RADIATION EMBRITTLEMENT OF NUCLEAR REACTOR PRESSURE VESSEL STEELS: AN INTERNATIONAL REVIEW (SECOND VOLUME)

A conference sponsored by
International Atomic Energy Agency
and ASTM Committee E-10 on
Nuclear Technology and Applications
Vienna, Austria, 8-10 Oct. 1984

ASTM SPECIAL TECHNICAL PUBLICATION 909
Lendell E. Steele, Naval Research Laboratory
editor

ASTM Publication Code Number (PCN)
04-909000-35

1916 Race Street, Philadelphia, PA 19103

Library of Congress Cataloging-in-Publication Data

Radiation embrittlement of nuclear reactor pressure vessel steels.

(ASTM special technical publication; 909)
"ASTM publication code number (PCN) 04-909000-35."
Includes bibliographies and index.
1. Nuclear pressure vessels—Congresses.   2. Steel—Effect of radiation on—Congresses.   I. Steele, L. E. (Lendell E.), 1928–   .   II. International Atomic Energy Agency.   III. ASTM Committee E-10 on Nuclear Technology and Applications.   IV. Series.
TK9211.5.R34   1986   621.48′332   86-10811
ISBN 0-8031-0473-1

NOTE

The Society is not responsible, as a body,
for the statements and opinions
advanced in this publication.

Printed in Ann Arbor, MI
August 1986

Foreword

This volume represents the second conference sponsored by the United Nations International Atomic Energy Agency, Unit of the United Nations (IAEA) and ASTM Committee E-10 on Nuclear Technology and Applications held in Vienna, Austria, 8–10 Oct. 1984. Lendell E. Steele, Naval Research Laboratory, served as specialist meeting chairman and editor of this publication.

Related
ASTM Publications

Effects of Radiation on Materials: Twelfth International Symposium (Volumes I and II), STP 870 (1985), 04-870000-35

Radiation Embrittlement and Surveillance of Nuclear Reactor Pressure Vessels: An International Study, STP 819 (1983), 04-819000-35

Effects of Radiation on Materials—11th International Symposium, STP 782 (1982), 04-782000-35

Effects of Radiation on Materials—10th International Symposium, STP 725 (1981), 04-725000-35

Effects of Radiation Structural Materials (9th Conference), STP 683 (1979), 04-683000-35

A Note of Appreciation
to Reviewers

The quality of the papers that appear in this publication reflects not only the obvious efforts of the authors but also the unheralded, though essential, work of the reviewers. On behalf of ASTM we acknowledge with appreciation their dedication to high professional standards and their sacrifice of time and effort.

ASTM Committee on Publications

ASTM Editorial Staff

Helen M. Hoersch
Janet R. Schroeder
Kathleen A. Greene
Bill Benzing

Contents

Introduction

This volume represents the second in what is expected to become a series of conference proceedings flowing from periodic international meetings. The latest of these meetings, which was held in Vienna, Austria, on 8–10 October 1984, was sponsored principally by the International Atomic Energy Agency, Nuclear Power Division. Other key supporters included approximately 20 member nations, the Secretariat of the IAEA Working Group on Reliability of Reactor Pressure Components, and ASTM Committee E-10 on Nuclear Technology and Applications. Historically, this Specialists Meeting grew from and continued a series of highly successful meetings begun in 1967 with irregularly scheduled follow-on meetings since that date.

The latest of the Specialists Meetings contained papers in four areas: (1) overviews of national positions on research or operational considerations; (2) periodic surveillance of radiation embrittlement and related research activities; (3) pressure vessel integrity and regulatory considerations; and (4) fundamental mechanisms of radiation embrittlement. Besides these formal sessions, detailed discussion was encouraged. This discussion provided much supplemental guidance to support the Summary that seeks to identify not only the results of this meeting but the crucial needs remaining in filling our knowledge base for this subject. In connection with the latter, there was remarkable unanimity concerning the gaps in our knowledge that will be the focus for future studies and later meetings. The collective appraisal of the scope of our knowledge on the subject of radiation embrittlement of reactor structural steels resides in two areas— assuring safety of currently operating systems through knowledge and enhancing future integrity through fundamental studies—the results of which will provide guidance for minimizing the negative consequences of high energy neutron radiation exposure of nuclear reactor components in the future.

The greatest benefit of this volume is the provision in one place of the results of critical studies from many nations, both those with and those now developing nuclear power plants for electricity production. It is believed, therefore, that this represents an international status report of lasting value. Further, the catalytic effects of this international interaction are most effective and, while not always evident from the cold written word, are most evident in the lively forum created during the meeting of specialists. Hopefully, the essence of these interactions is captured in the rather cryptic summary gleaned from the combination of formal sessions and the less formal discussion. Underlying the total effort is a dedication

to effective electric power generation using nuclear knowledge for imminently peaceful uses that may enhance the standard of living of all the world's peoples. This high goal has been vigorously promoted by the principal sponsor as well as the most unselfish scientist and engineer participants.

Special recognition is due the many knowledgeable and articulate contributors, both authors and discussors, who made this meeting the effective forum of knowledge that was the goal of all. Other individuals deserving special gratitude and credit include: Dr. H. J. Laue, director, IAEA Nuclear Power Division; Mr. R. Skjoeldebrand, his associate director; Mr. V. Lyssakov, scientific secretary for the meeting and the sponsoring IAEA Working Group; the many participating specialists who made the discussion so valuable; the reviewers who unselfishly shared their expertise; the ASTM Committee on Publications, an elite and tireless group; and, finally, the dedicated ASTM editorial staff.

Lendell E. Steele

Head, Thermostructural Materials Branch, Material Science and Technology Division, Naval Research Laboratory, Washington, DC; specialist meeting chairman and editor.

Overview of National Programs

Charles Z. Serpan, Jr.,[1] *and Pryor N. Randall*[1]

Irradiation Effects in Reactor Pressure Vessel Steels: A Nuclear Regulatory Commission Perspective

REFERENCE: Serpan, C. Z. Jr., and Randall, P. N., **"Irradiation Effects in Reactor Pressure Vessel Steels: A Nuclear Regulatory Commission Perspective,"** *Radiation Embrittlement of Nuclear Reactor Pressure Vessel Steels: An International Review (Second Volume), ASTM STP 909,* L. E. Steele, Ed., American Society for Testing and Materials, Philadelphia, 1986, pp. 5–12.

ABSTRACT: The embrittling effect of neutron irradiation on reactor pressure vessel steel and welds has a significant impact on the regulation of reactors by the U.S. Nuclear Regulatory Commission (NRC). Because the NRC is concerned with the continuing integrity and safety of the reactor's primary system, the neutron-irradiation-induced loss of fracture toughness and ductility must be carefully documented, understood, and controlled to assure that despite such loss, there is always a sufficient reserve of toughness and ductility to preclude crack initiation and uncontrolled propagation in the unlikely event of an accident. Aspects of embrittlement important to the NRC, which are discussed herein, include prediction of the transition temperature and upper-shelf-energy levels at critical vessel locations for the setting of pressure-temperature limits, for analysis of accident loadings such as pressurized thermal shock, and for evaluation of flaws found in inspection. Also discussed are the use of embrittlement-related neutron dosimetry and evaluation of vessel annealing.

KEY WORDS: pressure vessel steels, radiation effects, pressure vessel safety, radiation embrittlement, mechanical properties, neutron dosimetry, neutron spectrum, pressurized thermal shock

The embrittling effect of neutron irradiation on reactor pressure vessel steels has a significant impact on the regulation and licensing of reactors by the U.S. Nuclear Regulatory Commission (NRC). Because the NRC is concerned with the continuing integrity and safety of the reactor's primary system, the loss of fracture toughness and ductility during operation that results from neutron irradiation must be carefully documented, understood, and controlled to assure that despite such loss, there is always a sufficient reserve of toughness and ductility to preclude crack initiation and uncontrolled propagation in the event of an accidental pressure or thermal shock loading. The NRC discharges its obligation toward safety of reactors regarding radiation embrittlement through formulation

[1] Chief, Materials Engineering Branch, and senior materials engineer, respectively, Nuclear Regulatory Commission, Washington, DC 20555.

of regulations and Regulatory Guides, review and evaluation to assure compliance, and research activities to establish the technical basis for the regulatory instruments and decisions.

The facets of neutron-induced radiation embrittlement that are of importance to the NRC concern prediction of the Charpy-V specimen-based transition temperature and upper-shelf-energy level, for setting of pressure-temperature limits, for vessel safety analyses related to pressurized thermal shock and to flaws found in inspection, for evaluation of the effects of postirradiation annealing, and for embrittlement-related dosimetry. These facets of neutron-induced embrittlement are discussed in this paper along with the NRC regulations requiring calculation of embrittlement.

NRC Regulatory Requirements for Embrittlement

General Design Criterion 31, "Fracture Prevention of Reactor Coolant Pressure Boundary" (Ref 1), requires, in part, that the reactor coolant pressure boundary be designed with sufficient margin to ensure that, when stressed under operating, maintenance, testing, and postulated accident conditions: (1) the boundary behaves in a nonbrittle manner, and (2) the probability of rapidly propagating fracture is minimized. Appendix G, "Fracture Toughness Requirements," and Appendix H, "Reactor Vessel Material Surveillance Program Requirements," which implement, in part, Criterion 31, necessitate the calculation of changes in fracture toughness of reactor vessel materials caused by neutron radiation throughout the service life.

The principal examples of the NRC requirements that necessitate calculation of radiation damage are:

1. Paragraph V.A. of Appendix G requires: "The effects of neutron radiation . . . are to be predicted from the results of pertinent radiation effect studies. . . ." Procedures acceptable to the NRC for calculation of such radiation effects are provided in Regulatory Guide 1.99, "Radiation Damage to Reactor Vessel Material" (Ref 2), the second revision of which is under development, and the basis for which is presented in another paper in this volume [3].

2. Paragraph V.B. of Appendix G describes the basis for setting the upper limit for pressure as a function of temperature during heatup and cooldown for a given service period in terms of the predicted value of the adjusted reference temperature at the end of the service period.

3. The definition of reactor vessel beltline given in Paragraph II.F. of Appendix G requires identification of: ". . . regions of the reactor vessel that are predicted to experience sufficient neutron radiation damage to be considered in the selection of the most limiting material. . . ." Paragraphs III.A. and IV.A.1. specify the additional test requirements for beltline materials that supplement the requirements for reactor vessel materials generally.

4. Paragraph II.B. of Appendix H incorporates ASTM Practice for Conducting Surveillance Tests for Light Water-Cooled Nuclear Power Reactor Vessels (E

185-82) by reference. Paragraph 5.1 of ASTM E 185-82 requires that the materials to be placed in surveillance be those that may limit operation of the reactor during its lifetime, that is, those expected to have the highest adjusted reference temperature or the lowest Charpy upper-shelf energy at end of life. Both measures of radiation damage must be considered. In Paragraph 7.6 of ASTM E 185-82, the requirements for number of capsules and withdrawal schedule are based on the calculated amount of radiation damage at end of life.

The two measures of radiation damage used to comply with these NRC requirements are obtained from the results of the Charpy V-notch impact test. Appendix G to 10 CFR Part 50 requires that a full curve of absorbed energy versus temperature be obtained through the ductile-to-brittle transition temperature region. The adjustment of the reference temperature, ΔRT_{NDT}, is defined in Appendix G as the temperature shift in the Charpy curve for the irradiated material relative to that for the unirradiated material, measured at the 41 J (30-ft·lb) energy level. The second measure of radiation damage is the decrease in the Charpy upper-shelf-energy level, which is defined in ASTM E 185-82. Revision 2 of Regulatory Guide 1.99 will update the calculative procedures for the adjustment of reference temperature; however, calculative procedures for the decrease in upper-shelf energy will remain unchanged, because the preparatory work had not been completed in time to include them in Revision 2.

Aspects of Vessel Embrittlement

Following from the specific requirements for calculations, measurements and determinations just noted are a series of different aspects of embrittlement, wherein these required calculations, etc., are used to support plant operating actions and the parallel regulatory evaluations and approvals.

Pressure-Temperature Limits

The most common activity relating to embrittlement is the use of the data to set pressure-temperature limits for heatup and cooldown of the reactor vessel and primary system. Procedures for such calculations are set forth by the reactor vendors and are generally well known and used [4,5]. In these calculations, flaws are considered to be either on the inside or outside surface of the vessel. In fact, the latter are governing during heat-up. Thus, the calculation of attenuation of damage through the wall is an important step, which will be discussed later in this paper.

Pressurized-Thermal-Shock Analyses

A more recent and intense use of embrittlement data has been for vessel analyses considering the postulated conditions imposed by thermal shock resulting from emergency core coolant injection, followed by system repressurization; this accident scenario has been termed pressurized thermal shock (PTS).

Radiation embrittlement has had a very large influence on the PTS issue because it has been concluded that the resulting combined loadings from pressure and thermal stress plus the combined decrease in toughness from low vessel temperature and from radiation embrittlement could result in initiation from a very small flaw with small likelihood of arrest. The extent of crack propagation, as analyzed in PTS events, depends upon the change in fracture toughness through the vessel thickness, taking credit for the effects of higher temperature and reduced damage near the outside of the vessel wall. Thus, the exact level of toughness and the methods used for calculation and prediction of that toughness in the vessel wall are of great interest to NRC.

Predictions of the fluence and embrittlement (or fracture toughness level in reality) within an inch or so of the inner surface of reactor vessels have been extensively made for the PTS issue with little difficulty or question because the range of the extrapolation was not great. But the PTS issue forced additional extrapolations to midvessel thickness and beyond, because it was at these greater depths where arrest of propagating cracks occurred, thus concluding a PTS accident transient without breaching the vessel. The fluence-embrittlement extrapolation model for attenuation in deep penetration used in the past was based on fluence in terms of n/cm^2 $(E > 1 \text{ MeV})$. However, research results [6] showed that a different fluence parameter called dpa (displacements per atom) better represented the damaging effect of neutrons of all energy levels, and furthermore suggested that the attenuation behavior described by fluence "$E > 1$ MeV" was less conservative than that described by dpa. A description and calculation procedure for dpa is given in the ASTM Practice for Characterizing Neutron Exposures in Ferritic Steels in Terms of Displacements Per Atom (DPA) (E 693-79).

Formulation of the equation for use of dpa as the fluence parameter for deep penetration embrittlement analyses is discussed in Ref 3. At a depth of about 200 mm (8 in.) into a typical carbon steel reactor pressure vessel wall, the attenuation of dpa is about one half the attenuation of fluence $(E > 1$ MeV) [7]. Thus, the effect of using dpa as the measure of embrittlement toward the outside of reactor pressure vessel walls is more embrittlement (lower fracture toughness), than previously predicted by using fluence > 1 MeV. There is a second factor that further reduces the predicted attenuation through the vessel wall. The exponent in the fluence function for trend curves, which used to be 0.50, is now about 0.28, depending on the fluence level. The lower predicted level of fracture toughness toward the outside of vessels can result in deeper extension by cracks initiated during thermal shock and PTS accidents. Accordingly, the deeper crack penetration must be allowed for in plant-specific safety evaluations.

Vessel Outside Flaw Evaluation

More recently, the NRC has encountered another reason for interest in the level of embrittlement at the outer portions of the reactor vessel wall, because

in-service inspection revealed an indication of an exterior-surface flaw in the vessel of the Indian Point-2 PWR. Whereas previously, the embrittlement level at a vessel outer surface was estimated to be so low as to be insignificant, the embrittlement now must be considered to be much higher as a result of the higher damaging effects of the dpa exposure and the decrease in trend curve slope. Furthermore, analyses of the crack penetration from outside toward the vessel inside will show a more rapid advance because the steel is more brittle at every point than before based on fluence > 1 MeV. Thus, it is now just as important to know the fracture toughness of locations at or near the outer vessel wall for purposes of outer-surface crack initiation and propagation as it is for purposes of crack arrest for an inner-surface flaw under PTS.

Postirradiation Annealing

Recovery of fracture toughness of neutron-irradiated vessel steel to near-pre-service levels can be effected by postirradiation annealing, which is simply a heat treatment of irradiated steel at a temperature typically about 100°C (several hundred degrees Fahrenheit) above the normal operating temperature for a time period usually of one week. Annealing is important because it represents the only way to remove embrittlement and thus restore enough toughness and ductility so that a reactor can continue in service with a sufficient safe reserve against fracture during operation.

Postirradiation annealing of reactor pressure vessel steels and welds has been studied for several decades, with the result that a great deal is known about the general trends of recovery for reactor materials subjected to different time-at-temperature heating schedules and for various irradiation-anneal-reirradiation cycles. Because annealing has this remedial aspect, it is listed as one of the measures to be considered for mitigation and relief from potential vessel fracture resulting from PTS accidents. Nonetheless, the mass of information to date on annealing has been almost exclusively concerned with the degree of recovery of mechanical properties, and only a very small amount of work has been done on the engineering and mechanical aspects of annealing. That is, items not studied in detail include the thermal and mechanical stresses arising from the localized heating and the resulting potential for warping and misalignment of components, emplacement and removal of the heating system if self-heating is not used, control of airborne contamination from loosened contaminated particles if dry annealing plus forced air circulation is used, and criteria for vessel and plant requalification including proof of vessel mechanical property recovery.

Questions remaining about the mechanical metallurgy aspects of annealing are centered on plant-specific data of recovery for time-at-temperature schedules for a given plant, proof that the recovery determined from surveillance or other test specimens accurately reflect the *in situ* mechanical properties of the annealed vessel, re-embrittlement rate following annealing, and the cost benefit for annealing.

Embrittlement-Neutron Dosimetry

Neutron dosimetry is the time and damage-integrating parameter that is always used to measure the fluence values that index the mechanical property measurements of radiation damage in pressure vessel steels. Dosimetry is used as the primary measure of the number and energy level of the damage-causing neutrons, the basis for the neutron exposure parameter such as n/cm^2 ($E > 1$ MeV) or dpa. Neutron dosimetry also is used to benchmark the transport calculations that provide the methodology for extrapolation and prediction of embrittlement inside vessel walls based on surveillance test data, and the technology used for determining the flux at the vessel inner surface and the reduction in flux that can be achieved by replacement of active fuel from the core periphery with partially burned fuel or dummy elements.

The first two aspects of dosimetry are well known and have been just discussed in connection with embrittlement attenuation through the thickness of vessel walls. The next item concerns the methods used to predict the mechanical properties of a reactor vessel at times in the future, based on the results obtained from either test reactor or power reactor surveillance irradiation tests. Procedures for accomplishing this are given in the ASTM Recommended Practice for Extrapolating Reactor Vessel Surveillance Dosimetry Results (E 560-77), and ASTM Practice for Analysis and Interpretation of Light-Water Reactor Surveillance Results (E 853-81). This item is the crux of all neutron radiation embrittlement studies, because it is here that one must finally decide on a value of the embrittlement (or fracture toughness) that he believes exists in the steel or weld metal at a given location. The method set forth by the Regulatory Guide in Ref 2 gives as much credit as possible to the surveillance test results for individual plants, but because it is a regulatory document, it finally weighs-in just on the conservative side in recommending specific trend curves. Both the original version and Revision 1 of the guide were based on all pertinent data from both test reactor and power reactor surveillance irradiations; the current Revision 2 is based only on power reactor surveillance test data. This focusing, which eliminates the test reactor data base, has been considered necessary because of the unacceptable correlation between the test and power reactor data bases. Although research is underway to improve this correlation, it has not yet succeeded, and so remains as a great challenge to the research community to study and resolve the issue of how to set the correlation between the two sets of irradiation effects data. The key issue is the identification of the damage mechanisms that cause the embrittlement, recognizing that these mechanisms operate differently depending upon the concentration of constituent elements in the steel composition, the irradiation temperature, probably the dose rate of irradiation, the microstructure of the steel, and the population and energy level of the neutrons.

The last item regarding neutron dosimetry concerns the reduction in flux level at the vessel inner surface caused by removal of fresh fuel from the core outer row and replacement with either burned fuel elements or dummy elements. The contribution of neutron dosimetry to this activity is that it was first shown to be

technically worthwhile as a result of reactor physics neutron spectrum calculations [6], which form the theoretical/calculation balance to the parallel measurement aspect of dosimetry. The impetus for this activity and for the calculations came from the PTS issue, wherein practical means were being sought for keeping the level of vessel fluence and embrittlement below certain limits, thereby providing assurance that adequate vessel toughness would be present in the event that a PTS accident would occur. Although there was some opposition to this activity at first, because of the upsetting of carefully-derived fuel management schedules, it quickly became apparent that the benefits of the reduction in flux leakage from the core (manifested in relief from operational problems stemming from the PTS issue as well as more economical fuel operation) were well worth the effort to revise the fuel management schedules and provide for the burned or dummy elements in the appropriate locations of the outer core row. Because burned elements are placed at specific high flux locations, usually at corners where elements are located closest to the vessel wall, the peak flux locations on the vessel are now shifted to new locations. This necessitates a new series of reactor physics spectrum calculations to establish the new flux intensity level at the surveillance capsule locations, where the previous flux peaks usually occurred, and to establish the location and the intensity level of the new flux peak locations. As a further permutation of this activity, as the peak flux location shifts azimuthally around the vessel, the controlling material may change from base metal to weld metal (or vice versa) so that a location, which formerly may have been limiting because of the combination of high fluence and high levels of copper and nickel in the steel composition, might now be nonlimiting because the fluence is down to a level where embrittlement will no longer be so high over its lifetime. Conversely, a new limiting material would be established as the peak flux shifts to a new location where the material could have the characteristics, when combined with the higher fluence, to result in the highest level of embrittlement into the future. Thus, embrittlement continues to be inexorably combined with dosimetry for application to reactor vessel safety analyses, and improvements in understanding and accuracy of one element enhance the value of the other, while at the same time pointing to new areas where improvement is needed.

Conclusions

Great strides have been made in recent years in the understanding and application of radiation embrittlement technology for reactor pressure vessels. Fortunately, this understanding has kept pace with the recognition of new potential accident scenarios, such as pressurized thermal shock. At the same time, these technologies have also revealed paths for mitigation and elimination of the potentially unacceptable material conditions. While it is necessary, from a regulatory standpoint, to define potentially unsafe conditions and to set down calculative and operating procedures that may initially be conservative, the need is also recognized to not regulate any more than necessary to assure that we are *just* on the conservative side. The typical reason for erring on the side of conservatism

is the uncertainty in the value of the number used for analysis or final application to a plant; for example, the fluence value at the end of the next five-year operating period at the vessel inner surface for the newly-shifted peak flux point, or the RT_{NDT} value of the vessel steel 200 mm (8 in.) from the inside vessel wall, which is the location of the tip of a crack 15 mm (0.6 in.) deep on the outside surface of the vessel wall. Thus, there is a mutual obligation to study and reduce the uncertainties in data associated with both radiation embrittlement and with neutron dosimetry. The beneficial result will be greater assurance of safety, because the margins will be known more accurately, which then translates to the most efficient and economical operation of the plant, because there will be no excess and undefined amount of conservatism.

Acknowledgments

The authors wish to acknowledge that the analyses, results, conclusions, and technical positions reviewed and discussed in this paper are the products of the work of many persons including those within the NRC, those employed by contractors to the Office of Research, and by others both in the United States and abroad who are part of the cooperative programs underway in materials evaluations and in surveillance dosimetry improvement research. The contributions of our co-workers and collaborators are acknowledged with sincere appreciation.

References

[1] Appendix A, "General Design Criteria for Nuclear Power Plants," 10 CFR Part 50, "Licensing of Production and Utilization Facilities," Code of Federal Regulations, U. S. Government Printing Office, Washington, DC.
[2] Draft Regulatory Guide 1.99, Revision 2, "Radiation Damage to Reactor Vessel Materials," Nuclear Regulatory Commission, Washington, DC, in preparation.
[3] Randall, P. N., this publication, pp. 149–162.
[4] Hazelton, W. S., Anderson, S. L., and Yanichko, S. E., "Basis For Heatup and Cooldown Limit Curves," Westinghouse Electric Corporation, WCAP-7924-A, April 1975.
[5] Behnke, H. W., Lowe, A. L., Jr., Bloom, J. M., and Van der Sluys, W. A., "Methods of Compliance With Fracture Toughness and Operational Requirements of 10 CFR 50, Appendix G," Babcock and Wilcox Co., BAW-10046A, Rev. 2, Topical Report, June 1984.
[6] Guthrie, G. L., McElroy, W. N., and Anderson, S. L. in *Proceedings*, Fourth ASTM-EURATOM Symposium on Reactor Dosimetry, NUREG/CP-0029, Vol. 1, July 1982, Nuclear Regulatory Commission, Washington, DC, pp. 111–120.
[7] "LWR Power Reactor Surveillance Physics-Dosimetry Data Base Compendium," W. N. McElroy, Ed., NUREG/CR-3319 HEDL TME 84-2, Nuclear Regulatory Commission, Washington, DC, May 1984.

L. Myrddin Davies[1] and Terry Ingham[2]

Overview of Studies in the United Kingdom on Neutron Irradiation Embrittlement of Pressure Vessel Steels

REFERENCE: Davies, L. M. and Ingham, T., **"Overview of Studies in the United Kingdom on Neutron Irradiation Embrittlement of Pressure Vessel Steels,"** *Radiation Embrittlement of Nuclear Reactor Pressure Vessel Steels: An International Review (Second Volume), ASTM STP 909*, L. E. Steele, Ed., American Society for Testing and Materials, Philadelphia, 1986, pp. 13–33.

ABSTRACT: The paper describes work on irradiation embrittlement that has been undertaken in the United Kingdom since preparation of the Second Marshall Report on the Integrity of pressure water reactor (PWR) pressure vessels. Results from research programs concentrate specifically on work on steels for Magnox and PWR pressure vessel (PV) applications.

Models have been developed that describe the influence of copper precipitation on the yield stress changes in Magnox PV steels. Results from strength and microscopic examination confirm the significance of copper precipitation after long-term aging. The results provide support to the expression in the model to describe the time dependence of the copper precipitate contribution to the increase in yield strength.

Accelerated irradiation and surveillance data are present for both the Magnox and PWR PV steels. Modeling of data includes variations on neutron energy spectrum, neutron fluence, flux intensity, and irradiation temperature. The data for PWR PV materials have been used to examine the applicability of a recent draft revision of the U.S. Nuclear Regulatory Commission's Regulatory Guide 1.99 for estimating irradiation shifts on modern materials.

A study of mechanisms of embrittlement is reported including developments in positron annihilation studies and small-angle neutron scattering (both with and without the application of magnetic fields).

KEY WORDS: radiation effects, irradiation embrittlement, pressure vessel steels, pressure water reactors, neutrons, mechanical property changes, Charpy tests, yield stress, copper, phosphorus, mechanisms, modeling

In this paper, an attempt is made to present an overview of studies in the United Kingdom on neutron irradiation embrittlement of pressure vessels steels. It would be a difficult task to provide a comprehensive review of work in the United Kingdom. This paper is therefore essentially a partial view. We have

---

[1] Technical coordination officer, Central Electricity Generating Board, London, UK.
[2] Principal scientific officer, United Kingdom Atomic Energy Authority, Warrington, UK.

restricted the paper to an outline of the findings, in this area, of a major recent study, and we go on to consider the implications of those on the current scene in the United Kingdom. Attention is drawn to a recent draft revision to the U.S. Nuclear Regulatory Commission's (NRC) Regulatory Guide 1.99. Surveillance and Materials Test Reactor (MTR) data are considered in this context, and it is shown that the proposal is unrealistically pessimistic for welds typical of modern practice. We then proceed to provide a partial view of some recent developments in studies of Magnox steels because of their relevance to the general area of pressure water reactor pressure vessel (PWR PV) studies. Finally, we produce some closing comments that indicate areas of further study.

PWR Studies

Light Water Reactor Study Group

A Light Water Reactor Study Group (LWRSG) on the assessment of PWR PV integrity has existed in the United Kingdom since 1973. The first LWRSG report was published in 1976 [1]. The Study Group undertook the task of updating its first report in December 1979 and completed the task by December 1981. The second report [2] provided an evaluation of modern PWR PV technology and a comprehensive fracture assessment of a typical pressure vessel. The Study Group recommendations were classified as either "essential" or "for improved understanding," the former being regarded as necessary for the safe operation of PWRs installed in the United Kingdom. A pre-construction safety report (PCSR) for a PWR station at Sizewell in Suffolk has been prepared by the Central Electricity Generating Board (CEGB) and the National Nuclear Corporation (NNC) and submitted to H. M. Nuclear Installations Inspectorate (NII). The proposal to build the Sizewell 'B' PWR is currently the subject of a Public Inquiry. Deliberations at the Inquiry should be completed by the end of 1984 and the Inspector is expected to present his report to the Government at a later date.

Section 3 of the second Study Group report [2] discusses the mechanical and fracture toughness properties of pressure vessel materials.

In the context of this overview, three mechanisms were identified by the Study Group that could lead to a degradation of material properties during service life. These were: irradiation embrittlement, thermal aging, and strain aging. The

TABLE 1—*Specification for ASME SA508 Class 3 chemical composition (percent by weight).*

Carbon	0.25 max
Manganese	1.20 to 1.50
Phosphorus	0.025 max
Sulfur	0.025 max
Silicon	0.15 to 0.40
Nickel	0.40 to 1.00
Chromium	0.25 max
Molybdenum	0.45 to 0.60
Vanadium	0.05 max

TABLE 2—*Additional compositional requirements (percent by weight, maximum) for the Sizewell 'B' reactor vessel.*

	Forgings	Weld Metal
Carbon	0.20	0.15
Phosphorus	0.008	0.01
Sulfur	0.008	0.01
Copper	0.09	0.07
Vanadium	0.01	0.01
Aluminum	0.045	...
Antimony	0.008	0.008
Arsenic	0.015	0.015
Cobalt	0.02	0.02
Hydrogen	1 ppm (product)	...
Nickel	0.85	0.85
Tin	0.01	0.01
Silicon	0.3	...
Chromium	0.15	0.15

degree of embrittlement accruing from these mechanisms can be minimized by specifying pressure vessel materials having closely controlled chemical compositions that are readily achievable using current commercial practice.

A United Kingdom PWR PV will be fabricated using A508 Class 3 ring forgings. The American Society of Mechanical Engineers (ASME) specification for A508 Class 3 steel and the additional compositional requirements that have subsequently been imposed for the Sizewell 'B' pressure vessel are shown in Tables 1 and 2.

The principal elements that enhance the irradiation sensitivity of SA508 Class 3 steel and associated welds are copper and phosphorus. The upper limits on these elements have been restricted to Cu = 0.09% and P = 0.008% by weight for forgings and Cu = 0.07% and P = 0.010% by weight for welds. It can be seen from Table 3 that the maximum end-of-life neutron dose at the beltline of a four-loop PWR PV will be 2.3×10^{19} n/cm^2 ($E > 1$ MeV), whereas that for the weld closest to the reactor core will be only 5.8×10^{18} n/cm^2 ($E > 1$ MeV). The mechanical properties would not be expected to be changed significantly by the lower total dose experienced at the girth weld.

An analysis of materials test reactor data indicated that modern materials typical

TABLE 3—*End-of-life neutron doses in a four-loop PWR pressure vessel (40 year life).*

Position	Neutron Dose, n/cm^2 ($E > 1$ MeV)
Belt Line	
(i) Inner wall	2.3×10^{19}
(ii) ¼ T	1.3×10^{19}
(iii) ¾ T	2.7×10^{18}
Girth Weld	5.8×10^{18}

of current practice irradiated to a neutron dose of 3×10^{19} n/cm^2 ($E > 1$ MeV) would experience changes in transition temperature not exceeding 30°C [2]. Few data were available to assess changes in upper-shelf toughness when modern materials are irradiated but the limited evidence suggested that effects of irradiation, up to dose levels of interest, would not be significant. In view of the scarcity of data, the Study Group concluded that the effect of irradiation on upper-shelf toughness should be determined directly for relevant materials. The "essential" recommendation from the Study Group concerning embrittlement was:

> All analytical and mechanical tests used in US quality control procedure trials and irradiation surveillance should be included in the requirements for a vessel to be installed in the United Kingdom. In addition fracture toughness tests, for example on 12.5 mm thick compact tension specimens, or thicker as appropriate, should be included in the United Kingdom surveillance programme.

Precipitation, both within grains and on grain boundaries, and segregation of certain impurity elements, which may occur during long-term aging at 300°C, could contribute to an increase in the brittle-ductile transition temperature. The Study Group acknowledged that both chemical composition and fabrication procedures should be adequately controllable so that these thermal aging effects could prove to be insignificant. It was considered prudent, however, to include some allowance in fracture assessments for an increase in transition temperature, in nonirradiated regions, which would allow for any effect of thermal aging.

Strain aging promotes an increase in the brittle-ductile transition temperature and a reduction in both upper and lower-shelf toughness. The Study Group [2] noted that the strain aging phenomena cannot be isolated from the effect of warm prestressing, and that warm prestressing will result in a beneficial effect on the transition temperature—so that the combined effect of strain aging and warm prestressing on the transition temperature shift could be either positive or negative.

The Study Group concluded that there was insufficient knowledge concerning the extent to which the changes in transition temperature due to irradiation embrittlement, thermal aging, and strain aging would be additive. Taking into account the improved response of modern materials to such phenomena, the Study Group recommended that applying a transition temperature shift of 30°C to *all* regions of the vessel should encompass any toughness degradation during the operational life of a modern PWR PV.

Aspects relating to factors that may affect in-service material properties are covered in the following "Recommendations for Improved Understanding:"

> The materials surveillance programme should include specimens typical of the various components and welds of the vessels to evaluate the effect of long-term ageing, strain ageing and combined effects with neutron irradiation where appropriate at temperatures of about 300°C. It is expected that the effects on the transition temperature and the toughness values in modern steels and welds will be very small but sufficient

testing should be undertaken to show that this is the case for actual materials used for a particular vessel.

The inservice material surveillance programme should be supplemented by a programme to evaluate the effect of long-term thermal ageing, strain ageing, and combined effects with neutron irradiation where appropriate) at about 300°C on the fracture toughness of base materials and weld metal and also the temperature variation of sensitivity to these effects between about 250°C and 360°C.

Studies Related to Sizewell 'B'

Although the Study Group report was a generic study and did not consider the specific case of the Sizewell 'B' design, in developing their Safety case, the CEGB and NNC have taken account of the Study Group recommendations.

When considering the effect of irradiation on the shift in the brittle-ductile transition temperature, the case for Sizewell 'B' involved a more cautious approach by assuming that the shift will be not more than 50°C. This higher shift is based on both surveillance and MTR data for relevant materials and also evidence that the neutron fluxes shown in Table 3 could vary by ±20%. These results are summarized in Fig. 1. (Some of the data in this figure relate to higher phosphorus contents than the maximum level of 0.010% by weight for Sizewell 'B').

The effects of thermal and strain aging are considered to be minimal for the materials to be used in Sizewell 'B', but will be allowed for by assuming a 30°C shift in transition temperature for those parts of the vessel outside the core region.

Exact details of the surveillance program that would be used for Sizewell 'B' have yet to be decided. The Pre-Construction Safety Report and evidence to the Sizewell 'B' Power Station Public Inquiry indicate that the program will use standard Westinghouse-designed capsules. These will be located in guide baskets welded to the outside of the neutron shield pads and positioned directly opposite the center portion of the core. The program will use six capsules. A typical Westinghouse capsule would contain tension, Charpy V-notch impact, and fracture toughness specimens for base metals and welds in the proportions shown in Table 4. However, in view of the considerably reduced significance of the response to irradiation of girth welds and associated heat affected zones fabricated to the Sizewell 'B' specification (see Table 3), the exact numbers of specimens of a given material may well vary from the basic Westinghouse package.

The fracture toughness samples are likely to be 12.5-mm-thick compact specimens. These particular samples will be used to monitor the effect of irradiation on upper-shelf toughness. Where appropriate, the surveillance program will, as a minimum, conform with ASTM Practice for Conducting Surveillance Tests for Light Water-Cooled Nuclear Power Reactor Vessels (E 185-82). Details of the dosimeters that will be used to evaluate the neutron doses accumulated by the samples and the vessel wall have still to be finalized.

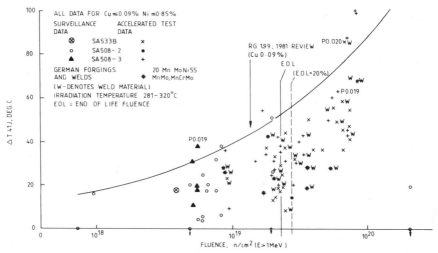

FIG. 1—*Reactor surveillance and accelerated test results on PWR PV steels with ≤0.09% by weight copper and ≤0.85% by weight nickel (Phosphorus contents are generally within 0.010 to 0.012% by weight, but certain high phosphorus points are identified.) [49].*

The U.S. Regulatory Position Concerning the Prediction of Neutron Damage

In the United States, estimates of neutron radiation damage are achieved using trend curves that are embodied in both Design Codes [3,4] and the U.S. Code of Federal Regulations [5]. Current regulations invoke the NRC Regulatory Guide 1.99 Revision 1 1977 [6]. The increase in transition temperature due to neutron damage is calculated using the expression:

$$A = T_{41}J = \frac{5}{9}[40 + 1000(\%Cu - 0.08) + 5000(\%P - 0.008)]$$

$$\times \left[\frac{f}{10^{19}}\right]^{1/2} °C \quad (1)$$

TABLE 4—*Contents of typical Westinghouse surveillance capsule.*

Material	Charpy Specimens	Tension Specimens	Fracture Toughness Specimens
Forging:			
Hoop direction	15	3	4
Axial direction	15	3	4
Weld metal	15	3	4
Heat affected zone	15	...	...

where

$$T_{41}J = \text{the transition temperature shift in °C indexed at 41-J Charpy V-notch impact energy,}$$
$$f = \text{fluence in n/cm}^2 \ (E > 1 \text{ MeV), and}$$
$$\%Cu, \%P = \text{the amounts of copper and phosphorus in percent by weight.}$$

The relationship is valid for $A > 27.8°C$ and $f < 6 \times 10^{19}$ n/cm^2 $(E > 1$ MeV). For Sizewell 'B', the material specification will call for copper and phosphorus contents of, respectively, 0.09 max and 0.008 max for base metals and 0.07 max and 0.010 max for weld metals. Inserting these values into Eq 1 provides the same limiting trend curve for both materials that reduces to

$$T_{41}J = 27.78 \left[\frac{f}{10^{19}}\right]^{1/2} \text{°C} \qquad (2)$$

Regulatory Guide 1.99 Rev. 1 is thought to be overly conservative at high fluences and the NRC is actively pursuing methods to revise the curves and thus reduce the conservatism. The first tentative steps towards revision were described at the 1981 International Atomic Energy Agency (IAEA) Specialists Meeting [7] where separate trend curves were presented for materials of low and high (>0.5% by weight) nickel content. The tentative trend curves for high nickel materials, (which would be relevant to Sizewell 'B') are given by

$$\Delta T_{41}J = \frac{5}{9} [30 + 1000(\%Cu - 0.05)] \left[\frac{f}{10^{19}}\right]^{0.35} \text{°C} \qquad (3)$$

Limiting curves for Sizewell 'B' materials would be for base materials

$$\Delta T_{41}J = 38.89 \left[\frac{f}{10^{19}}\right]^{0.35} \text{°C} \qquad (4)$$

and for weld metals

$$\Delta T_{41}J = 27.78 \left[\frac{f}{10^{19}}\right]^{0.35} \text{°C} \qquad (5)$$

The trend curves defined by Eqs 2, 4, and 5 are compared in Fig. 2. The end-of-life (EOL) fluences shown in the figures are those given in Table 3.

The 1981 Trend Curves have been superseded by a recent draft proposed revision to Regulatory Guide 1.99 [8]. These current NRC proposals were produced by combining correlation functions for surveillance data that had been

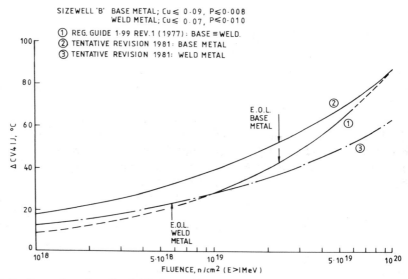

FIG. 2—*Comparison of predicted shifts in transition temperature for Sizewell 'B' materials using Regulatory Guide 1.99 Rev. 1 (1977) and tentative revisions made in 1981* [7].

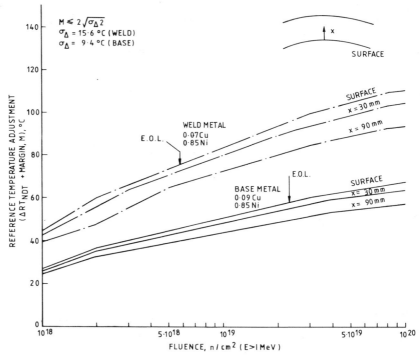

FIG. 3—*Predicted upper limits on shifts in transition temperature from draft revision of Regulatory Guide 1.99* [8].

derived independently by Guthrie [9] and Odette [10]. The mean irradiation-induced shift is given in the new proposal by

$$\Delta RT_{NDF} = \frac{5}{9} \, [C.F.] \cdot f^{(0.28 - 0.10 \, \log f)} \, °C \qquad (6)$$

where

    C.F. = a chemistry factor based on the copper and nickel contents that is tabulated separately for base and weld materials, and

    f = fluence normalized to 1×10^{19} n/cm^2 ($E > 1$ MeV).

Conservative adjusted reference temperatures (ART) are defined by

$$ART = Initial \; RT_{NDT} + \Delta RT_{NDT} + Margin \qquad (7)$$

where

    Margin $= 2 \cdot \sqrt{\sigma_I^2 + \sigma_\Delta^2},$

where

    σ_I, σ_Δ = standard deviations for Initial RT_{NDT} and RT_{NDT},

    σ_I = 0 if initial RT_{NDT} values are measured, and

    σ_Δ = 9.4°C for base metals and 15.6°C for weld metals or 0.5, RT_{NDT} whichever is the smaller.

The proposal also allows credit to be taken of the attenuation of neutron embrittlement with increasing penetration from the inner-wall surface of the pressure vessel. This attenuation factor is given by

$$\Delta RT_{NDT}(x) = \Delta RT_{NDT}(Surface) \times e^{-0.067x} \qquad (8)$$

where x is measured in inches.

    Limiting trend curves for Sizewell 'B' base metals and weld metals, derived using Eqs 6, 7, and 8, are presented in Fig. 3. The trend curves corresponding to positions 30 and 90 mm from the inner wall merely illustrate the allowance that can be taken for damage attenuation and have no specific significance with regard to PV integrity. The most striking feature in Fig. 3 is the significant increase in predicted shifts in reference temperature for the weld metal compared to those for the base metal. (It should be noted that the situation would be further aggravated for RPVs fabricated from plates where welds would be subject to neutron damage at peak flux.) The prediction of high shifts in reference temperature for weld metals is directly related to the inclusion of a higher chemistry factor for welds, the relatively high upper limit on nickel content (0.85), and inclusion of a margin, M, which is high (typically 100%) relative to the predicted

mean shift, ΔRT_{NDT}. In practical terms, the curves suggest that the girth weld, although well removed from the core region and receiving only minimal neutron flux (5.75 × 10⁹ n/cm²/s assuming 32 full-power years operation, 40 year life), would be a critical location on the basis of this Revision, for design assessments, and could be critical for in-service fracture assessments. Such a situation is at variance with our understanding of the sensitivity to irradiation embrittlement of modern PWR PV materials. A recent IAEA Coordinated Research Programme (CRP) [11] has demonstrated that, for materials having closely controlled chemical compositions, there is no significant difference between the irradiation-induced shift in transition temperature for base metals and associated welds. Relevant results from this program are shown in Fig. 4. Those results and the results shown in Fig. 1 indicate similar response from base materials and welds. Thus, available data for modern materials suggest that the current draft proposal for the Regulatory Guide revision will be unduly conservative when used to predict transition shifts for modern low-copper welds. One motivation behind the proposed revisions has been to reduce the degree of conservatism when applying Regulatory Guide 1.99 Rev. 1 in assessments of over-cooling transients. Such transients are of concern mainly in older RPVs fabricated from materials having less carefully specified chemical compositions. Recognition of possible problems of this nature at the design state has allowed them to be largely eliminated, for example, by using materials having closely controlled chemical compositions and incorporating specific design features.

Therefore, it would appear to be essential to give further detailed consideration to the current proposals for revising Regulatory Guide 1.99 to preclude the possibility of introducing unrealistically high predictions of irradiation-induced transition temperature shifts in modern materials, particularly weld metals fabricated using state-of-the-art welding technology.

Some Current Studies on the Embrittlement of PWR PV Steels

Druce et al [12–15] at Harwell are investigating the effects of thermal aging treatments in the temperature range of 300 to 550°C for times up to 20 000 h on a variety of steels that include A533 B Class 1 plate and A508 Class 3 forging materials (both as base materials and as simulated heat affected zone material) and also weldments. These studies show that base metal steels typical of modern practice are highly resistant to aging in the temperature range of 300 to 500°C. Typical increases in ductile-brittle transition temperature over the temperature range of their study were observed to be generally 40°C, while most specimens aged at 300°C showed no effects. Work on model alloys and simulated heat affected zone by Druce [12] and Brear and King [16] show the deleterious effects of large grain sizes (~200 μm) and impurity content. Phosphorus and antimony are significant in their effect and arsenic and tin can also promote embrittlement. Brear and King have suggested limits on arsenic, antimony, and tin of 0.048, 0.011, and 0.015% by weight, respectively, to produce effects equivalent to the maximum phosphorus content permitted by ASME for the PV beltline material

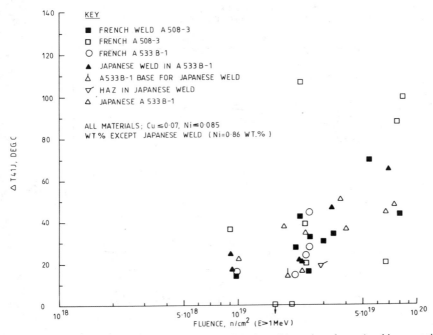

FIG. 4—*Comparison of Charpy 41-J transition shifts for weld metals and associated base metals tested in the IAEA CRP (after Ref 11).*

(0.012% by weight). Generally, lower austenitization temperature showed lower embrittlement on aging but coarser structures characteristic of higher austenitization temperatures promoted a greater degree of embrittlement on aging at the higher temperatures. However, aging at 300°C showed little effect.

Little [17] has investigated the combined effects of strain aging and irradiation at a temperature of about 290°C to a fluence of 3.1×10^{19} n/cm² ($E > 1$ MeV) on A533 B Class 1 and A508 Class 3 steel containing free nitrogen levels of 14 and 8 ppm, respectively. Some of the specimens were given a tensile prestrain of 5%. Some specimens were also thermally aged at 290°C. He found that C_v shifts in transition temperature due to strain aging were not additive to the corresponding shift from neutron irradiation because the irradiated prestrain and nonprestrained results were essentially coincident and because irradiation appears to suppress the C_v transition shift from strain aging.

For Phase 3 of the IAEA Coordinated Research Programme on optimizing RPV surveillance programs and their analyses, the UK contribution contains, as a cornerstone of its proposal [18], an investigation of the combined effects of irradiation embrittlement and strain age embrittlement on the fracture toughness temperature transition using 12.5-mm-thick compact specimens some of which will have been prestrained at ambient temperature prior to irradiation to an equivalent K_I value of 120 MPa$\sqrt{m}$. Results will be compared with those from Charpy tests and tension tests in the unirradiated, unirradiated and aged, and also

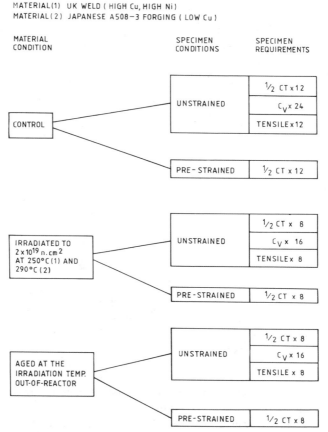

FIG. 5—*Deployment of specimens for the strain-aging experiment within the UK contribution to the IAEA-CRP* [18].

in the irradiated condition. The deployment of specimens for that part of the proposal is shown schematically in Fig. 5.

Small-angle neutron scattering techniques have been employed in the investigation of several irradiated pressure vessel steels [17,19] that had shown significant changes in mechanical property on irradiation but had shown little change in microstructure during electron microscope examination [20]. Enhanced scattering in PWR PV steels was related to the copper content but was affected by the presence of nickel and other elements. Figure 6 is from Jones and Buswell [19] and includes steels from Phase 2 [20] of the IAEA CRP (steels JW, Japanese weld containing 0.04% by weight copper; FF, French forging containing 0.06% by weight copper and the radiation sensitive UKW 0.2% by weight copper, 1.57% by weight nickel; Steels A and B were model alloys containing 0.01 and 0.22% by weight copper, respectively). An increase in the scattering intensity

with increasing Varsik and Byrne Chemistry Relationship [21] can be seen in Fig. 6. If the results were plotted against copper content only, then the results on UKW are located nearer the x axis in such a graph and evidence for a continuous enhanced scattering with both increasing copper and nickel is lost. Little [17] also confirms the additional scattering associated with increasing both nickel and phosphorus content.

Small-angle neutron scattering studies involving the determination of the ratio of the degree of scattering perpendicular to and parallel to magnetic fields applied to specimens have been carried out [19] to identify the nature of the scattering centers. (It will be remembered that Frisius et al [22] calculated ratios of 11.5 for pure copper precipitate and 1.3 for voids, and their measurements on model binary alloys gave ratios of 11.0.) Jones and Buswells [19] work provided ratios of about 2.5 for irradiated PWR steels and the UK weld used for Phase 2 of the IAEA [20] CRP that was very sensitive to irradiation. This work again provides a clear indication that real PWR PV steels behave in a manner more complex during neutron irradiation than model alloys. Such experimental and interpretive work is continuing [23].

Highton [24] has reported on the results from his positron annihilation studies where he found an increasing signal as a function of copper or chemistry relationship in unirradiated steels (He also reported on his observations on an increase in hardness as a function of heat treatment temperature in unirradiated PV steels.) Those studies are continuing [25] and preliminary results on model alloys indicate

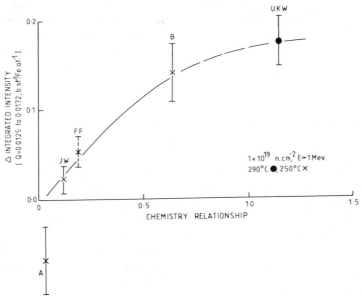

FIG. 6—*Irradiation-induced changes in integrated intensity versus Varsik and Byrne chemistry relationship for PWR steels, after accelerated irradiations at 250 and 290°C [19].*

an increasing signal (S value) as a function of decreasing irradiation temperature for the same composition.

Recent Magnox PV Steel Studies of Relevance to PWR PV Studies

Current assessments of Magnox pressure vessel integrity depend upon the original proof test using analyses based on fracture mechanics. Thus, values of fracture toughness are required that are relevant to the state of the vessel materials both at the time of the initial proof test and after a period of operation. For the proof test condition, values have been obtained from recent tests on material cut from the original reactor vessels at the time of construction. To obtain fracture toughness appropriate to material that has been in service and has thus been subjected to neutron irradiation, a number of approaches have been adopted:

(a) Techniques have been developed to allow the original monitoring scheme Charpy specimens to be used. Instead of impact testing, specimens are fatigue pre-cracked, side-grooved, and subjected to three-point bend loading. Papers outlining the analytical background to this work, along with analysis procedures, have been published by Neale [26,27]. The implementation of the techniques to hot-cell fracture toughness testing have been given by Neale and Priest [28–30] and a description of the CEGB's shielded fracture toughness testing facility was reported by Neale and Priest [31].
(b) The original monitoring schemes have been supplemented with standard fracture toughness specimens. Clearly, it will be some time before these will have experienced sufficient exposure to make testing worthwhile.
(c) Accelerated irradiation experiments have been undertaken. These have included tension, impact, and fracture toughness tests using both pre-cracked Charpy specimens and compact specimens. Data from these tests have been discussed by Priest, Charnock, and Stewart [32] and Priest, Charnock, and Neale [33].

In a recent series of papers Fisher et al [34–36] have presented a simple model to explain the influence of copper precipitation on the yield strength changes observed in Magnox PV steels. In terms of neutron irradiation embrittlement, the composition of older non-nickel modified PWR PV steels is generally similar to Magnox PV steels (see, for example, Table 5, which is reproduced in simplified form from Ref 34). The main differences are the generally higher copper, molybdenum, and carbon content of the PWR PV steels, and the lower nickel content in the Magnox steels. The differences in heat treatment and composition of Magnox and PWR PV steels are manifested in a difference in microstructure. The Magnox plate metallographic structure is ferrite/pearlite compared with tempered bainite/ferrite structures in PWR PV steels.

Fisher et al [34] have surveyed relevant studies on irradiation embrittlement. Their survey includes the period covering the results from the earlier work of

TABLE 5—*Typical analyses of the plate steels exposed in the low-temperature Magnox locations* [34].

Station	C	Si	Mn	S	P	Cu	Ni	Sn	Cr	Mo	Co	Ti	Al	Nb
1	0.19[a]	0.3	1.22	0.027	0.015	0.12	0.11	0[b]	0.1	0.03	0	0	0.01[c]	0
2	0.09	0.37	1.05	0.02	0.015	0.06	0.06	0.01	0.04	0	0.03	0.005[c]	0.008	0.01[c]
3	0.11	0.13	1.1	0.02	0.015	0.43	0.07	0.01	0.07	0.23	0.03	0.005[c]	0.018	0.01[c]
4	0.15	0.16	1.3	0.035	0.02	0.09	0.06	0.01	0.01	0.01	0.02	0.01[c]	0.051	0.01[c]
5	0.17	0.25	1.1	0.034	0.016	0.15	0.08	0.02[c]	0.07	0.02[c]	0.02[c]	0.02[c]	0.02[c]	0.02[c]

[a]Values are in percent by weight.
[b]0 indicates not determined.
[c]Indicates upper limit.

Potapovs and Hawthorne [37] that identified the detrimental effect of copper, through to the recent Field Ion Microscope studies [38–40] where Lott et al [40] confirmed the presence of copper-rich clusters in PWR steel irradiated to a neutron fluence of about 2×10^{19} n/cm^2 at 290°C. The small-angle neutron scattering studies of Frisius et al [22] led to the conclusion that the neutron irradiation embrittlement of the PV steels containing small quantities of copper is caused, at least partially, by radiation-induced precipitation of copper. Hawthorne's [41] observation, that PWR PV steels having high sulfur content reduced the detrimental effect of copper, is seen as confirming the observation of the presence of a copper-containing compound $Cu_{1.8}S$ [42] seen to be present in some Magnox steels. (The presence of this compound could provide misleading estimates of the amount of copper in solid solution in the steels because chemical analysis gives total copper content. Hence, bulk copper content may not be the most appropriate parameter to use in differentiating between steels of different sensitivity.)

In the studies on Magnox steels that support the model, copper precipitates 140 Å in. diameter were observed on aging for 20 000 h at 350°C and the measured increase in strength arising from the precipitation of copper was consistent with the value predicted from the theory of Russell and Brown [43]. The increase in yield strength detected in some surveillance specimens containing 0.4% by weight copper irradiated at 390°C derived solely from the precipitation of copper. (For a fuller description of the surveillance data and the thermal aging work, the reader is referred to Refs 34, 35, and 36.) The contribution to the change in yield strength from damage clusters is negligible at these irradiation temperatures (350 to 390°C) and the experimental data already available on model steels and ferritic steels show that copper precipitation will occur rapidly even without any enhancement from neutron irradiation, at these temperatures. For steels operated at lower temperatures (about 170 to 225°C), an increase in yield strength from copper precipitation would be expected from these alloys, but an enhancement of the precipitation process is expected during irradiation.

One input into the model assumes that the strengthening from dislocation loops on neutron irradiation is described by and, derived from the following equation, which is usually used to describe the change in yield strength on irradiation (after making allowances for composition and neutron spectra)

$$\Delta\sigma_{\text{damage}} = A(\phi t)^{1/2}$$

where A is a function of the irradiation temperature and aluminum or silicon content.

The copper in solution in the steels prior to irradiation is assumed to precipitate during irradiation, and the rate of precipitation is dependent on the rate of copper diffusion and, in turn, of the mobility and concentration of vacancies. (During irradiation, there is a supersaturation of vacancies so that the precipitation rate is enhanced to a temperature above the corresponding thermal temperature.)

Interestingly, the estimated size of copper precipitates is such that they would remain below the limit of resolution of electron microscope examination throughout the lifetime of Magnox stations.

Under irradiation at a temperature (T_{irr}), a reduced time to develop peak strength (tp') is calculated from the relationship

$$tp' = \left[\frac{C_v \text{ (thermal)}}{C_v \text{ (irradiated)}} \right] tp$$

where

C_v (thermal) = the thermal equilibrium concentration of vacancies;
C_v (irradiated) = the calculated vacancy concentration under irradiation at T_{irr}; and
tp = time to peak strength, unirradiated, but at T_{irr}, from existing data.

The maximum increase in yield strength from a particular copper concentration has been derived from iron-copper alloys and is described by the following equation

$$\Delta\sigma_{max} = [3.6 \times 10^3 (f)^{1/2} - 60] \text{ MN/m}^2$$

where f is the volume fraction of copper.

Having thus evaluated the separate contribution to yield strength of the damage loops, Fisher et al evaluate the overall superposition of the effects by the following summation

$$\Delta\sigma_{total}(t) = \Delta\sigma_{Cu}(t) + \Delta\sigma_{dam}(t)$$

Overall, this study has allowed the successful interpretation of yield stress measurements on plate steel monitoring specimens in low-temperature Magnox reactors.

In the small-angle neutron scattering experiments, mentioned earlier in this paper, by Jones and Buswell [19], results were given of a comparison between Magnox surveillance specimens irradiated at 220°C and accelerated tests at 180°C. Their results are reproduced, for convenience, as Fig. 7 where it can be seen that the results support the Fisher et al model that a fine distribution of copper particles is precipitated during long-term irradiation but that the process is less advanced in accelerated irradiations.

Buswell [44] has also compared results of irradiation-induced changes of proof stress and ductile–brittle transition temperatures from PWR surveillance data from Electric Power Research Institute (EPRI) [45] and MTR data from other published sources. He concluded that it was generally acceptable to consider the changes

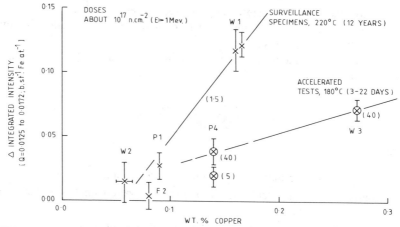

FIG. 7—*Irradiation-induced changes in integrated intensity versus copper content for Magnox steels, after long-term surveillance and short-term accelerated irradiations* [19].

in terms of copper content alone but the general agreement between surveillance and MTR data was lacking. The significant difference was that MTR data tended to show larger effects on steels typical of modern practice with copper contents less than about 0.1% by weight after irradiation to neutron doses of 1 to 2×10^{19} n/ cm^2 ($E > 1$ MeV) with the implication that results from MTR tests on such materials will be conservative for design application.

Buswell [44] also comments on the model produced by Odette [46], which is somewhat similar to that development by Fisher et al [36], but was developed to describe and interpret the EPRI data base on PWR PV surveillance results [45].

Closing Comments

Knowledge of the features underlying the strengthening processes in PWR PV steels during neutron irradiation has grown markedly in the past few years. In this paper, we have drawn attention to some of the recent developments in the United Kingdom, in particular, the encouraging agreement obtained between observed and predicted changes in yield stress of Magnox surveillance steels irradiated over a range of temperatures, fluxes, and spectra. Certainly, the initial application of such modeling techniques to PWR steels is showing promising signs of a capability to account for the changes found in both MTR and surveillance irradiations. However, there are additional features that need to be investigated further and the following are some examples: (1) there is evidence [40] for Mo_2C precipitates in PWR PV test specimens during irradiation, and this feature may provide an additional hardening source term for modeling mechanisms; (2) the role of nickel in aiding embrittlement when copper is present to significant levels needs to be understood for the analysis of older PWR PVs; (3)

the role of phosphorus requires to be understood; (4) recovery processes during annealing have been explained [47] by mechanisms different from those responsible for strengthening, and the mechanisms involved in strengthening and recovery should be consistent; (5) the increase in S value in positron annihilation studies with increase in both copper content and decreasing irradiation temperature [35] would indicate an increasing vacancy concentration that seems to contradict the mechanisms assumed in current models; etc.

There is a continued need to develop data bases on materials typical of current practices and from various sources of supply. In order to do this, there is a requirement for the continued development and standardization of test methods and techniques for both surveillance and post-irradiation testing processes. Many of these problems are being addressed in various national programs and in the phases of the IAEA Coordinated Research Programme and other international programs, such as the Surveillance Dosimetry Improvement Programme [48], but much work still remains to be done to understand irradiation embrittlement.

References

[1] Marshall, W. (chairman), "An Assessment of the Integrity of PWR Pressure Vessels," United Kingdom Atomic Energy Agency, 1976.
[2] Marshall, W. (chairman), "An Assessment of the Integrity of PWR Pressure Vessels," Second Report, United Kingdom Atomic Energy Agency, 1981.
[3] ASME III Appendix G, American Society of Mechanical Engineers, 1983.
[4] ASME XI Appendix A, American Society of Mechanical Engineers, 1983.
[5] 10 CFR 50, U.S. Code of Federal Regulations, 1980 (Fracture Toughness and Surveillance Program requirements).
[6] "Effects of Residual Elements on Predicted Radiation Damage to Reactor Vessel Materials," Regulatory Guide 1.99, Revision 1, U.S. Nuclear Regulatory Commission, Washington, DC, April 1977.
[7] Randall, P. N., "The Status of Trend Curves and Surveillance Results in US NRC Regulatory Activities," IAEA Specialists Meeting, Vienna, International Atomic Energy Agency, Oct. 1981.
[8] Randall, P. N., private communication to T. Ingham of "Draft Proposed Revision to Reg Guide 1.99," 14 June 84.
[9] Guthrie, G. L., "Charpy Trend Curves Based on 177 PWR Data Points," LWR PV SDIP, Quarterly Progress Report April 1983–June 1983, NUREG/CR-3391, Vol. 2, HEDL-TME 83-22, U.S. Nuclear Regulatory Commission, Washington, DC.
[10] Odette, G. R. and Lombrozo, P. M., "Physically Based Regression Correlations of Embrittlement Data from Reactor Vessel Surveillance Programmes," EPRI NP-3319, Final Report, Electric Power Research Institute, Jan. 1984.
[11] Steele, L. E., Davies, L. M., Ingham, T., and Brumovsky, M. in Effects of Radiation on Materials: Twelfth Conference, ASTM STP 870, F. A. Garner and J. S. Perrin, Eds., American Society for Testing and Materials, Philadelphia, 1986, pp. 863–899.
[12] Druce, S. G. and Edwards, B. C., Nuclear Technology, Vol. 55, Nov. 1981.
[13] Druce, S. G., AERE Report R11043, AERE Harwell, Nov. 1983.
[14] Druce, S. G., Gage, G., Jordan, G., and Hudson, J. A., "Effect of Thermal Aging on the Mechanical Properties of PWR Pressure Vessel Steels and Weldments," United Kingdom Atomic Energy Authority Report No. AERE-R 11460, April 1985.
[15] Druce, S. G. and Edwards, B. C., Proceedings, ANS Conference on Materials Performance in Steam Generators, Florida, 1980, American Nuclear Society.
[16] Brear, J. M. and King, B. L., CEGB CERL Report, LM/MATS 348, Central Electricity Generating Board, 1980.

[17] Little, E. A. in *Effects of Radiation on Materials: Twelfth Conference, ASTM STP 870*, F. A. Garner and J. S. Perrin, Eds., American Society for Testing and Materials, Philadelphia, 1986, pp. 1089–1126.
[18] Outline proposal for UK contribution to IAEA CRP, submitted July 1984.
[19] Jones, R. B. and Buswell, J. T., *Proceedings*, Brighton Conference, British Nuclear Energy Society, Vol. 2, April 1984.
[20] Davies, L. M., et al, "Analysis of the Behaviour of Advanced RPV Steels under Neutron Irradiation—The UK Programme," United Kingdom Atomic Energy Agency, April 1983.
[21] Varsik, J. D. and Byrne, S. T. in *Effects of Radiation on Structural Materials (9th Conference)*, *ASTM STP 683*, J. A. Sprague and D. Kramer, Eds., American Society for Testing and Materials, Philadelphia, 1979, pp. 252–266.
[22] Frisius, F., Kampmann, P. A., Beavan, P. A., Bunemann, D., and Wagner, R., "Small Angle Neutron Scattering Analysis of Irradiation Induced Microstructural Changes in Steel and Fe-Cu Alloys," 1981, Gesellschaft fuer Kernenergieverwertung in Schiffbau und Schiffahrt (atomic power) (Germany) (GKSS), 81/E/58.
[23] R. B. Jones, and J. T. Buswell, private communication from R. B. Jones, Sept. 1984.
[24] Highton, J. P. in *Radiation Embrittlement and Surveillance of Nuclear Reactor Pressure Vessels: An International Study, ASTM STP 819*, L. E. Steele, Ed., American Society for Testing and Materials, Philadelphia, 1983, pp. 117–129.
[25] Highton, J. P., private communication, Sept. 1984.
[26] Neale, B. K., *International Journal of Pressure Vessels & Piping*, Vol. 10, 1982, pp. 375–398.
[27] Neale, B. K., *International Journal of Pressure Vessels & Piping*, Vol. 12, 1983, pp. 207–227.
[28] Neale, B. K. and Priest, R. H., *Proceedings*, CSNI Workshop on Ductile Fracture Test Methods, Paris, 1982, pp. 464–476.
[29] Neale, B. K. and Priest, R. H., in *Elastic-Plastic Fracture Test Methods: The User's Experience*, *ASTM STP 856*, American Society for Testing and Materials, Philadelphia, 1983, pp. 375–393.
[30] Neale, B. K. and Priest, R. H., *Engineering Fracture Mechanics*, Vol. 19, No. 3, 1984, pp. 441–448.
[31] Neale, B. K. and Priest, R. H., *Proceedings*, International Conference on Fracture Toughness Testing, London, Paper 2, 1982.
[32] Priest, R. H., Charnock, W., and Stewart, A. T., in *Effects of Radiation on Materials—11th International Symposium, ASTM STP 782*, H. R. Brager and J. S. Perrin, Eds., American Society for Testing and Materials, Philadelphia, 1982, pp. 475–491.
[33] Priest, R. H., Charnock, W., and Neale, B. K., in *Effects of Radiation on Materials: Twelfth Conference, ASTM STP 870*, F. A. Garner and J. S. Perrin, Eds., American Society for Testing and Materials, Philadelphia, 1986, pp. 1150–1162.
[34] Fisher, S. B., Harbottle, J. E., and Aldridge, N., "Copper Precipitation in Magnox Pressure Vessel Steels: Part 1 Introduction," CEGB Report TPRD/B/0396/N84, Central Electricity Generating Board, Jan. 1984.
[35] Fisher, S. B., Harbottle, J. E., and Aldridge, N., "Copper Precipitation in Magnox Pressure Vessel Steels: Part 2: The Examination of Long Term Aged Steels," CEGB Report TPRD/B/0397/N84, Jan. 1984.
[36] Fisher, S. B., Harbottle, J. E., and Aldridge, N., "Copper Precipitation in Magnox Pressure Vessel Steels: Part 3, A Detailed Description of the Model and Its Applications," CEGB Report TPRD/B/0398/N84, Central Electricity Generating Board, Jan. 1984.
[37] Potapovs, U. and Hawthorne, J. R., *Nuclear Applications*, Vol. 6, 1969, p. 27.
[38] Brenner, S. S., Wagner, R., and Spitznagel, J. A., *Metallurgical Transactions A*, Vol. 9A, 1978, p. 1961.
[39] Goodman, S. R., Brenner, S. S., and Low, J. R., *Metallurgical Transactions*, Vol. 4, No. 10, 1973, p. 2371.
[40] Lott, R. G., Brenner, S. S., Miller, M. K., and Wolfenden, A., *Transactions*, American Nuclear Society, Vol. 38, 1981, p. 303.
[41] Hawthorne, J. R., in *Irradiation Effects on Structural Alloys for Nuclear Reactor Applications*, *ASTM STP 484*, American Society for Testing and Materials, Philadelphia, 1971, pp. 96–127.

[42] Fisher, S. B., Harbottle, J. E., and Aldridge, N., CEGB Report NO TPRD/B/0108/N82, Central Electricity Generating Board, 1982.
[43] Russell, K. C. and Brown, L. M., *Acta Metallurgica*, Vol. 20, 1972, p. 969.
[44] Buswell, J. T., CEGB Report TPRD/B/0351/N83, Central Electricity Generating Board, Oct. 1983.
[45] "Irradiated Nuclear PV Steel Data Base," EPRI NR 2428, Electric Power Research Institute, 1982.
[46] Odette, G. R., *Scripta Metallurgica*, Vol. 17, 1983, pp. 1183–1188.
[47] Pachur, D., *Arch. Eisenhuttenwesen*, Vol. 47, 1976, p. 501.
[48] Serpan, C. Z., *Nuclear Safety*, Vol. 22, No. 1, 1981.
[49] CEGB Evidence to the Sizewell B Public Inquiry, CEGB P12 Add 5, Central Electricity Generating Board, 1984.

Jürgen Ahlf,[1] Dieter Bellmann,[1] Jürgen Föhl,[2] Hans D. Hebenbrock,[1] Franz J. Schmitt,[1] and Werner Spalthoff[1]

Irradiation Behavior of Reactor Pressure Vessel Steels from the Research Program on the Integrity of Components

REFERENCE: Ahlf, J., Bellmann, D., Föhl, J., Hebenbrock, H. D., Schmitt, F. J., and Spalthoff, W., **"Irradiation Behavior of Reactor Pressure Vessel Steels from the Research Program on the Integrity of Components,"** *Radiation Embrittlement of Nuclear Reactor Pressure Vessel Steels: An International Review (Second Volume), ASTM STP 909,* L. E. Steele, Ed., American Society for Testing and Materials, Philadelphia, 1986, pp. 34–51.

ABSTRACT: Within the research program "Integrity of Components," reactor pressure vessel steels are irradiated in capsules in the swimming-pool-type research reactor FRG-2 at 290°C to different fluences of fast neutrons. Steel heats both conforming and not conforming to specifications with respect to chemical composition as well as to tensile and deformation properties are included.

So far, the results show that for the materials investigated the 41 J transition temperature shift from impact testing is always larger than the nil ductility transition (NDT) shift from drop-weight testing. This means that the mode of procedure of the regulatory rules leads to conservative values for the adjusted reference temperature even for material states near and beyond the specification limits.

From instrumented Charpy tests, the arrest load was determined. It was found that the irradiation-induced shift of the arrest load versus temperature curve corresponds closely to the NDT shift. By evaluating Charpy surveillance specimens along this line, one has a supplementary criterion for assessing irradiation embrittlement at hand.

At low fluences, the 41 J transition temperature shifts are conservatively predicted by the trend curves of Regulatory Guide 1.99, whereas at high fluences—though a little beyond the validity limits—these shifts lie above the extrapolated trend curves.

KEY WORDS: radiation effects, pressure vessel steels, reactors, steels, irradiation, neutron fluence, impact tests, tensile properties

The aim of the irradiation experiments within the research program "Integrity of Components," is to improve the understanding of the relationship between

[1] Head of Section for Irradiation Experiments, senior research physicist, head of the Mechanical Testing Laboratory, senior research metallurgist, and head of Hot Cell Laboratory, respectively, GKSS-Forschungszentrum Geesthacht GmbH, Geesthacht, West Germany.

[2] Deputy project manager for Safety of Components, Staatliche Materialprüfungsanstalt der Universität Stuttgart, Stuttgart, West Germany.

material properties (chemical composition, initial toughness) and response to neutron irradiation. From tension and toughness testing, before and after irradiation, along with a careful characterization of the neutron exposure, the irradiation response can be quantified. Special attention is paid to the safety margins for components of lower bound material properties exposed to extremely high neutron fluence, when fracture toughness is deduced from impact testing according to the regulatory rules. Comparison of experimental results from the irradiation experiments with trend curves is aimed at quantifying the safety margins of results from surveillance programs.

The results presented and discussed in this paper belong to a large matrix of experiments [1] comprised of irradiation experiments in different neutron fields with different kinds of specimens. Tensile and deformation properties are determined on the basis of tension, impact, drop-weight, and fracture toughness testing as well as hardness testing. The present results come from the first irradiation experiments in FRG-2 at Geesthacht and include tension, Charpy, drop-weight, and hardness testing that will be supplemented by fracture toughness testing (linear elastic as well as elastic-plastic) in the future program.

Materials

Two types of steel used for the pressure vessels of recent light-water reactors in the Federal Republic of Germany are investigated, namely, 22 NiMoCr 3 7 (corresponding to A508 Class 2) and 20 MnMoNi 5 5 (corresponding to A533 B Class 1). Several heats, some conforming to the specifications, others beyond them with respect to unfavorable chemical composition, low upper-shelf energy in impact testing, and high ductile to brittle transition temperature are included in order to cover realistic and postulated limiting situations [2–4]. The forgings are large enough to simulate a real component. Some forgings have been melted for the program (up to 200 000 kg), and others are rejected or withdrawn components.

The chemical compositions of the heats that are investigated here are shown in Table 1. Their impact toughness is shown in Fig. 1.

The KS 07 B material is an experimental heat that has been chosen intentionally because its chemical composition is outside of the specification. The specimens from KS 07 B were taken in the longitudinal direction (L and L-T). Because of the low upper-shelf energy in the transverse direction (~35 J), the conventional criteria for determining the ductile to brittle transition temperature and its shifts on irradiation could not be applied.

The KS 07 B, which is strongly irradiation sensitive because of its chemical composition, and KS 12, which is medium irradiation sensitive, are used as monitor materials. A set of Charpy specimens of each of these two materials is inserted into every irradiation capsule.

TABLE 1—Chemical composition of the materials investigated.

Material	C	Si	Mn	P	S	Cr	Mo	Ni	Al	Cu	V	Sn	Co	As	Sb	Nb	Ta	N	B	Ti	W
22 NiMoCr 3 7 specification VdTÜV 365 (4.72)																					
min	0.17	...	0.50	...	...	0.30	0.50	0.60	...	...	0.05	...	...	...	...	...	...	...	...	...	...
max	0.25	0.35	1.00	0.025	0.025	0.50	0.80	1.00	0.05 0.01	0.20	0.05	...	...	...	...	...	...	...	...	...	...
Restricted	≦0.20	0.20[a]	0.85[a]	≦0.008	≦0.008	≦0.40	≦0.55	1.20[a]	0.04	≦0.10	≦0.01	≦0.01	≦0.003	≦0.015	≦0.005	...	≦0.030	≦0.013	...	...	...
Base Metal																					
KS 01	0.25	0.24	0.71	0.009	0.022	0.41	0.75	0.95	0.046	0.11	0.012	0.01	0.019	0.017	<0.01	...	<0.01	...	...	...	...
KS 02 T/4	0.21	0.21	0.99	0.005	0.005	0.54	0.62	1.21	0.03	0.10	0.01	0.01	0.02	0.02	<0.01	<<0.01	...	...	...	...	...
KS 02 T/2	0.18	0.20	0.95	0.004	0.006	0.52	0.60	1.18	0.03	0.10	0.01	0.01	0.02	0.02	<0.01	<<0.01	...	...	...	...	...
KS 07 8[c]	0.27	0.29	0.62	0.022	0.034	0.49	1.03	0.74	<0.003	0.26	0.05	0.012	0.016	0.026	<0.005	...	...	...	...	...	...
20 MnMoNi 5 5 Specification VdTÜV Tentative Oct. 76																					
min	0.17	0.15	1.20	...	...	...	0.45	0.45	0.01	...	...	...	...	...	...	...	...	...	...	...	...
max	0.23	0.30	1.50	0.015	0.015	0.20	0.60	0.80	0.04	0.18	0.02	...	0.03	...	...	...	0.03	...	...	...	...
Restricted	0.15 0.25	0.10 0.35	1.15 1.55	≦0.012	≦0.012	≦0.20	0.40 0.55	0.45 0.85	0.010 0.040	≦0.12 (≦0.10)[b]	≦0.02	≦0.011	≦0.03	≦0.025	...	...	≦0.030	≦0.013	...	...	...
Base Metal KS 12	0.25	0.32	1.48	0.015	0.012	0.15	0.61	0.63	0.027	0.17	0.02	0.007	0.01	0.01	<<0.01	<<0.01	...	...	...	<<0.01	0.01

[a] Recommended value.
[b] ( )Core region.
[c] Experimental heat with low upper-shelf energy in transverse direction.

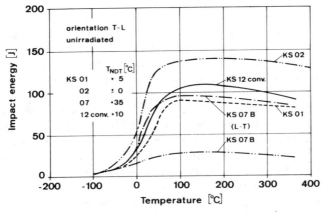

FIG. 1—*Impact energy of the materials investigated.*

FIG. 2—*Irradiation capsule for reactor pressure vessel steel specimens.*

Irradiation Experiments

The irradiation experiments are performed in capsules with a large specimen volume [5]. In Fig. 2, such a capsule is shown during assembly. The specimen volume has a height of 500 mm and a width of 260 mm; the depth is chosen according to the specimen carriage; it can be varied between 60 mm and 120 mm.

The temperature distribution in the specimen volume is measured by about 50 chromel-alumel thermocouples. For temperature control, three electrical heaters, one above the other, are installed on the frontside and on the backside of the specimen volume; additional heaters are mounted on the sides. From the time averages of the thermocouple signals, a three-dimensional temperature profile is determined by approximation with a polynomial; from that polynomial, an average irradiation temperature is calculated for each specimen at the crack tip. Within a specimen set in a capsule, the deviation from the mean value is less than 5 K.

The capsules are irradiated in border positions of FRG-2. The FRG-2 is a swimming-pool-type research reactor operated at 15 MW. To reduce gamma heating in the specimens, shields of stainless steel 74 mm thick are arranged between the capsules and the reactor core.

Evaluation

Dosimetry

The fluence distribution in the capsules is determined from the activation of iron-nickel wires (63.8% iron and 36.2% nickel, by weight) distributed in the specimen volume on the basis of neutron spectra, which have been obtained from two-dimensional transport calculations with DOT IV [6] using the EURLIB Library condensed to a 51 energy group structure. The dosimetry cross sections are taken from ENDF/B-V. The cross sections of the neutron exposure units, fluence ($E > 1$ MeV) and dpa, respectively, are defined as follows

$$\sigma(E > 1 \text{ MeV}) = \frac{\int_0^\infty \sigma(E)\Phi(E)dE}{\int_{1\text{ MeV}}^\infty \Phi(E)dE}$$

$$\sigma(\text{dpa}) = \frac{\int_0^\infty \sigma_d(E)\Phi(E)dE}{\int_{1\text{ Mev}}^\infty \Phi(E)dE} = \frac{\text{dpa}}{\int_{1\text{ MeV}}^\infty \Phi(E)dE}$$

where $\sigma_d(E)$ = cross section for Frenkel defects in iron [7] according to ASTM Practice for Characterizing Neutron Exposures in Ferritic Steels in Terms of Displacements Per Atom (E 693-79).

In order to reduce fluence gradients in the direction perpendicular to the core, the capsules are turned around their vertical axis several times during an irradiation period. Therefore, each point in the capsule outside the middle plane sees two different neutron spectra; this is taken into account in the evaluation of the monitor activation.

To determine the ^{54}Mn activity from the reaction ^{54}Fe$(n,p)^{54}$Mn and the ^{58}Co activity from the reaction ^{58}Ni$(n,p)^{58}$Co, the wires are scanned along a germanium (lithium) detector.

The fluence distribution in the specimen volume, as determined from the monitor wire activation, is approximated by a polynomial in the three space coordinates, so that an individual exposure can be assigned to each specimen at the crack tip. The fluence variation within one specimen set is less than 5%.

Testing of Irradiated Specimens

The hot cell facilities for testing irradiated materials are described in detail in Ref 8.

For tension and fracture toughness testing, three machines with maximum loads of 50, 250, and 2500 kN, respectively, are available. Testing is possible in the temperature range from -196 to $+300°C$. Tension specimens and fracture toughness specimens of CT and WOL type up to 100 mm thickness can be tested.

Standard Charpy V-notch specimens are tested on an instrumented 300 J pendulum ram, impact testing machine that is fully automated; again the accessible temperature range is from -196 to $+300°C$. In addition to the conventional values determined in the noninstrumented test, characteristic parameters of the

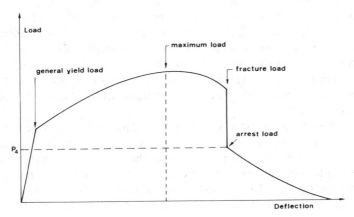

FIG. 3—*Load-deflection diagram (schematic).*

load-deflection curve, schematically shown in Fig. 3, are measured as a function of the testing temperature, for instance, the arrest load [9].

With a drop-weight testing machine installed in a lead cell, it is possible to test the Pellini P2 specimens according to ASTM Recommended Practice for Conducting Drop-Weight Test to Determine Nil-Ductility Transition Temperature of Ferritic Steels (E 208-81). The specimens are brought to the test temperature in a constant temperature chamber working with a combined liquid nitrogen cooling and electric heating system. Then they are transferred automatically to the anvil and tested immediately.

For hardness testing (Brinell, Rockwell, or Vickers), a universal testing apparatus is installed in a lead cell. Additional shielded devices for measuring lateral expansion, reduction of area, etc., are available.

Results and Discussion

Most of the results are from the KS 01 and KS 02 heats, both of type 22 NiMoCr 3 7 steel. Some results of KS 07 B (22 NiMoCr 3 7, modified) and KS 12 (20 MnMoNi 5 5) that are used as monitor materials are included. The properties of the unirradiated materials are generally determined from specimens cut in the vicinity of those taken for irradiation.

Tensile Properties and Hardness

Tension specimens from KS 01, KS 02, and KS 07 B were irradiated in several capsules at 290°C to target fluences of $2 \cdot 10^{23}$ m^{-2} and $7.5 \cdot 10^{23}$ m^{-2} ($E > 1$ MeV), respectively.

The tensile properties at room temperature and at 300°C are shown in Table 2. Yield strength and tensile strength as a function of temperature are shown in Figs. 4, 5, and 6. In the unirradiated as well as in the irradiated state, these parameters decrease with increasing temperature up to 200°C and are constant for higher temperatures. Yield strength as well as tensile strength increase on irradiation. The increase is largest for KS 01 and smallest for KS 07 B. Also, the curves show that the yield strength ratio remains nearly constant over the whole temperature range. The elongation decreases a little with increasing fluence, whereas the reduction of area does not show any trend as can be seen from the data of Table 2.

The Vickers hardness (HV10) was determined for all four irradiated materials. The irradiated Charpy specimens were used for the measurements. The results are collected in Table 3, which also contains the change in yield strength in the last column for comparison. The increase of hardness is quite different for the materials investigated. To what extent the increase of hardness is correlated to the changes in tensile and deformation parameters will be investigated further.

TABLE 2—*Tensile properties of the materials investigated (irradiation at 290°C).*

Fluence, 10^{23} m^{-2}, $E > 1$ MeV	dpa, %	Testing Temperature, °C	$R_{eH}/R_{p0.2}$, MPa	R_m, MPa	A_5, %	Z, %
KS 01, 22 NiMoCr 3 7, Orientation T						
0	0	23	438	586	25	55
1.96	3.8	23	549	679	21	60
8.02	15.6	23	669	764	18	42
0	0	300	375	547	20	45
1.95	3.7	300	462	617	17	44
7.56	14.7	300	549	699	14	40
KS 02, 22 NiMoCr 3 7, Orientation T						
0	0	23	500	656	20	62
2.17	4.2	23	569	687	21	66
7.05	13.7	23	694	792	19	66
0	0	300	426	580	21	56
2.09	4.1	300	502	634	17	60
7.27	14.1	300	599	719	15	59
KS 07 B, 22 NiMoCr 3 7, Orientation L						
0	0	23	739	886	19	64
1.5	3.0	23	824	944	20	61
5.5	10.7	23	909	1014	18	57
0	0	300	622	786	14	58
1.5	3.0	300	729	867	17	60
5.5	10.7	300	779	909	15	51

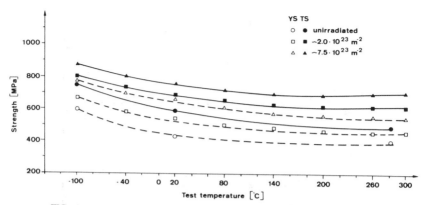

FIG. 4—*Change of yield and tensile strength of steel KS 01 by irradiation.*

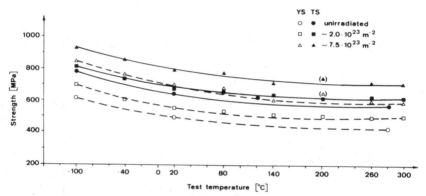

FIG. 5—*Change of yield and tensile strength of steel KS 02 by irradiation.*

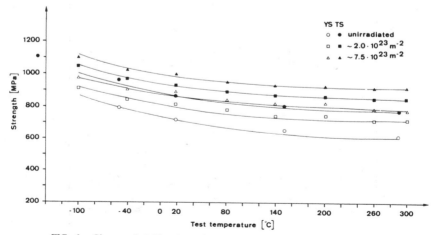

FIG. 6—*Change of yield and tensile strength of steel KS 07 B by irradiation.*

TABLE 3—*Hardness of the materials investigated (irradiation at 290°C).*

Fluence, 10^{23} m^{-2}, $E > 1$ MeV	dpa, %	Hardness HV10^a	Increase of Hardness, %	Increase of Yield Strength at 20°C, %
		KS 01 GW, 22 NiMoCr 3 7		
0	0	214	. . .	. . .
2.14	4.1	239	12	24
7.78	15.1	258	21	46
		KS 02 GW, 22 NiMoCr 3 7		
0	0	195	. . .	. . .
2.04	3.9	233	19	13
8.26	16.0	281	44	22
		KS 07 B GW, 22 NiMoCr 3 7		
0	0	272	. . .	. . .
1.56	3.0	314	15	12
7.89	15.5	336	24	22
		KS 12 GW, 20 MnMoNi 5 5		
0	0	235	. . .	. . .
2.09	4.1	254	8	. . .
8.33	16.3	279	19	. . .

^{a} GW = base metal.

Impact Energy and NDT Temperature

Charpy V-notch specimens of all four steels KS 01, KS 02, KS 07 B, and KS 12 and the Pellini P2 dropweight specimens of KS 01 and KS 02 were irradiated to $2 \cdot 10^{23}$ m^{-2} and $7.5 \cdot 10^{23}$ m^{-2} ($E > 1$ MeV).

In the instrumented impact test, the absorbed energy, lateral expansion, shear fracture portion, and arrest load were measured as a function of temperature. The data for absorbed energy, lateral expansion, and shear fracture portion have been approximated by the gaussian integral; the corresponding transition temperatures were taken from the approximated curves. The measurements of the arrest load P_4 (see Fig. 3) have been evaluated in the following manner: the arrest load at the drop weight temperature, T_{NDT}, in the unirradiated state has been determined as a material specific reference arrest load; for the irradiated state, the temperature at which the arrest load is equal to this reference arrest load is defined as the transition temperature T_{P4} (in the unirradiated state T_{P4} is identical to T_{NDT} by definition). The irradiation conditions and the results of impact testing are contained in Table 4.

The irradiation conditions and the results of drop-weight testing are contained in Table 5.

The impact energy versus testing temperature curves for KS 01, KS 02, KS 07 B, and KS 12 are shown in Figs. 7 to 10. Note that the specimens of KS 07 B are in the L-T orientation. The shift of the transition temperature and the decrease of the upper-shelf energy as a function of fluence are clearly visible. The 41 J shift is given in Table 6.

TABLE 4—Results of instrumented impact tests.

Fluence, 10^{23} m^{-2} $E > 1$ MeV	dpa, %	Irradiation Temperature, °C	T_{41J}, °C	t_{68J}, °C	$T_{0.9mm}$, °C	$T_{50\%}$, °C	T_{P4}, °C	Upper-Shelf Energy, J
			KS 01, ORIENTATION T-L					
0	0	...	6	43	15	5	5 [10]	86
2.14	4.1	290	56	103	63	56	50	77
7.78	15.1	288	128	209	139	116	100	72
			KS 02, ORIENTATION T-L					
0	0	...	−41	−23	−27	−7	0 [10]	157
2.04	3.9	288	7	29	23	33	40	138
8.26	16.0	286	98	136	124	118	105	113
			KS 07 B, ORIENTATION L-T					
0	0	...	0	22	16	−1	30 [11]	119
1.56	3.0	287	58	80	78	72	75	118
7.89	15.5	290	117	181	165	112	130	93
			KS 12, ORIENTATION T-L					
0	0	...	25	49	38	29	10 [3]	129
2.09	4.1	289	102	148	118	111	75	96
8.33	16.3	287	140	175	161	140	110	100

TABLE 5—*Results of drop weight tests.*

Fluence, 10^{23} m^{-2}, $E > 1$ MeV	dpa, %	Irradiation Temperature, °C	T_{NDT}, °C
		KS 01, Orientation T-L	
0	0	...	5 [10]
1.99	3.8	291	45
7.07	13.7	289	100
		KS 02, Orientation T-L	
0	0	...	0 [10]
2.02	3.9	289	40
7.79	15.1	288	105

Comparison of the results for steels KS 01 and KS 02 shows that the 41 J transition temperature shifts are nearly equal for the lower fluence, whereas these shifts differ by 16 K at the higher fluence. The decrease of upper-shelf energy is less for KS 01, which has, apart from this, a lower upper-shelf energy in the unirradiated state than KS 02. For both steels, the reduced upper-shelf is reached at a relatively high temperature of about 200°C as a result of a significant flattening of the impact energy versus temperature curves.

The KS 07 B and KS 12 materials exhibit comparable transition temperature shifts and decreases of the upper-shelf energy at the same fluence levels ($2 \cdot 10^{23}$ m^{-2} and $7.5 \cdot 10^{23}$ m^{-2}, respectively) despite the higher copper content as compared to KS 01 and KS 02.

In Figs. 11 and 12, the arrest load, P_4, is plotted against the testing temperature for steels KS 01 and KS 02 in the unirradiated state and for the two fluence levels. The curves are shifted to higher temperatures on irradiation similar to the impact energy curves.

It was suggested earlier to estimate the NDT temperature on the basis of P_4 versus temperature measurements [12]. In this work, it was attempted to correlate the shift of the P_4 versus temperature curve on irradiation to the corresponding NDT shift. It was found that for the steels investigated, the shift of the arrest load transition temperature, T_{P4}, as defined earlier is in very good agreement with the shift of T_{NDT} from the drop-weight test. This is shown in Figs. 11 and 12 and can be seen from the numerical values given in Table 6. The reason for this correlation is probably because in both tests the parameters that characterize the crack arrest behavior are determined.

An important safety consideration is that the drop-weight NDT shift is always less than the 41 J shift for the steels investigated. This agrees with other investigations [3,13,14].

In Fig. 13, the 41 J transition temperature shifts, measured in the impact test, are compared to the trend curves of Regulatory Guide 1.99 [15]. For the lower fluence, the measured shifts are well below the trend curves whereas at the higher fluence the shifts lie above the extrapolated trend curves. For steel KS 01, a

TABLE 6—Comparison of measured transition temperature shifts according to different criteria with different trend formulas taking into account the chemical composition.

Fluence, $E > 1$ MeV, 10^{23} m^{-2}	dpa, %	Measured Values			Reg. Guide,[a] K	Guthrie,[b] K	Randall,[c] K	KTA,[d] K
		ΔT_{41J}, K	ΔT_{P4}, K	ΔT_{NDT}, K				
				KS 01				
~2.0	~4	50	45	40	61	53	59	73
~7.5	~16	122	95	95	116	76	66	...[e]
				KS 02				
~2.0	~4	48	40	40	48	53	59	62
~7.5	~16	139	105	105	96	78	66	...[e]
				KS 07 B				
1.56	3.0	58	45	...	173[f]	112	125	...[e]
7.89	15.5	117	100	...	233[f]	174	149	...[e]
				KS 12				
2.09	4.1	77	65	...	132	73	81	130
8.33	16.3	115	100	...	236[f]	106	91	...[e]

[a] $\Delta T = \dfrac{1}{1.8}\,[40 + 1000\,(\mathrm{Cu} - 0.08) + 5000\,(\mathrm{P} - 0.008)\cdot f^{0.5}$.

[b] $\Delta T = \dfrac{1}{1.8}\,[-10 + 470\,\mathrm{Cu} + 350\,\mathrm{NiCu}]\cdot f^{0.27}$ [18].

[c] $\Delta T = \dfrac{1}{1.8}\,[-54 + 555\,\mathrm{Cu} + 255\,\sqrt{\mathrm{CuNi}}]\cdot f^{0.26-0.06\cdot\ln f}$ [16].

$f = \Phi t/10^{23}$ m^{-2} ($E > 1$ MeV), concentration in percent by weight.

[d] KTA 3203.

[e] Beyond validity range [17].

[f] Upper limit curve [15].

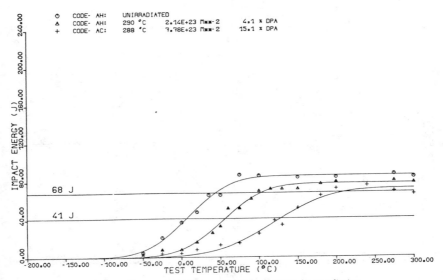

FIG. 7—*Change of impact energy of steel KS 01 by irradiation.*

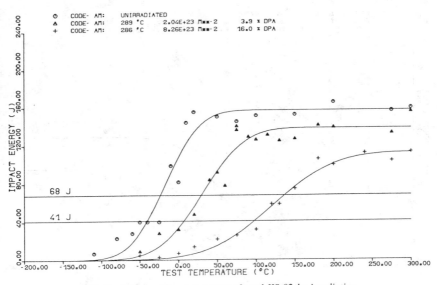

FIG. 8—*Change of impact energy of steel KS 02 by irradiation.*

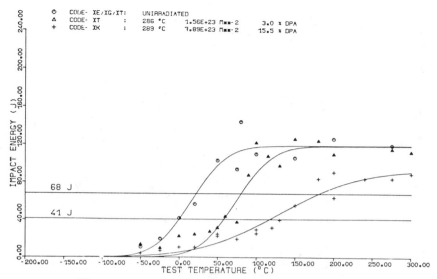

FIG. 9—*Change of impact energy of steel KS 07 B by irradiation.*

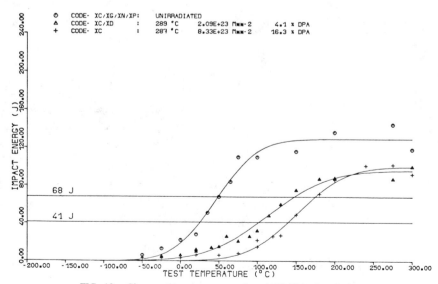

FIG. 10—*Change of impact energy of steel KS 12 by irradiation.*

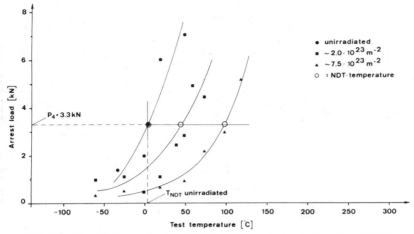

FIG. 11—*Change of arrest load and NDT temperature by irradiation of steel KS 01.*

transition temperature shift is added, which had been determined earlier from an irradiation to a fluence of $2 \cdot 10^{23}$ m^{-2} ($E > 1$ MeV) in the VAK reactor that is a small prototype boiling-water reactor. This value compares well with the data found in this investigation despite the fact that the neutron spectra and the fluence rates are different.

In Table 6, four columns are added that contain the 41 J shifts as predicted by Regulatory Guide 1.99 [15], its proposed revision [16], the recent German KTA Rule 3203 [17], and by the empirical formula of Guthrie [18]. Whereas Regulatory Guide 1.99 leads to predictions in accordance with the experimental results (except the high fluence shift of KS 02), the proposed revision and also the Guthrie formula predict the high fluence shifts too low; the predictions of KTA 3203 with its restricted validity range are conservative.

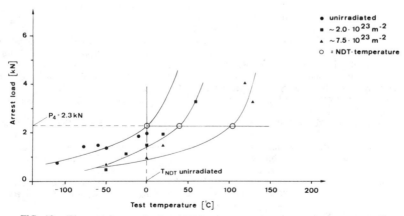

FIG. 12—*Change of arrest load and NDT temperature by irradiation of steel KS 02.*

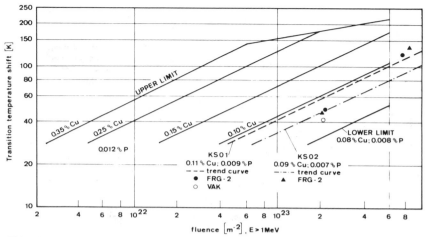

FIG. 13—*Comparison of measured ΔT(41 J) values with trend curves of Regulatory Guide 1.99.*

References

[1] Föhl, J., et al, "Irradiation Experiments in the Research Program Safety of Components," 5th MPA Seminar on Safety of the Pressure Boundary of Light Water Reactors, 11 and 12 Oct. 1979, Stuttgart.

[2] Issler, L., "Status of the Research Program Safety of Components," 5th MPA Seminar on Safety of the Pressure Boundary of Light Water Reactors, 11 and 12 Oct. 1979, Stuttgart.

[3] Föhl, J., Leitz, C., and Anders, D., *Nuclear Engineering and Design*, Vol. 72, 1982, pp. 65–79.

[4] Kussmaul, K., "The Integration of the Tensile- and C_v-Tests in an Experimentally Verified Engineering Fracture Mechanics Approach," 7th MPA Seminar on Safety of the Pressure Boundary of Light Water Reactors, 8 and 9 Oct. 1981, Stuttgart.

[5] Ahlf, J., Bellmann, D., and Martens, H., Operating Experience with Capsules for RPV Steel Irradiations with Large Specimen Volume, P. V. D. Hardt and H. Röttger, Eds., *Irradiation Technologie*, Brüssel, 1983, p. 593.

[6] Bellman, D., Ahlf, J., Wille, P., and Prillinger, G., "Neutron Dosimetry in Irradiation Capsules for Large RPV Steel Specimens," Fourth ASTM-EURATOM Symposium on Reactor Dosimetry, 22–26 March, 1982, NUREG/CP-0029, Vol. 1, p. 579.

[7] *Annual Book of ASTM Standards*, American Society for Testing and Materials, Philadelphia.

[8] Hebenbrock, H. D., Schmitt, F. J., and Spalthoff, W., "Fracture Mechanical Testing Methods for Irradiated Pressure Vessel Steels," GKSS 82/E/54, 1982.

[9] Müller-Roos, J. and Richter, G., "Instrumented Impact Test, a Contribution to Investigate Fracture of Steels," GKSS Annual Report 1979, 1980, pp. 35–45.

[10] Sinz, R., et al, "Research Program Safety of Components, Materials and Weld Connections," TWB 1/1, 1981.

[11] Föhl, J., et al, "Research Program Safety of Components, Vol. Irradiation," TWB 5/1, Dec. 1981.

[12] Berger, C., et al, "Determination of Brittle Fracture and Fracture Mechanics Parameters by Means of Impact Test Specimens, German Association for Materials Testing," 11th Session of the Working Group on Fracture Phenomena, 9–11 Oct. 1979, Stuttgart.

[13] Klausnitzer, E. N., Gerscha, A., and Leitz, C., in *Effects of Radiation on Structural Materials (9th Conference), ASTM STP 683*, J. A. Sprague and D. Kramer, Eds., American Society for Testing and Materials, Philadelphia, 1979, pp. 267–277.

[14] Schmitt, F. J., Spalthoff, W., Ahlf, J., and Bellmann, D., "Evaluation of Neutron Irradiation

Embrittlement of Pressure Vessel Steels," IAEA Coordinated Program, Final Report, International Atomic Energy Agency, June 1983.

[15] U. S. Nuclear Regulatory Commission Regulatory Guide 1.99 Rev. 1 (April 1977), "Effects of Residual Elements on Predicted Radiation Damage to Reactor Vessel Materials," Nuclear Regulatory Commission, Washington, DC.

[16] Randall, P. N., "NRC Perspective of Safety and Licensing Issues Regarding Reactor Vessel Steel Embrittlement Criteria for Trend Curve Development," ANS Annual Meeting, Detroit, American Nuclear Society, 14 June 1983.

[17] Safety Rule of KTA No. 3203, "Surveillance of the Irradiation Embrittlement of Materials from the Pressure Vessel of Light Water Reactors," March 1984.

[18] Guthrie, G. L. and Randall, P. N., "Comparison of Guthrie and MPC Formulas for the Mean Values of ΔRT_{NDT} for Representative Copper and Nickel Content in Pressure Vessel Steels," 1982, to be published.

Surveillance and Other Radiation Embrittlement Studies

Ralf Ahlstrand,[1] Kari Törrönen,[2] Matti Valo,[3] and Bruno Bärs[3]

Surveillance Programs and Irradiation Embrittlement Research of the Loviisa Nuclear Power Plant

REFERENCE: Ahlstrand, R., Törrönen, K., Valo, M., and Bärs, B., "**Surveillance Programs and Irradiation Embrittlement Research of the Loviisa Nuclear Power Plant**," *Radiation Embrittlement of Nuclear Reactor Pressure Vessel Steels: An International Review (Second Volume), ASTM STP 909,* L. E. Steele, Ed., American Society for Testing and Materials, Philadelphia, 1986, pp. 55–69.

ABSTRACT: The surveillance programs of Loviisa 1 and 2 nuclear power plants consist of irradiations of Charpy V-notch, Charpy-size three-point bend, and tensile specimens. The specimens are located outside the core barrel. The program consists of six sets of irradiation capsules that are taken out according to a special schedule.

The results from the first surveillance tests from Loviisa 1 showed that the shift in transition temperature (both Charpy-V and crack-opening displacement) was higher than expected. These results introduced a modification to the original withdrawal schedule of the surveillance capsules. The subsequent test results confirmed the shift in transition temperature.

In addition to the normal surveillance program, new surveillance capsules have been placed into both reactors before and after the core modification including round compact tension (CT) specimens. Parallel programs to validate the reliable use of small specimens for fracture toughness measurements and a special instrumented impact tester have been conducted.

The accuracy of the fluence measurements has been improved by the implementation of some novel procedures.

To study the amelioration of radiation embrittlement, an annealing study was carried out using the broken halves of the Charpy bars from surveillance testing.

KEY WORDS: radiation embrittlement, surveillance program, fracture toughness, neutron dosimetry, pressure vessels, nuclear reactor materials, chemical composition, heat treatment, radiation effects, pressure vessel steels

In Finland, four commercial light water reactors are currently in operation. In Loviisa, we have two Soviet-built pressure water reactor (PWR) type nuclear power stations (NPS), and in Olkiluoto, two boiling water reactor (BWR) type

[1] Head of Materials Engineering Office, Imatran Voima Power Company, Helsinki, Finland.
[2] Head of Materials Technology Section, Technical Research Centre of Finland, Metals Laboratory, Espoo, Finland.
[3] Senior research officers, Technical Research Centre of Finland, Reactor Laboratory, Espoo, Finland.

NPS of Swedish design. Last year (1983), 37% of the electricity was produced by the nuclear power plants. In this presentation, we will concentrate only on the Loviisa PWR plants that are owned and operated by Imatran Voima Power Company.

In Loviisa, we have two identical blocks with a capacity of 440 MW each. The plants are Soviet designed VVER-440 type reactors. Loviisa 1 has been in commercial operation since May 1977 and Loviisa 2 since January 1981. The load factors of the plants can be seen in Table 1.

The cumulative load factor for Loviisa 1 is 74.2% and for Loviisa 2 it is 80.0%.

The main systems and components in Loviisa were made in the Soviet Union; some smaller systems, for example, water demineralizing plant, ice condenser, steel containment, instrumentation, and the primary cooling pumps are Finnish or other western design.

Surveillance Program of the Loviisa Reactor Pressure Vessels

Description of the Program

The reactor pressure vessel (RPV) of Loviisa 1 and 2 including technical data of the plant is presented in Fig. 1.

The material of the RPV is a quenched and tempered Cr-Mo-V alloyed ferritic steel of type 15X2MφA. Typical chemical compositions of the core area base metal and weld metal are given in Table 2. The vessel is assembled from circular forgings. Submerged-arc welding is used with post-weld heat treatment at 620 to 660°C. In the lower part of the core region outside the peak fluence, there is a horizontal weld seam.

The original surveillance program of the Loviisa reactor includes 936 test specimens. The specimens are loaded into small capsules that are connected to a long chain. The test specimens are divided into six test sets that are loaded symmetrically outside the core barrel with 60° azimuthal distance. Charpy V, precracked Charpy V, and tension specimens are included in the original surveillance program. Each surveillance set consists of 39 test capsules containing either two Charpy-size or six tension specimens. The specimens are cut from base metal, weld, and heat affected zone (HAZ) of the core region material.

The temperature during irradiation has been estimated to be below 290°C by using melting binary alloys. None of the alloys has been melted, the lowest

TABLE 1—*Load factors, %.*

	Year						
NPS	1977	1978	1979	1980	1981	1982	1983
Loviisa 1	83.1	78.1	75.8	36.7	80.6	84.2	86.6
Loviisa 2	...	...	...	...	70.5	77.7	90.4

Technical data (one unit):

Thermal output	1375 MW
Electric output, gross	465 MW
Electric output, net	445 MW
Thermal efficiency, net	32,4 %
Operating pressure	123 bar
Number of loops	6
Coolant: borated water	
Coolant flow	abt. 9000 kg/s
Coolant temperature at inlet	267 °C
Coolant temperature at outlet	296 °C
Height of reactor core	2,42 m
Diameter of reactor core	2,80 m
Number of control rods	37
Number of fuel assemblies	313
Number of steel elements	36
Number of pins per assembly	126
Quantity of enriched fuel	38 t UO_2
Annual refuelling	14 t
Concentration of fresh fuel	3,6...2,4 % U^{235}
Nominal duration of reloading cycle	7000 hrs
Average burn-up of the fuel	28,6 MWd/kgU

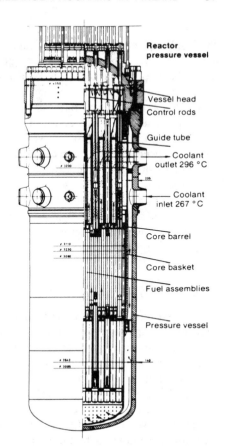

FIG. 1—*Reactor pressure vessel and technical data of Loviisa NPS.*

melting point being 290°C. The neutron flux is measured with iron, cobalt, niobium, and copper dosimeters.

The water gap between the surveillance specimens and the reactor wall is 156 mm. The lead factor at the surveillance position is about 12 for the base metal and 15 for the core weld specimens. Due to the high lead factor, most of the surveillance specimens are removed during the first few years of operation.

TABLE 2—*Typical chemical composition, percent by weight.*

	C	Si	Mn	S	P	Cu	Cr	Ni	Mo	V	Co
Base metal	0.05	0.39	1.2	0.013	0.031	0.17	1.5	0.17	0.48	0.2	0.01
Weld	0.15	0.26	0.41	0.015	0.01	0.13	2.74	0.18	0.64	0.33	0.009

The first surveillance set from Loviisa 1 was removed after one year. The three subsequent sets (Nos. 2, 3, and 5) were withdrawn after three years and set No. 6 after four years of operation. Only one set (No. 4) of the original surveillance program is still in the reactor of Loviisa 1. In Loviisa 2, the first set was removed after one year and the second set after three years of irradiation. One set of Loviisa 2 material was put into the Loviisa 1 four years ago to obtain early information of reduced flux irradiation due to modified core.

In addition to the original surveillance program, three additional surveillance sets have been inserted after commissioning containing more sophisticated test specimens, dosimeters, and temperature indicators (see the following section). The first additional set was irradiated for only one year (1978 to 1979). The second set has been in the Loviisa 1 reactor for four years and was removed in August 1984. The third set was put into Loviisa 2 in September 1984. During the next revision, a new set with test specimens from Phase 3 of the International Atomic Energy Agency (IAEA) Co-ordinated Research Programme will be inserted.

Surveillance Test Results

The test results from the first surveillance tests of Loviisa 1 showed a higher transition temperature shift of the core weld than expected. The results are shown in Fig. 2. Impact energy, lateral expansion, percentage of shear area, and different standard transition temperature criteria give consistent transition temperature shift values within $\pm 10°C$. The use of 35-J level for impact energy transition shift is based on the Soviet fracture mechanics calculation norms.

The Charpy impact tests were conducted according to ASTM Recommended Practice for Notched Bar Impact Testing of Metallic Materials (E 23-82) procedure with the exception of the tup radius, which was according to DIN standards.

The neutron fluence of the irradiated weld specimens was 4.65×10^{19} n/cm^2

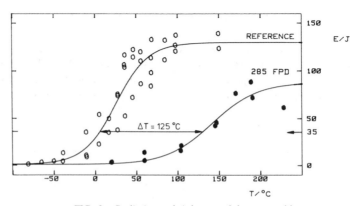

FIG. 2—*Radiation embrittlement of the core weld.*

($E \geq 1$ MeV) after 285 full power days (FPD) of irradiation. The base metal and HAZ showed a much smaller embrittlement rate than the weld material.

Test results from the first additional surveillance set that was irradiated to about the same fluence (295 FPD) gave a smaller shift for the core weld ($\Delta T = 75°C$). The test specimens were, in this case, cut from the weld root that is cleaner than the main part of the weld.

In Loviisa 2, only the first surveillance set has been tested so far. The shift in transition temperature was much smaller than in Loviisa 1 (first set). The reason for the difference in embrittlement rate is discussed in the following section.

Influence of Residual Elements on Steel Embrittlement

The variation in neutron embrittlement of RPV steels is due mainly to variation of impurity content. Several investigations have been carried out and equations derived to estimate metal irradiation performance [1–4]. Five equations from the literature are considered

$$\Delta T_\phi = -118 + 14800 \text{ P} + 990 \text{ Cu} \tag{1}$$

$$\Delta T_\phi = 2 + 1300 \text{ (P} - 0.005)\sqrt{\text{Cu}} \tag{2}$$

$$\Delta T_\phi = 23 + 317(\text{Ni})^2 \times \text{Cu} + 333 \text{ (Cu} - 0.08)$$
$$+ 3640 \text{ (P} - 0.008) \tag{3}$$

$$\Delta T_\phi = 40 + 1000 \text{ (Cu} - 0.08) + 5000 \text{ (P} - 0.008) \tag{4}$$

$$\Delta T_\phi = 232 \text{ As}^{1/3} + 515 \text{ P}^{1/3} + 180 \text{ Cu}^{1/3} - 115 \tag{5}$$

The fluence factors are excluded from some of the equations in order to compare the relative influence of the residuals P, Cu, and Ni (phosphorus, copper, and nickel). The mean value of the residual elements of the tested welds are given in Table 3.

The calculated (Eqs 1 through 5) and the measured relative shifts in transition temperature from test results with about the same fluence is shown in Table 4. It appears that Eq 1 gives the best correspondence with measured results.

TABLE 3—*Residuals of Loviisa 1 and 2 and the first additional weld samples.*

	Cu	P	Ni	As
Loviisa 1	0.17	0.031	0.17	0.015
Loviisa 2	0.22	0.019	0.16	0.014
Additional sample	0.12	0.020	0.14	0.015

TABLE 4—*Measured and calculated relative embrittlement rates.*

	$\dfrac{\Delta T \text{ LO2}}{\Delta T \text{ LO1}}$	$\dfrac{\Delta T \text{ Additional Sample}}{\Delta T \text{ LO1}}$	$\dfrac{\Delta T \text{ Additional Sample}}{\Delta T \text{ LO2}}$
	MEASURED		
	0.76	0.60	0.79
	CALCULATED		
Eq 1	0.75	0.58	0.78
Eq 2	0.66	0.55	0.83
Eq 3	0.80	0.57	0.72
Eq 4	0.96	0.57	0.54
Eq 5	0.90	0.77	0.86

Radiation Embrittlement at RPV Wall Position (Loviisa 1)

The surveillance test results can be extrapolated to the RPV wall position according to Soviet fracture mechanics calculation norms using a cubic root formula

$$\Delta T_{\text{RPV}} = \left[\frac{\Phi_{\text{RPV}}}{\Phi_{SC}} \right]^{1/3} \times \Delta T_{SC} \qquad (6)$$

where

ΔT_{RPV} = the shift at vessel wall position (°C),
ΔT_{SC} = measured shift from surveillance tests (°C),
Φ_{RPV} = neutron fluence [n/cm²] at vessel wall position, and
Φ_{SC} = neutron fluence at surveillance capsule position.

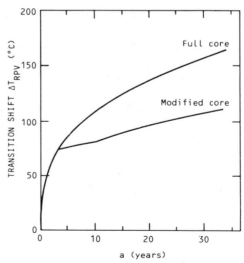

FIG. 3—*Shift in transition temperature for the core weld (Loviisa 1).*

With Eq 6, the cumulative shift in transition temperature at reactor wall position (ΔT_{RPV}) can be estimated. In Fig. 3, the cumulative shift, ΔT_{RPV}, for Loviisa 1 reactor pressure vessel core weld (at inner wall position) is drawn on the basis of the first surveillance set results. The effect of core modification after three years of operation can be seen in this figure.

In the figure, the ΔT_{RPV} at the same position with full core is also shown. At this moment, after seven years of operation $\Delta T_{RPV} = 78°C$. In three years from now, the neutron fluence in another azimuthal direction will dominate and the damage rate will increase again. The shift in transition temperature at the end of life (30 years) will be $\Delta T_{RPV} = 109°C$. This shift gives a much smaller transition temperature than the acceptance limit 149°C proposed recently by the U.S. Nuclear Regulatory Commission (NRC) for the horizontal core welds.

Improvement of the Surveillance Program

New Specimens and Test Methods

Due to the design of the surveillance chain positioning in the Loviisa RPVs, it is possible to insert new chains after removal of the original ones. As discussed earlier, two such chains have already been irradiated and additional chains are planned. For these new irradiation chains, new specimens could be added to obtain fracture mechanics data also.

Because of the size limitations of the capsule, the largest standard type specimen size could be obtained with the round compact tension (CT) specimen configuration shown in Fig. 4. The thickness of the specimen with standard ASTM configuration is 12.5 mm.

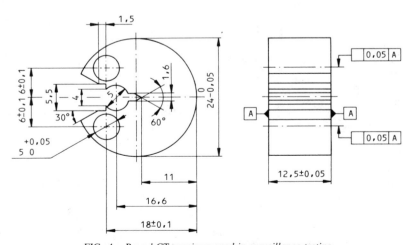

FIG. 4—*Round CT specimen used in surveillance testing.*

A study was undertaken to evaluate the reliability of the *J-R* curve data obtained with the relatively small round CT specimen. Additionally, the possibility to use Charpy-size precracked specimens was studied. One heat of A533 B and one heat of 15X2MφA steel were chosen for the study. Besides the round CT and precracked Charpy configuration, 25-mm-thick normal CT specimens and 15-mm-thick three-point bend specimens were used.

Tests were carried out using a fully computerized single specimen unloading compliance test method in a temperature range of −120°C to +300°C [5]. The results indicated a good agreement with CT and three-point bend specimens, and a satisfactory agreement with precracked Charpy configuration, Fig. 5.

Further development work with, for example, experimental compliance calibration for precracked Charpy specimens has been undertaken. Tests with irradiated specimens will start during this fall. Additional verification of the reliability of the small specimen data will be obtained as a part of the IAEA Co-ordinated Research Programme.

A further study aimed at achieving more information from the Charpy testing has also been undertaken. A new impact hammer with inverted test geometry, Fig. 6, was developed and patented [6–8]. In this test configuration, the specimen rests against a stationary and instrumented tup and the moving anvil hits both ends of the specimen. Two improvements can be achieved with the system: reduced oscillations of the specimens [7] and the possibility to use crack tip opening (CTOD) monitoring during impact [8]. A laser-based optic device has been developed together with MPA, Stuttgart, for the hammer, and preliminary

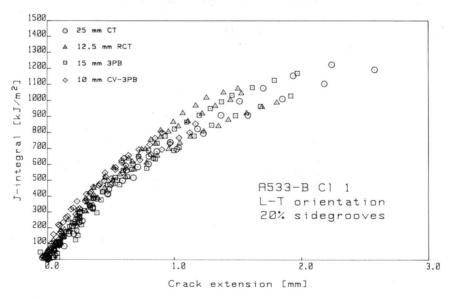

FIG. 5—*Comparison of* J_i-*R curves measured with four different specimen geometries at room temperature for A533 B. The results of two tests are shown for each geometry* [5].

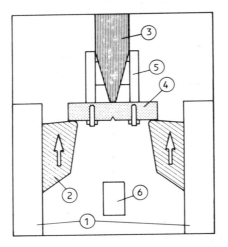

① Moving hammer
② Anvil (span width 40 or 80 mm)
③ Instrumented tup
④ Specimen
⑤ Mechanical specimen lifting device
⑥ Optic COD measuring device

FIG. 6—*Schematic description of the impact tester based on the inverted test geometry* [8].

results indicate, that it is possible to obtain dynamic *J*-integral values from the crack opening displacement (COD) information, Fig. 7 [8]. An additional hammer for hot cell use will be constructed during 1985.

Fluence Monitoring

In order to reduce the influence of fluence uncertainties, standardized relative measurements have been developed and applied. The procedure is based on relative measurements of the neutron fluence (Φ_T above a threshold energy, E_T) at the surveillance chain (*SC*) and at the inner surface of the RPV and on standardization.

For practical purposes, the fluence dependence of the embrittlement of the RPV steel can be approximated by Eq 6. Thus, only fluence ratios are needed to determine the RPV embrittlement parameter from the corresponding measured *SC* embrittlement parameter (Fig. 8).

The ratios, ϕ_{TSC}/ϕ_{TRPV}, of the threshold fluxes (above $E_T = 2.8$ MeV and later above $E_T = 0.9$ MeV) were experimentally determined by using steel samples (with niobium content) from the inner surface of the RPV, from the mechanical test specimens of the steel from the *SC*, and niobium foils in the *SC* as activation detectors. The main method to avoid systematic errors was to use

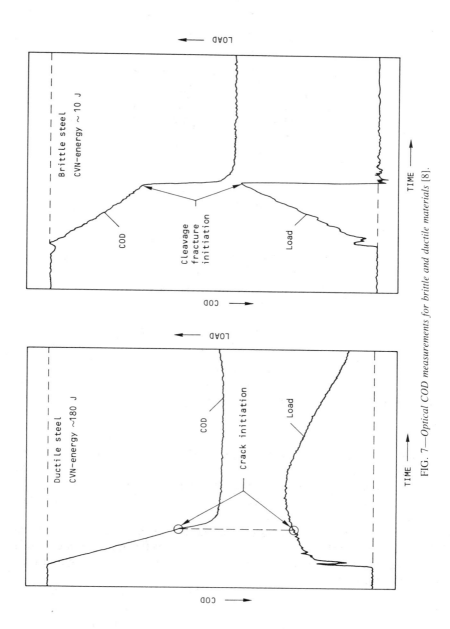

FIG. 7—*Optical COD measurements for brittle and ductile materials [8].*

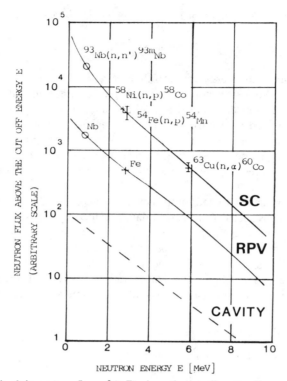

FIG. 8—*Sketch of the neutron fluxes* $\Phi(>E)$ *above the cut-off energy,* E, *versus the neutron energy,* E, *for RPV, SC, and cavity. Some measured values* $(+, \bigcirc)$ *are indicated. Accurate relative measurements of the flux ratio* Φ_{TRPV}/Φ_{TSC} *with iron samples have been made and similar measurements with niobium samples* $(\bigcirc)$ *are well under way. The flux-ratio is needed roughly at the threshold (0.9 MeV) of the niobium reaction (Eq 8).*

steel samples (and at the later stage niobium), the same reaction cross sections, etc., to determine the ratio of threshold fluxes. In the initial stage of the development, the reaction

$$^{54}\text{Fe}(n,\ p)^{54}\text{Mn} \tag{7}$$

with a threshold energy $E_T = 2.8$ MeV was used. In this manner, the influence of the relatively large systematic errors in the cross sections were almost completely eliminated and the accuracy significantly improved [9]. The main uncertainty left arises from the extrapolation of the threshold flux ratio Φ_{TSC}/Φ_{TRPV} from 2.8 MeV to the cut off energy $E_0 = 1$ MeV of interest. The first stage of this novel application is described in Ref 9.

In order to reduce the influence of the uncertainty arising from the spectrum extrapolation, research and development work has been initiated and successfully

carried out. The second stage of basic improvements is based on the reaction

$$^{93}\text{Nb}(n, n')^{93\text{m}}\text{Nb} \qquad (8)$$

with a low threshold energy (about 0.9 MeV). The niobium foils in the *SC* provided by the Soviet reactor supplier and the separated niobium in the steel samples scraped from the welded austenitic cladding of the pressure vessel in Loviisa 1 were used as neutron dosimeters. The first preliminary results from the research and development work using niobium are very promising, although all alternatives and procedures have not yet been tested. Some basic achievements and results have been reported at the Fifth ASTM-EURATOM Symposium on Reactor Dosimetry [*10*].

The spectrum shapes needed for the computation of the effective reaction cross sections were constructed from design data provided by the Soviet reactor supplier. Although these data agree well with the experimental results at the *SC*, additional efforts to verify the shape of the neutron spectrum at the pressure vessel would be very useful due to the limited amount of experimental data and due to the changes made in the core configuration. Partly for that reason, neutron dosimeters have also been inserted into the cavity outside the RPV.

Annealing of Irradiated Specimen

Thermal annealing behavior of irradiated pressure vessel steel 15X2MφA has been studied by micro hardness measurements using material from tested surveillance specimens. The material was taken from Charpy samples that have shown small absorption energy and hence experienced negligible deformation. Hardness specimens were cut out from weld samples in such a way that the fusion line was in the middle of the 4 by 5 by 24-mm size samples. They were mechanically polished and annealed in argon atmosphere. The applied load was 1 kg. The samples had received a large fast neutron dose of $1.45 \cdot 10^{20}$ n/cm^2 ($E > 1$ MeV).

Figure 9 shows the original hardness profiles. The curves are averages of measurements from about 25 samples with fusion lines adjusted at zero point in *x*-axes. Irradiation increased the microvickers hardness in weld by 42% and in base metal, which is here mostly HAZ, by 27%. The figure shows that the weld hardness reaches the HAZ hardness level that leads to more homogeneous hardness profiles in irradiated than in the reference samples.

Temperatures of 360, 420, and 480°C were chosen for annealing. Figure 10 shows the results measured after isothermal heat treatments. As can be seen from this figure, it is not possible to describe the decrease in hardness with one time constant. Just at the beginning, the time constant is of the order of 1 h, after that, the dominant time constant is a few tens of hours. The first few measuring points were left out when the exponential fittings were made for the measured points in Fig. 10. For this reason the fitting parameters describe only the long

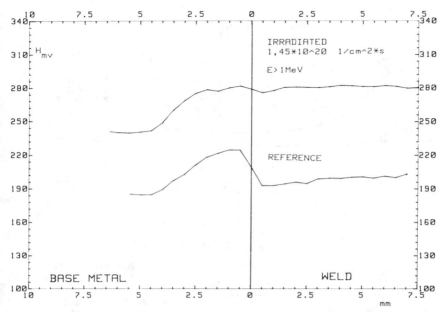

FIG. 9—*Hardness profiles of reference and irradiated samples across the fusion line.*

time annealing behavior, which is relevant if technical pressure vessel annealings are considered.

If the annealing model, given by Pachur [*11*]

$$\Delta H(T, t) = \Delta H_i \cdot \exp[-\lambda_i(T)t] + \dots \tag{9}$$

where

$$\lambda_i(T) = \lambda_0 \cdot \exp(-U_i/kT) \tag{10}$$

is used with his value for the frequency factor $\lambda_0 = 1.4 \cdot 10^{10}$ 1/s, one gets from the time constants given in Fig. 10, activation energies between 1.9 and 2.3 eV.

Figure 10 indicates further that the temperature required in a possible pressure vessel anneal is above 420°C.

Annealing studies of irradiated samples are continuing. At the moment, hardness measurements as a function of annealing temperature (isocronal) are carried out in order to identify the different annealing mechanisms.

For rehardening studies, specimens representing different annealing temperatures and different original fluence values have been loaded in one surveillance capsule in Loviisa power plant for a two-year irradiation period. Tested surveillance samples serve also as a source of irradiated material for these studies.

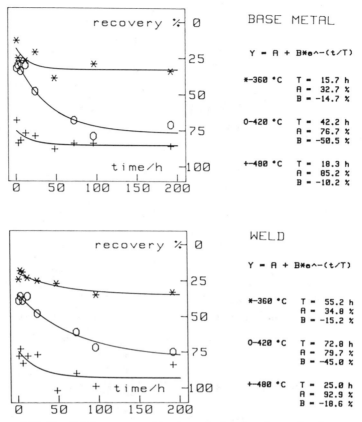

FIG. 10—*Relative recovery of hardness as a function of annealing time.*

Summary

The surveillance program and test results of Loviisa 1 and 2 nuclear power plants have been described. Additional surveillance irradiations with fracture mechanics specimens together with supporting test method development and verification have been carried out. Improvements in neutron dosimetry have been obtained. Annealing behavior of irradiated steel has been evaluated.

References

[1] Steele, L. E., "Neutron Irradiation Embrittlement of Reactor Pressure Vessel Steels," Technical Report No. 163, International Atomic Energy Agency, Vienna, 1975.

[2] Brumovsky, M., "Radiation Damage and Annealing of Cr-Mo-V Steel," International Atomic Energy Agency, IWG-RRPC-79/3, Vienna, 1979.

[3] Guionnet, C., et al in *Effects of Radiation on Materials, 11th International Symposium, ASTM STP 782,* H. R. Brager and J. S. Perrin, Eds., American Society for Testing and Materials, Philadelphia, 1982, pp. 392–411.

[4] Regulatory Guide 1.99 Rev. 1, Nuclear Regulatory Commission, Washington, DC, 1977.
[5] Saario, T., Wallin, K., Saarelma, H., Valkonen, A., and Törrönen, K. in *Automated Test Methods for Fracture and Fatigue Crack Growth, ASTM STP 877,* American Society for Testing and Materials, Philadelphia, 1985, pp. 26–268.
[6] Patents: FI 60 313, 1981; European Patent EP 0027257 BI, 1983; U. S. Patent 4425786, 1984.
[7] Rintamaa, R., Rahka, K., Wallin, K., Ikonen, K., Talja, H., Kotilainen, H., and Sirkkola, E., "Instrumented Impact Testing Machine with Reduced Specimen Oscillation Effects," Espoo 1984, Technical Research Centre of Finland (VTT), Metals Laboratory Research Reports 290.
[8] Rintamaa, R., Saario, T., and Wallin, K., "Procedures for the Determination of the Static and Dynamic Fracture Behaviour Using Three-Point Bend Specimens," 5th European Conference on Fracture, Lisbon, 17–21 Sept. 1984.
[9] Bärs, L. B., Liuhto, P. A., and Serén, T. O., *Kernenergie,* Vol. 27, 1984, pp. 342–347.
[10] Bärs, B. and Karnani, H., "Use of Niobium for Accurate Relative Fast Neutron Fluence Measurements at the Pressure Vessel in a WWER-440 NPP," to be presented at the Fifth ASTM-EURATOM Symposium on Reactor Dosimetry, Geesthacht, FRG, 24–29 Sept. 1984.
[11] Pachur, D., *Nuclear Technology,* Vol. 59, 1982, pp. 463–475.

Pierre Petrequin,[1] *Mohamed Al Mundheri,*[2] *and Pierre Soulat*[1]

Effect of Irradiation on the Elasto-Plastic Toughness of Pressure Vessel Steels

REFERENCE: Petrequin, P., Al Mundheri, M., and Soulat, P., "**Effect of Irradiation on the Elasto-Plastic Toughness of Pressure Vessel Steels,**" *Radiation Embrittlement of Nuclear Reactor Pressure Vessel Steels: An International Review (Second Volume),* ASTM *STP 909,* L. E. Steele, Ed., American Society for Testing and Materials, Philadelphia, 1986, pp. 70–95.

ABSTRACT: A study on the effect of irradiation on the toughness of pressure vessel materials in the ductile regime has been undertaken. Compact tension (CT) specimens of two pressure vessel steels (A533 B and A508 Class 3) and a weld material of fitting chemical composition were irradiated and received neutron fluences of 3 and 8 × 10^{19} n/ cm^2. The *J-R* curves of these materials were determined between 100 and 290°C. Only a very small influence of irradiation was observed for tests at 290°C. In irradiated condition, the effect of the test temperature is not noticeable. At lower temperature, but in the ductile regime, the weld material appears to be more sensitive to neutron irradiation than the two steels. The forged material exhibited a surprisingly high shift of transition temperature since cleavage rupture occurred up to 100°C.

A method using tension tests on round notched specimens with different root radii was employed to obtain an alternative value of J_c. This method relates the J_c value to a critical growth of cavities that is determined from the tension test on notched specimens. A good agreement between this method and the conventional one was obtained for the A533 B steel. For the forged material, the results were more questionable and this was attributed to inhomogeneities in the distribution on nonmetallic inclusions for this material. This method is expected to be very useful for the determination of J_c for irradiated materials.

KEY WORDS: radiation effects, pressure vessel steels, elasto-plastic toughness, embrittlement

The effect of neutron irradiation on reactor pressure vessel steels is currently considered as affecting the brittle to ductile transition temperature as well as the elasto-plastic toughness in the ductile regime. Impact Charpy-V tests and tension tests are very extensively employed for evaluating these phenomena in both research studies and surveillance programs of in-service reactors. The Charpy-V transition curves determine the effect of irradiation on the transition temper-

[1] Head and head of group, respectively, Service de Recherche Metallurgique Appliquee, French Atomic Energy Commission (CEA), CEN Saclay, France.

[2] Detached from IRAKI Atomic Energy Organization, preparing for Doctor of Science, Service de Recherche Metallurgique Appliquee, French Atomic Energy Commission (CEA), CEN Saclay, France.

ature, but this method is inadequate to produce reliable information on the effect of irradiation in the ductile regime. As fracture mechanics analyses are used to assess the safety of reactor vessels, the need of the fracture mechanics properties of the materials becomes more and more apparent. At lower temperature, in the brittle regime, the linear elastic parameters, K_{Ic}, can be used. The assessment of the effect of irradiation is done by shifting the reference curve of K_{Ic} towards higher temperature of an amount depending on the neutron irradiation conditions. This kind of analysis cannot be used at the service temperature of reactor pressure vessel walls, which operate in the range 250 to 300°C, which correspond to the ductile regime, at least for newer steels. The need of elasto-plastic parameters for characterizing the toughness of steels is evident.

The stable crack growth resistance curves (J-R curves) appear as being more and more used for characterizing the upper-shelf toughness and, in many places, a considerable effort has been made to evaluate the effect of neutron irradiation on them [1–4]. However, because results are relatively scarce and testing techniques change many times before an American Society for Testing and Materials (ASTM) standard is issued, the available results are very difficult to compare (By the way, it is not possible to derive any significant trend on the effect of neutron irradiation on upper-shelf toughness).

A study, part of the International Atomic Energy Agency (IAEA) coordinated research program of the analysis of the behavior of advanced reactor pressure vessel steels under neutron irradiation, was developed by the French Atomic Energy Commission (CEA). In this study, the influence of neutron irradiation on the elasto-plastic toughness (J_c and J-R curves) was determined on three pressure vessel materials before and after neutron irradiation at two levels of fluence. In parallel, a tentative investigation was made for deriving the critical elasto-plastic toughness, J_c, from a tension test on notched round specimens with different notch radii. This method was applied only on unirradiated materials.

Materials and Testing Techniques

Materials

Three materials for reactor pressure vessel steels were used in this study: one forged steel and one plate material corresponding to ASTM Standards A508 Class 3 and A533 B Class 1. The third material was a weld metal coming from a submerged-arc weldment with chemical composition fitting those of the plate and the forging.

The three materials are typically industrial products with thicknesses of 230 mm for the forging (referred to as FF), 300 mm for the plate (referred to as FP), and 230 mm for the weldment (referred to as FW).

The chemical composition as well as the heat treatments and the tensile properties at room temperature and 290°C are given in Tables 1 and 2, respectively.

TABLE 1—Chemical composition and heat treatments.

Denomination	Reference of Steel	Chemical Composition, % by weight														Heat Treatment[a]
		C	S	P	Si	Mn	Ni	Cr	Mo	Cu	V	Sb	Sn	As	Al	
A533 B Class 1	FP	0.23	0.002	0.008	0.23	1.46	0.66	0.03	0.51	0.04	0.002	0.005	0.005	0.019	0.028	1
A508 Class 3	FF	0.15	0.009	0.009	0.24	1.36	0.68	0.24	0.46	0.063	0.008	0.01	0.008	0.022	0.031	2
Weld	FW	0.06	0.008	0.012	0.37	1.50	0.79	0.07	0.62	0.04	0.008	0.005	0.007	0.057	0.01	3

[a]Heat Treatment

WQ = Water Quenched   AC = Air Cooled   FC = Furnace Cooled

1	900°C – 7 h 40 min	640°C – 10 h 35 min	610°C – 24 h
2	865°C to 880°C	630 to 650°C – 5 h 30 min	615°C – 8 h
3			617°C – 8 h

TABLE 2—*Tensile properties.*

Irradiation Temperature, °C	Fluence, 10^{19} n/cm², $E > 1$ MeV	20°C Yield Strength, MPa	20°C Ultimate Tensile Strength, MPa	20°C Total Elongation, %	20°C Uniform Elongation, %	290°C Yield Strength, MPa	290°C Ultimate Tensile Strength, MPa	290°C Total Elongation, %	290°C Uniform Elongation, %
		A533 B Class 1 FP							
...	UNIR	478	626	21.5	10.2	462	608	22.6	10.7
		474	617	22.7	9.5	462	613	22.6	11.3
289	2.46	533	671	18.2	9.2	501	653	21.5	10.5
		533	669	18.9	9.2	509	663	24.5	10.3
285	7.47	580	708	19.9	9.4	510	647	20.4	10.5
		581	707	18.7	9.2	504	646	23.8	11.2
		A508 Class 3 FF							
...	UNIR	527	638	22.0	8.6	464	541	22.1	6.2
		548	689	21.8	9.5	514	619	17.3	7.9
285	2.40	533	670	18.9	9.2	555	655	18.2	8.0
		533	671	18.2	9.2	560	663	19.1	8.0
284	7.37	580	708	19.9	9.4	573	673	18.3	9.1
		581	707	18.7	9.2	573	662	16.9	8.3
		Weld FW							
...	UNIR	529	611	21.0	6.4	447	584	19.6	8.6
		524	540	20.0	8.1	481	587	20.3	8.6
286	2.31	561	650	20.0	8.6	531	625	18.2	8.1
		569	649	13.2	8.0	527	624	19.6	8.6
285	7.36	656	680	15.6	5.1	561	653	17.8	7.7
		602	679	19.3	9.0	533	626	18.4	7.1

Specimens and Experimental Techniques

For the evaluation of the *J-R* resistance curves, compact tension (CT) specimens as defined in ASTM Test Method for Plane-Strain Fracture Toughness of Metallic Materials (E 399-83) and ASTM Test Method for J_{Ic}, a Measure of Fracture Toughness (E 813-81) were used. In unirradiated and irradiated conditions, CT specimens with a nominal thickness of 12.5 mm were used. Side grooves of about 20% of the nominal thickness were machined by grinding after fatigue precracking to reach the initial crack length corresponding to an a/w ratio of 0.6. The tests were conducted on two electro-hydraulic closed-loop testing machines of 100 kN capacity, one of which being installed in a hot cell.

To determine the *J-R* resistance curves, the unloading compliance technique was used. The loading pin's displacement was measured by a clip gage installed on machined knives on the specimen and was controlled by a microcomputer. Unloading sequences of less than 20% were introduced in order to generate about 30 to 50 compliance measurements during the tests. Tests were run at 100, 200, and 290°C. On the forged materials, in irradiated condition, tests were also run at 50, 70, and 150°C. The test temperature was obtained by using a light radiation furnace controlled by thermocouples attached to the specimens.

On the other hand, the critical elasto-plastic toughness J_c was determined from tension tests on notched specimens. Three kinds of round notched specimens with a diameter of 10 mm and notch root radii of 10, 4, and 2 mm, respectively, were used. Details of the specimens are given on Fig. 1. A diametral extensometer was attached at the root of the notch in order to control the diametral contraction during the pulling of the specimen. The details about the analysis of the results are given in a later section of this paper.

The CT specimens were machined at one fourth or three fourths of the thickness of the wrought products whose direction of the major deformation was parallel to the plane of the crack extension (TL orientation). For the weld, the specimens were machined at one fourth of the thickness in the bottom part of the weld. The direction of the welding was parallel to the plane of crack extension.

Irradiation Experiments

The three materials were irradiated in the TRITON 6.5 MW swimming pool type research reactor at the Fontenay-aux-Roses Nuclear Center. The rigs were installed in the first periphery around the core with a neutron flux of about 1.10^{13} $n/cm^2 \cdot s$.

The irradiation rigs employed, named SIAT, were a compact pack of specimens, heated by neutrons and gamma effects. The temperature was monitored by controlling a thin gas gap around the device (control of gas mixture and pressure). The neutron exposure parameters were determined from ^{63}Cu and ^{59}Co foil detectors in each rig and from the results of previous dosimetry experiments. More details are given in Ref 5.

The two irradiation experiments referred to as FT945 and FT946 with goal

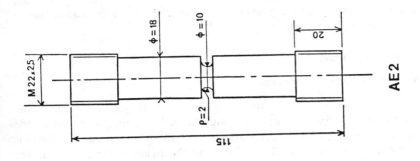

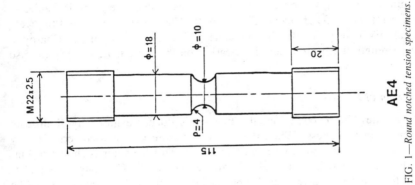

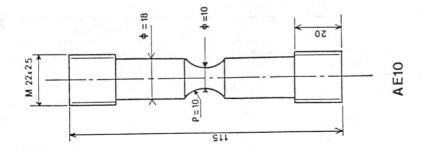

FIG. 1—*Round notched tension specimens.*

fluences of 3×10^{19} and 8×10^{19} n/cm^2 $E > 1$ MeV and a temperature of 290°C were made. Each experiment contained 16 specimens of each material. The capsules were rotated at mid-experiment in order to minimize the transversal irradiation gradients. The axial gradient was about 25%. The average temperature and fluence of the specimens are given in Table 3.

J-R Curve Determination

Analysis of Test Data and Results

The test data were analyzed following ASTM E 813-81. However, some differences were introduced, the more significant being that the slope of the blunting line was assumed to be three times the flow stress and that the limit for the linear regression was fixed to 0.10 times the ligament size. The validity criteria were generally fulfilled for J_c. For the maximum extension criteria, some points corresponding to the tougher materials were in violation of about 20%. Finally, J_c, dJ/da, the tearing modulus T, the J value for a crack extension Δa of 1 mm, and the K_{Ic} value were evaluated. These values are given in Tables 4, 5, and 6 for the A533 B steel (FP), the A508 Class 3 steel (FF), and the weld material (FW), respectively. In the same tables, the values of the Charpy-V impact strength that were determined earlier on the same materials [5] are also given.

Discussion of Results

In the unirradiated condition, the two steels do not exhibit any significant differences in toughness. When the test temperature is increased, only a very slight decrease in the $J-R$ curve can be noticed. This behavior is shown in Fig. 2 for the A533 B steel. The weld metal presents at 100°C a toughness that is higher than that of the two steels, but at 290°C, the reverse situation can be observed as can be seen in Fig. 3 where the test temperature alters very significantly its $J-R$ curve. The results obtained at 100°C are in good agreement with

TABLE 3—Results of irradiation of CT specimens.

Steel	Kind of Specimen	Temperature Average, °C	Fluence Average	
			$\Phi_R(E > 1$ MeV$)$ 10^{19} n/cm^2	10^{-2} dpa
		FT 945		
FP	CT	288	2.99	4.62
FF	CT	287	2.94	4.53
FW	CT	285	2.70	4.16
		FT 946		
FP	CT	282	7.72	11.90
FF	CT	287	8.10	12.48
FW	CT	285	7.30	11.26

TABLE 4—Test results for J-R curves on A533 B steel (FP).

Test Temperature, °C	J_c, kJ/m²	dJ/da, MPa	T	J_c(1 mm), kJ/m²	K_{Jc} MPa√m	J_c Average, kJ/m²	dJ/da Average, MPa	T Average	J_c(1 mm) Average, kJ/m²	K_{Jc} Average, MPa√m	Charpy-V Impact Strength, J
UNIRRADIATED											
100	173	291	199	464	186	153	283.5	194	436.5	174.5	165
100	133	276	189	409	163						
200	133	233	157	366	161	128.5	239.5	161.5	368	158	172
200	124	246	166	370	155						
290	125	183	121	308	154	129.5	198.5	131	328	156.5	...
290	134	214	141	348	159						
3 × 10¹⁹ n/cm²											
100	145	234	133	379	170	173	235.5	134	408.5	185.5	159.5
100	201	237	135	438	201						
200	187	133	74	318	191	169.5	149.5	84	318	181.5	160
200	152	166	94	318	172						
290	139	162	91	301	162	126.5	172.5	97	299	154.5	...
290	114	183	103	297	147						
7.7 × 10¹⁹ n/cm²											
100	167	176	91	343	183	175.5	192.5	99.5	368	187.5	130
100	184	209	108	393	192						
200	138	225	122	363	164	139.5	185.5	100.5	325	167	...
200	141	146	79	287	166						
290	160	165	85	325	174	165	183.5	94.5	348.5	177	...
290	170	202	104	372	180						

TABLE 5—Test results for J-R curves on A508 Class 3 steel (FF).

Test Temperature, °C	J_c, kJ/m²	dJ/da, MPa	T	J_i(1 mm), kJ/m²	K_{Ic} √m	J_c Average, kJ/m²	dJ/da Average, MPa	T Average	J_i(1 mm) Average, kJ/m²	K_{Jc} Average, MPa √m	Charpy-V Impact Strength, J
UNIRRADIATED											
100	209	239	141	448	204	194	224.5	132.5	418.5	196.5	178
100	189	210	124	389	189						
200	191	180	113	371	202	146.5	186	116.5	332.5	171.5	162
200	102	192	120	294	141						
290	175	141	93	316	182	191	168	111	359	188.5	...
290	207	195	129	402	195						
2.94 × 10¹⁹ n/cm²											
70	222	207	101	429	209	222	207	101	429	209	191.5
100	142	248	121	390	167	164	248	121.5	412	179	
100	186	249	122	435	191						
200	180	218	109	398	187	158	199	99.5	357	174.5	182
200	136	180	90	316	162						
290	107	208	107	315	142	151	234	120.5	385	167	
290	195	260	134	455	192						
8.1 × 10¹⁹ n/cm²											
50	17		cleavage		62	...	...	...	...	...	53
50	48		cleavage		103						
100	74		cleavage		128	...	...	...	...	...	116
100	85		cleavage		138						
150	61	255	155	316	116	87.5	203	123.5	290.5	133	176
150	114	151	92	265	150						
200	151	141	71	295	171	151	144	84.5	295	160.5	178
200	116	156	98	272	150						
290	113	184	90	297	146	108	190	93	297	142.5	...
290	102	196	96	298	139						

TABLE 6—Test results for J-R curves on weld materials FW.

Test Temperature, °C	J_c, kJ/m²	dJ/da, MPa	T	J_c(1 mm), kJ/m²	K_{Jc} MPa $\sqrt{m}$	J_c Average, kJ/m²	dJ/da Average, MPa	T Average	J_c(1 mm) Average, kJ/m²	K_{Jc} Average, MPa $\sqrt{m}$	Charpy-V Impact Strength, J
					UNIRRADIATED						
100	235	253	171	488	216	217.5	252	170.5	469.5	208	186
100	200	251	170	451	200						
200	184	153	104	337	189	193	159	108.5	352	193.5	203
200	202	165	113	367	198						
290	102	133	91	235	139	102	143.5	98.5	245.5	139	⋯
290	102	154	106	256	139						
					2.7×10^{19} n/cm²						
100	124	230	129	354	157	134.5	227	127	361.5	163.5	194.6
100	145	224	125	369	170						
200	123	251	142	374	154	135.5	240	135.5	375.5	161.5	189
200	148	229	129	377	169						
290	108	184	79	299	155	103.5	161.5		268.5	146	⋯
290	99	139		238	137						
					7.30×10^{19} n/cm²						
100	102	211	99	313	142	95	214	100.5	309	137	179
100	88	217	102	305	132						
200	99	160	74	259	138	104	166	76.5	270	141.5	184
200	109	172	79	281	145						
290	98	130	70	228	136	93.5	141	75.5	234.5	133	⋯
290	89	152	81	241	130						

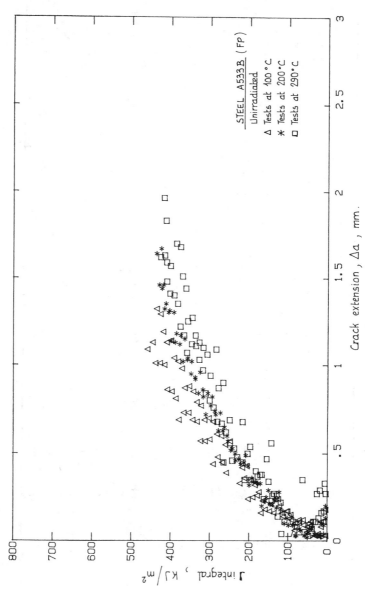

FIG. 2—J-R curves of A533 B steel; test temperature effect on unirradiated specimens.

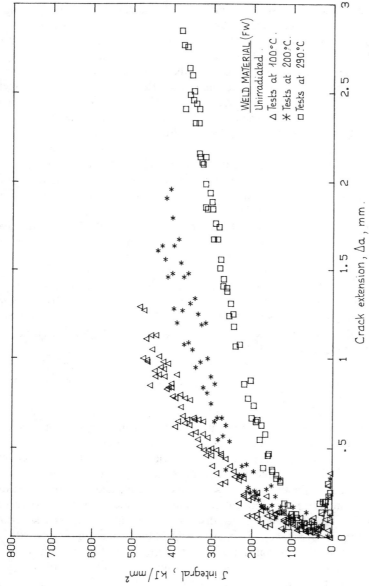

FIG. 3—J-R curves of weld material; test temperature effect on unirradiated specimens.

the Charpy-V impact values that are higher for the weld metal than for the two steels.

At 290°C, this kind of correlation is not possible to achieve because no impact data are available. The results obtained at 290°C on the FF material are close to those obtained by Ingham for the same steel and published in Ref 4 as shown in Fig. 8. However, Ingham's data appear to be at the upper part of the results obtained here.

In irradiated condition, the J-R curves of the FP material are practically identical to those obtained in the unirradiated condition. However, for the higher fluence (7.72×10^{19} n/cm², $E > 1$ MeV) as shown in Fig. 4, the test temperature was observed to have no effect, whereas a slight effect was noticeable in unirradiated condition. On the weld material (FW), the trend is the same and again, for the higher fluence (7.30×10^{19} n/cm², $E > 1$ MeV), it cannot be observed on Fig. 5 that the test temperature had any influence. This indicates that for the weld metal, the J-R curves at 100°C are significantly lowered after irradiation, but no change can be seen for tests at 290°C. This phenomenon is illustrated in Figs. 6 and 7.

The behavior of the FF material is more complex. First of all, the scatter seems to be greater for this steel than for the other two materials. Second, it appeared relatively sensitive to the radiation embrittlement although its chemical composition is very adequate for good behavior under irradiation (low copper and phosphorus). This sensitivity to radiation embrittlement appeared when it was impossible to produce J-R curves at 100°C in the more irradiated condition (8.10×10^{19} n/cm², $E > 1$ MeV). Cleavage fracture occurred very rapidly, restricting the J-R curve to a very short portion. At 150°C, the J-R curves were obtained without any problem.

In the same manner as for the other materials, the effect of irradiation on the J-R curves is not very strong. As can be seen on Fig. 8, the same trend is observed, that is, the effect of test temperature is practically unobservable in the more irradiated condition. The behavior of this steel confirms previous results indicating that the transition temperature measured with Charpy-V tests was about 90°C for an identical level of irradiation (Steel F6 in Ref 5).

The results given in Tables 4, 5, and 6 reflect the general trends mentioned for the J-R curves. The more significant features are the very low J_c values obtained at 100°C for the A508 Class 3 steel in irradiated condition (cleavage) and the sensitivity to test temperature of the weld material, which is observable in unirradiated condition and which disappears when irradiated. This situation is illustrated in Fig. 9, which shows the variation of the J values for a crack extension of 1 mm against the neutron fluence for the different test temperatures.

In conclusion of this section, there is only a small influence of irradiation, even for high fluences, on the elasto-plastic toughness at operating temperature (290°C) for these materials with low copper and low phosphorous. At lower temperature (100°C), irradiation reduces the toughness of the weld material. The A508 Class 3 steel exhibits cleavage at low temperature, revealing a relatively

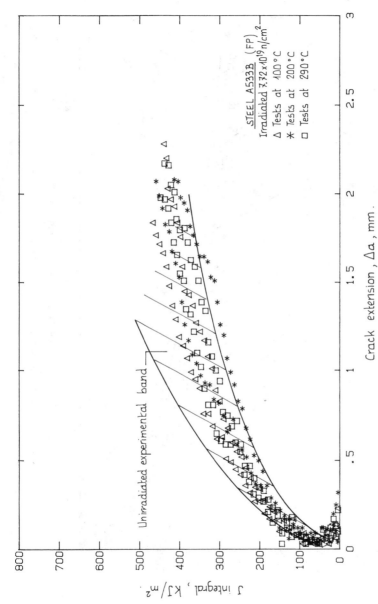

FIG. 4—J-R curves of A533 B steel: influence of irradiation and test temperature.

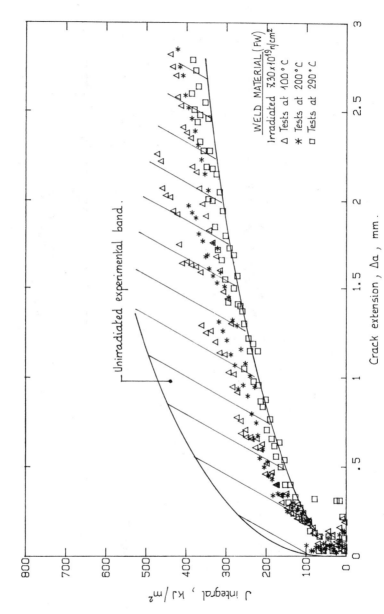

FIG. 5—J-R curves of weld material: test temperature effect on irradiated specimens (7.30×10^{19} n/cm², E > 1 MeV).

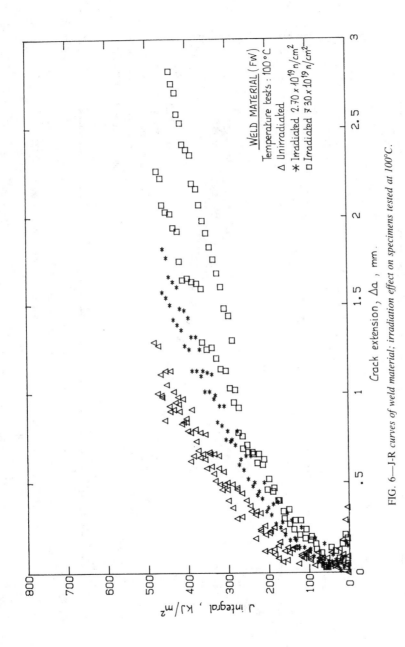

FIG. 6—*J-R curves of weld material: irradiation effect on specimens tested at 100°C.*

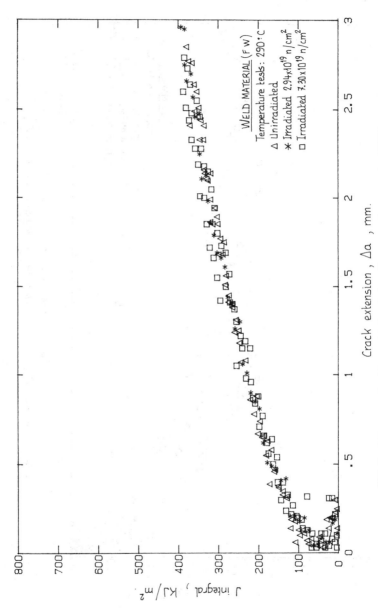

FIG. 7—J-R curves of weld material; irradiation effect on specimens tested at 290°C.

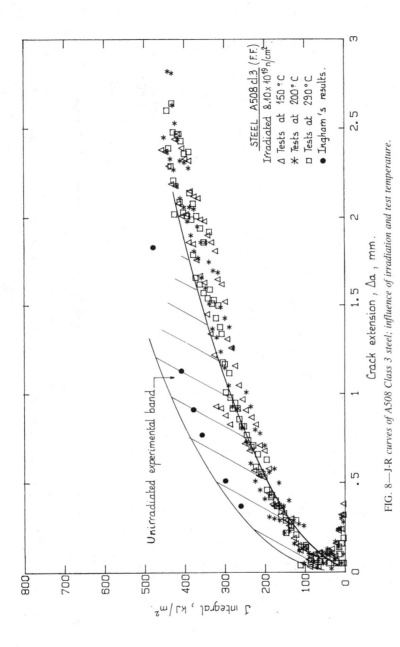

FIG. 8—J-R curves of A508 Class 3 steel: influence of irradiation and test temperature.

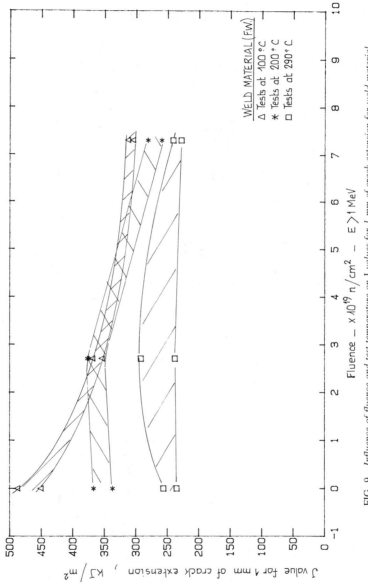

FIG. 9—Influence of fluence and test temperature on J values for 1 mm of crack extension for weld material.

high shift of transition temperature. But, in the ductile regime, the J-R curves are practically unaffected by irradiation.

Determination of J_c from Tension Tests on Notched Round Specimens

The critical value of J for the onset of stable crack growth is difficult to determine. That is the reason why a conventional value was proposed in ASTM E 813-81 for J_c. As the scatter remains relatively high, it is difficult to analyze the effect of external variables such as temperature, especially if their influence is not very great. That is why we tried to obtain an evaluation of the value of J_c from tests completely different from those done on cracked specimens.

Description of the Method

The method consists of simulating the constraint at the crack tip by using round specimens with different notches. The basic idea is comparable to that of Gillemot [6], but he employed an energetic criteria. The method that we used, developed by Mudry [7] and Lautridou [8], employs a microscopic criteria of ductile failure.

In this approach, the growth of cavities formed around nonmetallic inclusions is predicted from the strain and stress fields in confined plasticity. Starting from solutions using Hutchinson [9] and Rice and Rosengren fields [10] or a perfectly plastic field, it can be shown that the growth of the cavity described in terms of the ratio R/Ro (Ro and R being the radius of the cavity in the initial state and after straining, respectively) can be related to the J-integral value. With this analysis, the critical value for J_c can be related to a critical cavity growth $(R/Ro)_c$ by the relationship

$$J_c = 4.5 \, \sigma_Y \, (\Delta a)_c \, \ln \, (R/Ro)_c \qquad (1)$$

where σ_Y is the yield strength of the material, $(R/Ro)_c$ is the critical growth ratio of the cavity, and $(\Delta a)_c$ is the length of the critical elementary volume in which this phenomenon occurs.

The problem is now to determine the critical values of $(\Delta a)_c$ and $(R/Ro)_c$ from tests on round notched specimens.

The $(\Delta a)_c$ parameter is considered adjustable, but it is not very different from the distance between nonmetallic inclusions in a plane. The value of 0.2 mm, retained here, was derived from the study on a very similar material described in Ref 7.

The $(R/Ro)_c$ critical value is derived from tension tests on round notched specimens. For the three specimens (AE 10, AE 4, and AE 2) shown in Fig. 1, a numerical calculation using the method described was made [7] and lead to

the following simplified extrapolation formulas

$$AE\ 10: \ln (R/Ro)_c = 0.890\ \bar{\epsilon} - 0.044 \tag{2}$$

$$AE\ 4: \ln (R/Ro)_c = 1.186\ \bar{\epsilon} - 0.009 \tag{3}$$

$$AE\ 2: \ln (R/Ro)_c = 1.80\ \bar{\epsilon} - 0.075 \tag{4}$$

In these formulas, $\bar{\epsilon}$ is the critical rupture strain measured from the tests. The FP and FF materials were tested at 100, 200, and 290°C. The load versus diameter curves of the specimens were obtained. A typical example is given in Fig. 10 where it can be seen that a sudden decrease in load appears, which is associated to cracking at the center of the specimen. From the critical diametral contraction, the true axial critical strain, $\bar{\epsilon}$, is derived.

Finally, from Eqs 1, 2, 3, and 4 and introducing the experimental ϵ values, it is possible to derive the J_c of the materials.

Results and Discussion

Tables 7 and 8 give the results that were obtained. In Fig. 11, the different values of J_c derived from the two test methods are compared for the FP steel (A533 B). It can be noticed that the agreement is relatively good. The values coming from the round specimens are, however, systematically higher than those measured with the CT specimens. This effect could be attributed to the fact that in the model for rupture initiation in the round specimens, a critical value of crack extension of 0.2 mm has been used, whereas the J_c value is assumed to be corresponding to the very onset of the stable crack growth. For the FF material (A508 Class 3), the scatter is higher. Also, in one test on a AE 2 specimen, a premature failure was observed corresponding to a very low value of J_c.

An examination of the rupture surface with a scanning electron microscope has shown the presence in practically all sections of the specimen of "nests" of nonmetallic inclusions. This indicates that for this material the $(\Delta a)_c$ parameter taken as 0.2 mm is very likely not well adapted. As indicated earlier, this parameter is related to the distance between particles, its value being very difficult to fix if the material is nonhomogeneous and if the $(\Delta a)_c$ values change from place to place.

In conclusion of this section, one can indicate that the testing technology using round notched specimens seems to be a very promising method, leading to a good evaluation of J_c. However, it is necessary to be very careful in extending this method to other materials because it necessitates a numerical analysis of the specimens, introducing the different variables characterizing the plastic behavior of the material.

In the case of irradiated pressure vessel steels, one can assume that the method is applicable since it is known that neutron irradiation, at least for the fluences generally studied, has a limited influence on the tensile properties and the plastic behavior of the steel.

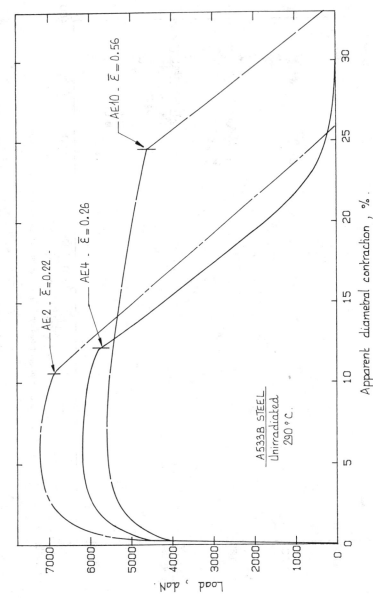

FIG. 10—*Typical load—diametral contraction curves on A533 B steel at 290°C using specimens Type AE 2, AE 4, and AE 10.*

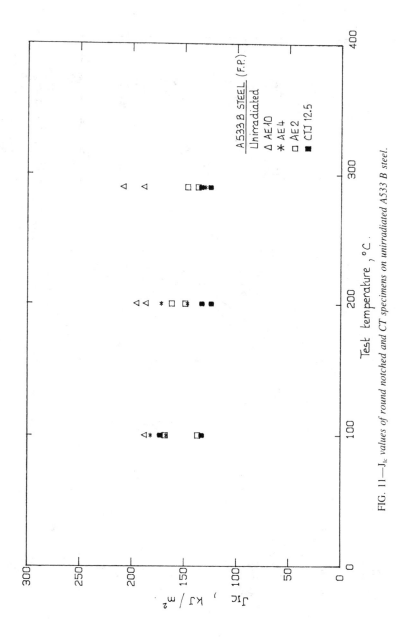

FIG. 11—J_{Ic} values of round notched and CT specimens on unirradiated A533 B steel.

TABLE 7—*Test results for unirradiated round notched specimens on A533 B steel (FP).*

Notch Root Radius	Test Temperature, °C	Rupture Strength, σ_R, MPa	Rupture Strain, %	Calculated J_c, kg/m²	Yield Strength, MPa
10	100	756.9	54.9	188.00	
10	100	932.7	51.0	173.30	
4	100	743.4	32.5	166.70	470
4	100	816.9	35.5	181.73	
2	100	1050.1	26.2	167.76	
2	100	1084	22.2	137.30	
10	200	943.7	57.5	196.00	
10	200	951.0	55.2	187.50	
4	200	920.5	33.9	172.20	466
4	200	941.7	28.8	146.86	
2	200	1032.3	25.6	161.80	
2	200	1050.7	23.9	149.00	
10	290	813.5	61.5	209.20	
10	290	1016.3	56.2	189.20	
4	290	887.1	25.6	130.26	462
4	290	931.6	25.9	131.74	
2	290	1077	23.8	147.00	
2	290	1080.9	22.2	135.00	

TABLE 8—*Test result for unirradiated round notched specimens on A508 Class 3 steel (FF).*

Notch Root Radius	Test Temperature, °C	Rupture Strength, σ_R, MPa	Rupture Strain, %	Calculated J_c, kg/m²	Yield Strength, MPa
10	100	984	56.7	216	
4	100	1137	47.5	261	523
2	100	1127	28.5	207	
10	200	1018	48	174	
4	200	904	39.2	215	506
2	200	1074	26.1	179	
2	200	1048	14.5	84.6	premature failure
10	290	955	42.7	148	
4	290	1110	35	179	489
2	290	1136	23.5	153	

Conclusions

From this study on the influence of irradiation on the elasto-plastic toughness of pressure vessel materials, the following conclusions can be drawn.

1. In unirradiated condition, the test temperature has only a weak influence on the J-R curves of the two steels studied (A533 B and A508 Class 3). The J-R curves are only slightly lowered when the test temperature is increased from 100°C up to 290°C.

2. Conversely, the *J-R* curves of the weld metal are significantly lowered when the test temperature is increased. The toughness of the weld is better than that of the two steels at 100°C but poorer at 290°C.
3. In irradiated condition, test temperature had little influence on toughness.
4. At 290°C, practically all of the *J-R* curves of irradiated material are identical to the *J-R* curves of the unirradiated materials.
5. The A508 Class 3 steel tested exhibits a relatively high sensitivity to radiation embrittlement at high fluences since cleavage occurs up to 100°C, although its content in copper and phosphorus are low.
6. Round notched tension specimens were used to evaluate the J_c of the two steels. A good prediction was obtained for the A533 B steel. The results obtained for the A508 Class 3 are more questionable. This is attributed to some inhomogeneity of the distribution of nonmetallic inclusions. However, this method is considered very promising for an alternative determination of J_c on irradiated materials.

Acknowledgments

The authors would like to very gratefully thank A. Pineau from Centre des Materiaux-Ecole des Mines, Paris who suggested the method of determination of J_c from round notched specimens and oriented the work of M. Al Mundheri during his thesis. The International Atomic Energy Agency who gave support to this study in the frame of the Coordinated Research Program on Advanced Pressure Vessel Steels and the French Safety Authorities (IPSN) who commissioned this work are greatly acknowledged. Many thanks are due to all the people who performed the tests and helped the authors in the preparation of this paper.

References

[1] Soulat, P., Petrequin, P., and Houssin, B. in *Radiation Embrittlement and Surveillance of Nuclear Reactor Pressure Vessels: An International Study, ASTM STP 819*, L. E. Steele, Ed., American Society for Testing and Materials, Philadelphia, 1983, pp. 64–85.
[2] Loss, F. J., Menke, B. H., and Vagins, M., "Elastic Plastic Toughness of Irradiated Low Shelf Nuclear Vessel Steels," *Transactions,* Sixth International Conference, SMIRT, 1981.
[3] Higer, A. L., Loss, F. J., and Menke, B. H., "J-R Curve Characterization of Irradiated Low Upper Shelf Welds," Report NUREG/CR-3506-MEA-2028, U.S. Nuclear Regulatory Commission, Washington, DC, April 1984.
[4] Ingham, T., Morland, E., Baguley, G., and Belcher, W. P. A., "The Influence of Irradiation on the Upper Shelf Toughness of SA508 Class 3 Steels," Analysis of the Behaviour of Advanced Reactor Pressure Vessel Steels Under Neutron Irradiation: The UK programme UKAEA, report for the International Atomic Energy Agency, Coordinated Research Programme, April 1983, pp. 194–245.
[5] Petrequin, P. in *Radiation Embrittlement and Surveillance of Nuclear Reactor Pressure Vessels: An International Study, ASTM STP 819*, L. E. Steele, Ed., American Society for Testing and Materials, Philadelphia, 1983, pp. 29–52.
[6] Gillemot, F. and Kapitany, A. in *Radiation Embrittlement and Surveillance of Nuclear Reactor Pressure Vessels: An International Study, ASTM STP 819*, L. E. Steele, Ed., American Society for Testing and Materials, Philadelphia, 1983, pp. 174–185.
[7] Mudry, F., "Etude de la Rupture Ductile et de la Rupture par Clivage d'Aciers Faiblement Allies," thesis, University de Technologie de Compiegne, 1982.

[8] Lautridou, J. C., "Etude de la Dechirure Ductile d'Aciers a Faible Resistance—Influence de la Teneur Inclusionnaire," thesis, Ecole Nationale des Mines de Paris, 1980.

[9] Hutchinson, J. W., *Journal of the Mechanics and Physics of Solids*, Vol. 16, 1968, pp. 13–31.

[10] Rice J. R. and Rosengren, G. F., *Journal of the Mechanics and Physics of Solids*, Vol. 16, 1968, pp. 1–13.

Claudio Maricchiolo,[1] Pietro P. Milella,[2] and Alfredo Pini[1]

Prediction of Reference Transition Temperature Increase Due to Neutron Irradiation Exposure

REFERENCE: Maricchiolo, C., Milella, P. P., and Pini, A., **"Prediction of Reference Transition Temperature Increase Due to Neutron Irradiation Exposure,"** *Radiation Embrittlement of Nuclear Reactor Pressure Vessel Steels: An International Review (Second Volume), ASTM STP 909,* L. E. Steele, Ed., American Society for Testing and Materials, Philadelphia, 1986, pp. 96–105.

ABSTRACT: A new approach of radiation damage data reduction is presented. The approach, called Constant Chemistry Analysis (CCA), is based on the systematic analysis of radiation damage observed on groups of steels having practically the same chemistry, in terms of copper and nickel content, individually considered.

For each group, a chemistry factor (CF) and exponent describing the reference transition temperature shift (ΔRT_{NDT}) trend versus fluence has been inferred.

Finally, a prediction formula for the overall trend is derived bestfitting the chemistry factors and the exponents previously determined. This particular approach emphasizes the role played by copper and nickel on the build-up of radiation damage.

The major finding is that saturation may take place in steels with very high copper/nickel ratio after great damage in the early stage (low fluence).

Furthermore, nickel seems to not contribute in an adverse manner to the radiation damage but it rather helps to reduce the ΔRT_{NDT} up to a content of about 1.0% over which it starts to develop an independent negative effect.

The steels considered in the analysis are A533 and A508 irradiated in test reactors in the United States, Germany, Japan, France, and Sweden with a copper and nickel content spanning from 0.02% to 0.22% and from 0.5% to 1.4%, respectively. The fluence ($E > 1$ MeV) was ranging from 1×10^{19} n/cm^2 to 9×10^{19} n/cm^2.

KEY WORDS: neutron irradiation, transition temperature, copper, nickel, reactor pressure vessel steels, radiation effects, embrittlement

Assessing the capability of a reactor pressure vessel to withstand an accident condition without loss of integrity, a fundamental role is played by the knowledge of the embrittlement of steel exposed to neutron irradiation. While data are becoming available from surveillance programs of power reactors, other data are more readily accessible from test reactors where exposure up to and over 3×10^{19}

[1] Mechanical engineers, Comitato Nazionale per l'Energia Nucleare ed Energie Alternative, Directorate for Safety and Health Protection, Roma, 00144 Italy.

[2] Head of Materials Technology Branch, Comitato Nazionale per l'Energia Nucleare ed Energie Alternative, Directorate for Safety and Health Protection, Roma, 00144 Italy.

n/cm^2 ($E > 1$ MeV) can be achieved within several months due to higher fluxes. This has led to the "vexata quaestio" of whether or not a material irradiated in a test reactor can be experiencing greater damage and showing no saturation effect at all.

On the other hand, most of the data coming from surveillance programs are referring to a steel, A302 B, no longer used in the nuclear industry. In addition, since exposures up to and over 3×10^{19} n/cm^2, which is the end of life fluence (EOLF) of a vast majority of reactor vessels, obviously cannot be reached in a few years in power plants (most of the aforementioned data are concentrated at fluences below or close to 1×10^{19} n/cm^2).

These two observations alone can justify the present need for test reactor data for new generation steels not only for research purposes but also for design consideration.

This has led the Directorate for Safety and Protection (DISP) of the Italian Comitato Nazionale per l'Energia Nucleare ed Energie Alternative (ENEA) to investigate the radiation damage of new steels, namely A533 B Class 1 and A508 Class 3, collecting and analyzing all the data available pertaining to such steels irradiated in test reactors and tested in the United States, Germany, Japan, France, and Sweden.[3] The aim was to derive a prediction formula for ΔRT_{NDT} to be used for the new generation of pressure water reactor (PWR) power plants to be built in Italy in the framework of the National Energy Plan (PEN).

The Charpy-V curves for the steels considered were not always immediately available, as in the case of French data where ΔRT_{NDT} were gathered by the source without the possibility of an independent check. A total of 80 data points have been collected so far. The fluence ranged from 0.9×10^{19} n/cm^2 to 9×10^{19} n/cm^2 ($E > 1$ MeV). The irradiation temperature was 288°C. Some steels (six) showed a ΔRT_{NDT} so much different than expected, that they have been disregarded until a possible explanation can be formulated.

Reference Transition Temperature

The reference transition temperature (RT_{NDT}) is normally measured on the Charpy-V curve at 68 J (50 ft · lb) according to a procedure well defined by the ASTM Notched Bar Impact Testing of Metallic Materials (E 23–82). Problems arising from embrittlement of old vessel steels whose notch ductility would not have eventually reached that energy level have changed that procedure, lowering the reading to 41 J (30 ft · lb) for the RT_{NDT} and, hence, for the ΔRT_{NDT}.[4]

The present study, however, is based on the 68-J ΔRT_{NDT}, because observation has revealed that readings at this energy level for the steels may be 10°C or more higher than readings done at 41 J, as Fig. 1 depicts. Moreover, the Italian Design

[3] Maricchiolo, C., Milella, P. P., Pini, A. and Sessa, M., "Raccolta di dati di infrangilimento da Radiazione su Acciai al Carbonio Bassolegati," ENEA/DISP ACO-MAT, Rapporto Tecnico, 1984.
[4] Metal Property Council Subcommittee 6 on Nuclear Materials, *Journal of Testing and Evaluation*, Vol. 11, No. 4, July 1983, pp. 237–260.

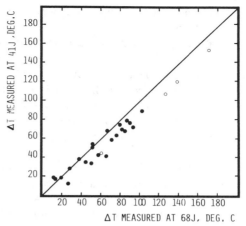

FIG. 1—*Plot of* ΔT *shift at 68 J versus* ΔT *measured at 41 J.*

Criteria for the new PWR-type power reactors explicitly call for an upper-shelf toughness of at least 100 J, even at the EOLF.

First, it was checked whether the Guthrie PTS equation, developed mainly for A302 B steel and based on the 41 J transition temperature shift, could hold also for A533 B Class 1 and A508 Class 3 without any further refinement. Figure 2 is a plot of residual versus fluence for 74 steels considered in this study, where residual is defined as the difference between the ΔRT_{NDT} measured on the Charpy-

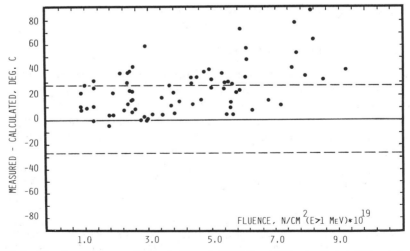

FIG. 2—*Plot of residual versus fluence for 74 steels (A533 B or A508) using Guthrie PTS equation.*

V curves and that calculated using the PTS equation that is[5]

$$1.8 \, \Delta RT_{NDT} = (-10 + 470 \, Cu + 350 \, Cu \, Ni)f^{0.27} \qquad (1)$$

where f is the fluence divided by 10^{19}, and Cu and Ni are the copper and nickel contents, in percent, respectively.

As can be seen, practically all of the data fall above the zero line, indicating a nonconservatism in the prediction formula considered (Eq 1). Moreover, almost half of the data points are above the 2σ line. The standard deviation, σ, for the Guthrie PTS equation is equal to 13°C (24°F). This finding has suggested the derivation of a completely new equation rather than a simple adjustment to the old one.

Constant Chemistry Analysis

The steels considered in this study have been grouped in a box matrix according to their copper and nickel contents, Fig. 3. Each box is delimiting copper and

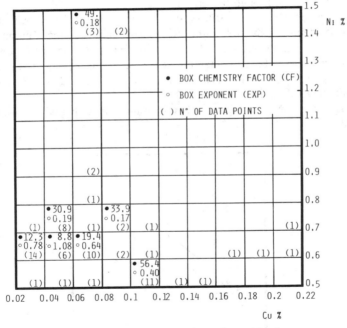

FIG. 3—Box matrix for the steels considered.

[5] Guthrie, G. L., "Development of Trend Curve Formulas Using Surveillance Data," *LWR-Pressure Vessel Surveillance Dosimetry Improvement Program: January–March 1982*, NUREG/CR-2805, Vol. 1, HED-TME 82-18, U.S. Nuclear Regulatory Commission, Washington, DC, Dec. 1982.

nickel within very narrow ranges such that steels occupying anyone could be considered as having the same chemistry, in terms of copper and nickel. This particular approach enables the researcher to focus his attention to classes of steels that can be considered as having almost the same response to neutron irradiation. The numbers in brackets in the boxes of Fig. 3 indicate how many steels with the same chemistry fall within the box.

It is assumed that the damage (in terms of increase in the transition temperature, ΔT, introduced by neutron irradiation) can be expressed in the form of an exponential of the type

$$\Delta T = CF \cdot f^n \qquad (2)$$

where f is the fluence divided by 10^{19}, CF is the chemistry factor, and n is an exponent to be determined.

The analysis has been done separately for each box in which there were at least three steels; hence, three data points relating ΔT to the fluence. The limitation clearly stems from the law of degradation that, being exponential, needs at least three points to be inferred. In reality, the minimum number should be two, since the curve has to pass through the origin.

Figures 4 and 5 show the result of such an analysis for Boxes 3,2 and 1,2. Each box is identified by two numbers: the first indicates the column in the matrix of Fig. 3, and the second indicates the row starting from the bottom. The results for each of the boxes containing at least three data points are presented in the matrix of Fig. 3. The closed point indicates the CF of the box, and the open point shows the relative exponent.

Looking at the matrix of Fig. 3, it is important to note that while an increase

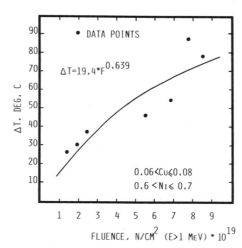

FIG. 4—*Chemistry factor and exponent for Box 3,2 inferred from best fitting of box data points.*

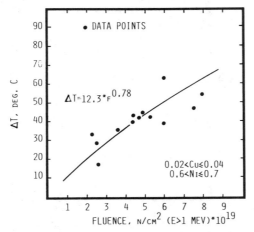

FIG. 5—*Chemistry factor and exponent for Box 1,2 inferred from best fitting of box data points.*

in the CF can be eventually seen going from left to right, that is, from low copper to high copper, no trend can be actually guessed at as to an increase in the nickel content due to lack of consistent data going from bottom to top.

In order to ascertain any particular trend, it can be very useful to plot both the CF and the exponents versus the nickel/copper ratio, as shown in Figs. 6 and 7. While the downward trend of Fig. 6 with increasing copper content was expected for the CF, it was surprising to discover the opposite trend as far as the nickel was concerned. This finding contradicts the current belief that a synergistic effect between copper and nickel would eventually enhance the radiation damage.

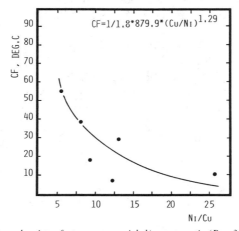

FIG. 6—*Plot of box chemistry factors versus nickel/copper ratio (Box 3,10 is not included).*

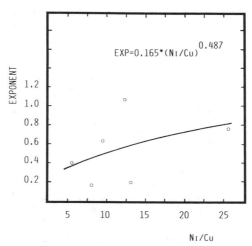

FIG. 7—*Plot of box exponents versus nickel/copper ratio (Box 3,10 is not included).*

Equally, if not more surprising, was the upward trend shown by the exponent, depicted in Fig. 7, that has been always considered constant, that is, independent of the chemistry factor.

The analytical expression found for the curves plotted in Figs. 6 and 7 are the following

$$1.8 \ CF = 879.9(Cu/Ni)^{1.29} \tag{3}$$

$$Exp = 0.165(Ni/Cu)^{0.487} \tag{4}$$

Knowing Eqs 3 and 4, it is finally possible to derive the reference transition temperature shift prediction formula by simply writing

$$1.8 \ \Delta RT = [879.9(Cu/Ni)^{1.29}]f^{0.165(Ni/Cu)^{0.487}} \tag{5}$$

Some further refinements were made to Eq 5 to better describe the behavior of those steels having either very low copper (<0.04%) or very high (>1.0%) nickel content. The final form turns out to be

$$1.8 \ \Delta RT_{NDT} = [879.9(Cu/Ni)^{1.29} + Ni^{8.5} + (0.08/Cu)^{1.7}]f^{[0.165(Ni/Cu)^{0.487}]} \tag{6}$$

Equation 6 has been checked against all of the data available included in the matrix of Fig. 3. The result is plotted in Fig. 8 as residual versus fluence. The standard deviation, σ, is equal to 13°C. Also plotted in Fig. 8 is the 2σ line.

Figure 9 is a plot of Eq 6 for different copper contents and nickel equal to 0.8% compared to the U.S. Nuclear Regulatory Commission's Regulatory Guide

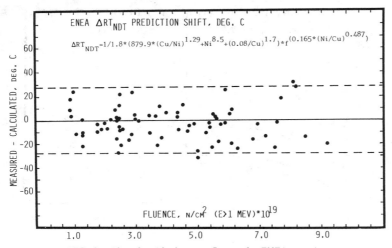

FIG. 8—*Plot of residual versus fluence for ENEA equation.*

1.99 Rev. 1 trend curves for the same chemistries. It must be kept in mind that while Regulatory Guide 1.99 Rev. 1 curves are upper bound trends, the ENEA curves represent mean values to which 2σ shall be added.

Figure 10 shows the same comparison with Regulatory Guide 1.99 Rev. 2, which shows a saturation effect at high fluences not present in the ENEA trend curve yet predicted by Eq 6, because as the nickel/copper ratio decreases the exponent of the fluence goes to zero indicating total saturation. About 40% of the data analyzed by P. N. Randall to derive Regulatory Guide 1.99 Rev. 2 had a nickel/copper ratio of about 0.75 to 1.0, since they were relative to old steels with high copper and almost no nickel. For those values of the nickel/copper

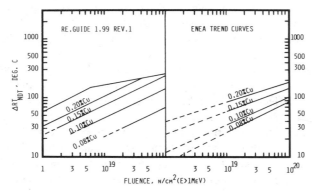

FIG. 9—*Plot of Regulatory Guide 1.99 Rev. 1 and ENEA formula versus fluence for several copper contents with nickel = 0.8% and phosphorus = 0.012%.*

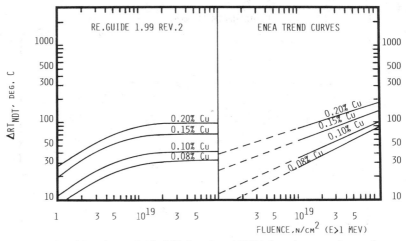

FIG. 10—*Plot of Regulatory Guide 1.99 Rev. 2 and ENEA formula versus fluence for several copper contents with nickel = 0.8%.*

ratio, the exponent of Eq 6 becomes equal to 0.143 to 0.165 and saturation predominates. For new steels with a nickel/copper ratio of about 10, that exponent swells to 0.5 eliminating any saturation.

Figure 11 is a plot of the ENEA prediction curves and experimental data (closed points) normalized to a fluence of 1×10^{19} n/cm^2 versus copper content for several nickel contents. As can be seen, as nickel increases up to 1%, the radiation damage sharply decreases. Since nickel also enters into the exponent of fluence, this trend decreases, by percent, at higher fluences.

Discussion and Conclusions

1. A reference transition temperature prediction shift equation was derived for high nickel, low copper steels of the A533 B Class 1 and A508 Class 3 type, using the Constant Chemistry Analysis (CCA) method. Experimental data coming from test reactors have been checked against the prediction equation indicating very good agreement.
2. Nickel was found to reduce the damage introduced by neutron irradiation up to a content of about 1.0% over which it develops an independent high negative effect. The beneficial effect of nickel below 1.0% decreases by percent as the fluence increases.
3. The fluence term contribution to damage appeared to depend on the nickel/copper ratio, that is, the prediction shift equation turned out to have a fluence term elevated to a power containing a nickel/copper factor. This suggested that saturation could take place any time the nickel/copper ratio decreases below unity.
4. Since the prediction equation was derived analyzing and interpolating data

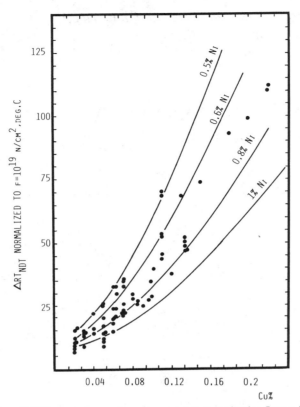

FIG. 11—*Plot of ENEA trend curve and experimental data normalized to fluence 1×10^{19} n/cm²
versus copper content for several nickel contents.*

coming from relatively few lots of steels having practically the same chem-
istry (CCA analysis), it is felt that more lots are needed to better infer the
CF and exponent to be introduced into the prediction equation itself. The
ENEA is actually planning research in this direction.

5. It must be kept in mind that the transition temperature shift equation derived
by ENEA, Eq 5, has an empirical base. As such, it cannot be used outside
the data base chemistry range ($0.5\% \leq \mathrm{Ni} \leq 1\%$, $0.02\% \leq \mathrm{Cu} \leq 0.22\%$)
utilized for its derivation. This limitation also applies to Conclusions 2 and
3, which might not be true outside that range.

K. S. Sivaramakrishnan,[1] *Subrata Chatterjee,*[2]
S. Anantharaman,[2] *K. S. Balakrishnan,*[2] *U. K. Viswanathan,*[2]
and Pradip R. Roy[3]

Boiling Water Reactor (BWR) Pressure Vessel Surveillance Program

REFERENCE: Sivaramakrishnan, K. S., Chatterjee, S., Anantharaman, S., Balakrishnan, K. S., Viswanathan, U. K., and Roy, P. R., **"Boiling Water Reactor (BWR) Pressure Vessel Surveillance Program,"** *Radiation Embrittlement of Nuclear Reactor Pressure Vessel Steels: An International Review (Second Volume), ASTM STP 909,* L. E. Steele, Ed., American Society for Testing and Materials, Philadelphia, 1986, pp. 106–117.

ABSTRACT: A302 B steel cladded with stainless steel is used as the pressure vessel material for the two 210 MW(e) boiling water reactors commissioned during 1968. Fabricated surveillance specimens, representative of the pressure vessel steel, were kept in the reactor at wall, shroud, core, and steam dryer locations of the reactor. Charpy V-notch impact and tension specimens from base, weld, and heat affected zone (HAZ) from these locations, except at the core, were tested in the hot cell.

It has been found that maximum shift corresponding to Charpy 41-J index temperature was observed for the base material at the shroud location and the estimated value was 38°C. The corresponding index temperature was 18°C. The irradiation capsules had iron, copper, and nickel flux monitors. These were analyzed for estimating the fluences (>1 MeV), which were found to be $(2.2 \pm 0.4) \times 10^{18}$ n/cm^2 for wall and $(1.5 \pm 0.3) \times 10^{19}$ n/cm^2 for the shroud locations.

The shift in index temperatures was compared with the trend curves of Regulatory Guide 1.99.1.

KEY WORDS: pressure vessel surveillance, A302 B base, welds, heat affected zone, TAPS reactors, index temperature, index temperature shift, upper-shelf energy, tensile strength, chemical composition, fast neutron fluence, radiation effects, pressure vessel steels, welded joints, irradiation, embrittlement

The pressure vessel is a vital component of a reactor, and assurance of its structural integrity is a must as this has a direct bearing on safe operation of the reactor. Composed mostly of ferritic types of steels, pressure vessels have a tendency to become embrittled with exposure to neutron irradiation present in the reactor core.

[1] Head, Post Irradiation Examination Section, Radiometallurgy Division, Bhabha Atomic Research Centre, Bombay, India.

[2] Scientific officers, Post Irradiation Examination Section, Radiometallurgy Division, Bhabha Atomic Research Centre, Bombay, India.

[3] Associate director, Metallurgy Group, Bhabha Atomic Research Centre, Bombay, India.

The Tarapur Atomic Power Station (TAPS) reactors are designed so that the maximum fast fluence of the reactor pressure vessel does not exceed 2.3×10^{18} n/cm^2 (>1 MeV). Extensive experimental data generated from studies carried out in research reactors or accelerated locations in power reactors (fast flux is higher than 10^{12} n/cm^2/s), has shown that changes in mechanical properties for exposures up to this fluence are acceptable. Nevertheless, it is prudent and conservative to perform pressure vessel material surveillance programs to monitor material property changes where the threshold exposure of 1×10^{17} n/cm^2 is exceeded [1,2].

Another pertinent reason for the necessity of surveillance programs arises from the fact that the pressure vessel wall experiences fast flux of the order of only 10^9 n/cm^2/s, about three orders less than the flux levels of research reactors or other accelerated locations of power reactors and from where most of the experimental results are available. Presently, available experimental results from the low-flux irradiations obtained from some reactor surveillance programs point out the saturation behavior of embrittlement, which has not been observed in high-flux irradiations. As such, irradiation behavior predictions from high-flux experiments are likely to give higher values of irradiation-induced embrittlement [3-5].

Thus it becomes very important to have all the metal heats of the steel used in the operating reactor evaluated for radiation damage under the actual operating conditions of the reactor, which is achieved by the in-reactor surveillance program.

The results obtained from the TAPS surveillance program, as completed to date, are presented.

Material Preparation and Irradiation

Charpy V-notch impact specimens and tension specimens were made from A302 B base metal used to fabricate the TAPS reactor pressure vessel. A test weld representing a vessel welded joint was fabricated from the vessel base metal. Impact and tension specimens representing the weld heat affected zone (HAZ) and the weld were fabricated from the test weld material. The specimens were fabricated in accordance with ASTM Practice for Conducting Surveillance Tests for Light Water-Cooled Nuclear Power Reactor Vessels (E 185-82) specifications.

The gage length of the weld tension specimens was made entirely of the weld metal by taking the specimens parallel to the weld length and parallel to the plate surface. The weld Charpy specimens were made parallel to the rolling direction; perpendicular to the weld line with the notch located in the weld. The weld HAZ Charpy specimen was made parallel to the weld Charpy specimen but its notch root radius was located at the intersection of the base metal and weld deposit. The weld and weld HAZ Charpy V-notches were parallel to the original plate surface. The gage length of weld HAZ tension specimen was parallel to the rolling direction and perpendicular to the weld line. The major axis of both base

TABLE 1—*Chemical composition of the materials.*

Material	C	Si	Mn	Mo	Ni	Cu	P
Base	0.2	0.18	1.10	0.29	0.440	0.125	0.008
Weld	0.2	0.15	1.16	0.49	0.375	0.093	0.007
HAZ	0.2	0.32	1.12	0.42	0.487	0.120	0.008

tension and impact specimens were parallel to the rolling direction and the notch perpendicular to the original plate surface.

Table 1 gives the chemical composition of base, weld, and the weld HAZ in percent by weight.

The specimen capsules scheduled for a given neutron fluence were kept together in a single basket. Figure 1 [1,2] shows a typical surveillance basket that contained three or four capsules containing impact specimens and four or five capsules containing tension specimens.

A typical tensile capsule is shown in Fig. 2 [1,2]. Sub-size tension specimens of 25.4-mm gage length were used.

A typical impact specimen capsule in shown in Fig. 3 [1,2]. The fluence

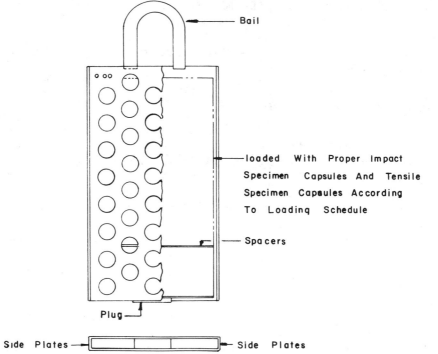

FIG. 1—*Capsule basket containing impact specimen capsules and tension specimen capsules.*

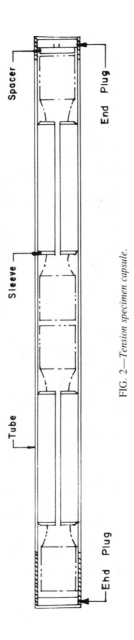

FIG. 2—*Tension specimen capsule.*

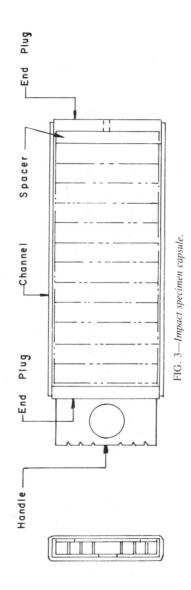

FIG. 3—*Impact specimen capsule.*

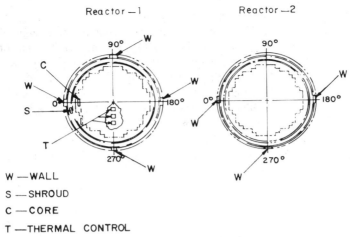

FIG. 4—*Location of capsule baskets in the reactor core.*

experienced by the specimens could be measured from iron, nickel, and copper monitors kept inside the capsule [1,2].

The tensile and impact capsules were filled with dry helium. Reactor water pressure assured good contact between the capsule and the specimens. Because the boiling water reactor is a constant temperature bath at 288°C ± 10°C, no temperature monitors were kept separately.

The baskets were kept in the wall (W), shroud (S), and core (C) locations of the TAPS reactor. These are situated at the middle of core elevation. Three baskets kept in the steam dryer locations (T) in the reactor, where neutron flux levels are insignificant, serve as thermal control specimens. These specimens are used to measure the effect of temperature only, as opposed to temperature and neutron flux that the other capsules undergo [6]. Figure 4 [1,2] shows the location of the baskets in the reactor.

Experimental Details

The baskets and the capsules contained in them were properly identified inside the hot cell. The baskets and the capsules were remotely cut open and the specimens were removed by gentle tapping. Flux monitors were carefully retrieved from the impact capsules and the fluence values were monitored[4] [7]. Yield strength, ultimate tensile strength, and total elongation values were measured on the tension specimens by using a remotized Instron testing machine. Tests were performed at room temperature at a constant strain rate of 8.3×10^{-4} s^{-1}. Impact tests were carried out with a remotely operated 36 kg · m Charpy

[4] Personal communication with Dr. V. C. Deniz, head, Experimental Reactor Physics Section, Bhabha Atomic Research Centre, Trombay, Bombay, India, 16 May 1984.

pendulum as per ASTM Recommended Practice for Notched Bar Impact Testing of Metallic Materials (E 23-82) requirements, in the temperature range of -120 to $+280°C$. Although Charpy 41-J, 68-J, and 0.89 mm lateral expansion index temperatures were used, the adjustment of the reference temperature was determined from the shift corresponding to Charpy 41-J index temperature.

It needs to be mentioned here that although there are 12 locations in the two reactors, where the surveillance specimens were kept, only specimens from one wall location of each reactor, one shroud location, and one steam dryer location of one of the reactors were tested at present. All these specimens were removed from the reactors after 10 years of reactor operation. The irradiation temperature of the specimens was $288°C \pm 10°C$.

Results

The results of tension tests carried out on the specimens removed from the steam dryer, wall, and shroud locations are given in Table 2. The values indicated are the average of three tests carried out on each material. The results of Charpy impact tests from these corresponding locations are given in Table 3 and Figs. 5, 6, 7, and 8. The number of specimens tested for each location is indicated within parentheses. The fluence, >1 MeV, experienced by the specimens at the wall and shroud locations were estimated as $(2.2 \pm 0.4) \times 10^{18}$ ns/cm^2 and $(1.5 \pm 0.3) \times 10^{19}$ ns/cm^2, respectively.

The results of tests on specimens taken from steam dryer locations were used as the base unirradiated data due to the non-availability of both the archive

TABLE 2—*Tension test results.*

Location	Yield Strength, MPa	Ultimate Tensile Strength, MPa	Elongation, %
	BASE MATERIAL		
Steam dryer	419.0	582.8	36.0
Wall	475.9	627.6	35.7
Shroud	500.0	637.9	29.0
Wall[a]	513.8	658.6	31.4
	APED[b] MATERIAL		
Wall[a]	493.1	633.3	31.7
	WELD MATERIAL		
Steam dryer	462.1	598.3	32.5
Wall	524.1	635.2	30.5
Shroud	556.9	674.1	29.0
	HAZ MATERIAL		
Steam dryer	405.2	556.9	31.5
Wall	464.3	625.3	29.0
Shroud	525.9	631.0	26.5

[a] TAPS-2. All other locations are from TAPS-1.
[b] Atomic Power Equipment Department correlation monitor [6].

TABLE 3—*Charpy impact test results.*

Location	Index Temperature, °C			Upper-Shelf Energy, J
	$C_{V\,41\,J}$	$C_{V\,68\,J}$	$C_{V\,0.89mm}$	
	BASE MATERIAL			
Steam dryer	− 20	− 4	− 10	165
Wall	− 6	+ 14	+ 14	140
Shroud	+ 18	+ 36	+ 32	135
Wall[a]	− 6	+ 20	+ 18	129
	APED[b] MATERIAL			
Wall[a]	+ 4	+ 16	+ 16	118
	WELD MATERIAL			
Steam dryer	− 48	− 34	− 42	148
Wall	− 26	+ 6	− 6	128
Shroud	− 8	+ 32	+ 28	113
	HAZ MATERIAL			
Steam dryer	− 82	− 58	− 70	201
Wall	− 56	− 38	− 40	163
Shroud	− 46	− 24	− 28	163

[a] TAPS-2. All other locations are from TAPS-1.
[b] Atomic Power Equipment Department correlation monitor [6].

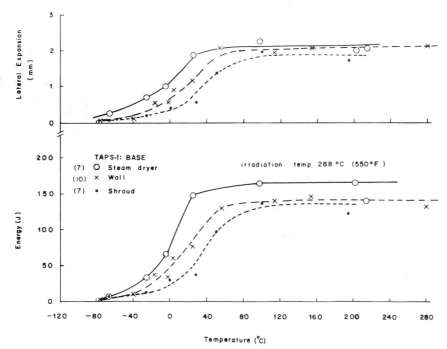

FIG. 5—*Charpy V-notch results on base metal at steam dryer, wall, and shroud locations of TAPS-1.*

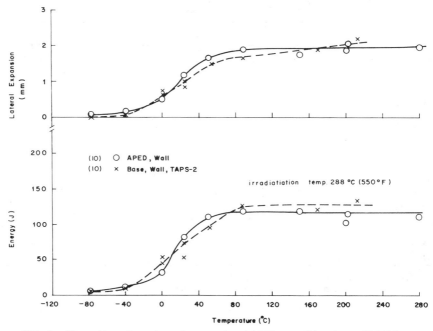

FIG. 6—*Charpy V-notch results on base metal and APED at wall locations of TAPS-2.*

specimens and test report on the unirradiated material used for the pressure vessel construction. This can be justified by the fact that the steam dryer is located at the very top of the pressure vessel and the neutron flux level at this location is not significant enough to cause any considerable change in the parameters estimated [8]. Moreover, the flux monitors contained in the impact test specimen capsules, when analyzed, did not indicate any measurable activation.[5]

The specimens at the wall locations at their time of removal had neutron exposure corresponding to 6.5 effective full power years. The lead factor at the shroud location being 6.8, the specimens in these locations had neutron exposure corresponding to 45 effective full power years, which is higher than 40 years of end-of-life design lifetime of the reactor pressure vessel. Therefore, shift in Charpy 41-J index temperature observed in specimens from the shroud location can be safely considered for the determination of the index temperature shift corresponding to the end-of-lifetime of the reactor pressure vessel.

Figure 5 shows that for the base metal, the increase in the Charpy 41-J index temperature was 14°C for the wall location and 38°C for the shroud location. The corresponding upper-shelf energy values were reduced from 165 J by 25 J and 30 J, respectively. These specimens were from TAPS-1.

---

[5] Personal communication with Dr. V. C. Deniz (see Footnote 4).

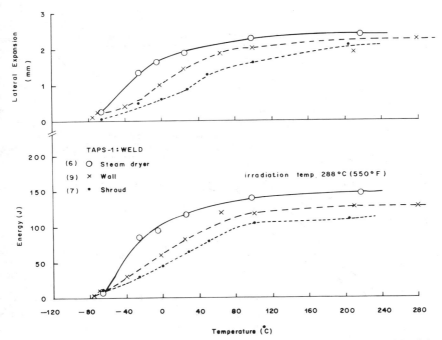

FIG. 7—*Charpy V-notch results on weld at steam dryer, wall, and shroud locations of TAPS-1.*

Figure 6 shows that for the base metal from TAPS-2, the increase in the Charpy 41-J index temperature was also 14°C for the wall location. The upper-shelf energy was reduced from 165 J by 36 J. The APED specimens showed the Charpy 41-J index temperature to be comparable to the base metals.

Figure 7 shows that for the weld metal, the increase in the Charpy 41-J index temperature was 22°C for the wall location and 40°C for the shroud location. The corresponding upper-shelf energy values were reduced from 148 J by 20 J and 35 J, respectively.

Figure 8 shows that for the HAZ, the increase in the Charpy 41-J index temperature was 26°C for the wall location and 36°C for the shroud location. The corresponding upper-shelf energy values were reduced from 201 J by 38 J for both locations.

Discussion

The tension test results show that yield strength of all the materials had increased with increasing neutron exposure.

The impact test results show that although the unirradiated Charpy 41-J index temperatures were different for the base, weld, and HAZ materials, the shift in the corresponding index temperatures were very similar, typically around 20°C

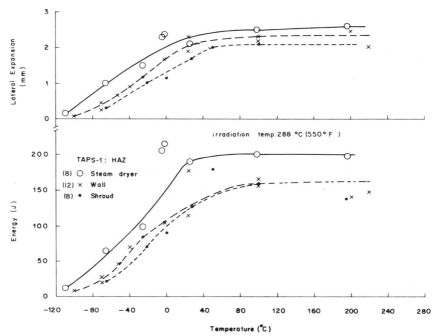

FIG. 8—*Charpy V-notch results on HAZ at steam dryer, wall, and shroud locations of TAPS-1.*

for wall locations and around 38°C for shroud location. The differences in the values of index temperatures of the unirradiated materials could possibly be attributed to the different specimen orientations used in these materials.

It becomes important to note that if Regulatory Guide 1.99.1 trend curves [9] were to be used for predicting shift in the index temperature, the corresponding values would have been 22, 14, and 21°C for the base, weld, and HAZ at the wall location and 58, 36, and 54°C for these corresponding materials at the shroud location. Comparison of the values so obtained from the trend curves with the impact test results reveals that whereas for the wall location (corresponding to a low fluence of 2.2 × 10[18] n/cm[2]) trend curve predicts the shift in the index temperature within ±8°C, for the shroud location (corresponding to a fluence value as high as 1.5 × 10[19] n/cm[2]), the trend curve over-predicts the shift in the index temperature by as much as 20°C.

A similar comparison of the impact test results with the trend curve [10] for ASTM A302 B reference plate (containing 0.2% copper) shows that the shift in the index temperature corresponding to shroud location (fluence of 1.5 × 10[19] n/cm[2]) of the latter is higher by about 30 to 45°C.

Conclusions

The results of the surveillance program indicate a maximum shift of index temperature of 38°C for a fluence of $(1.5 \pm 0.3) \times 10^{19}$ n/cm^2. The maximum index temperature at this fluence is about 18°C.

These results also show that the Regulatory Guide trend curves over-predict the shift in the index temperature at higher fluence values of the order of 1×10^{19} n/cm^2, implying thereby the fact that towards the end-of-life reactor operation, the vessel wall is less embrittled than what the trend curves predict.

Acknowledgment

The authors wish to thank their colleagues in Post Irradiation Examination Section of Radiometallurgy Division, Spectroscopy Section of Radiochemistry Division, and Experimental Reactor Physics Section, all of Bhabha Atomic Research Centre for experimental help, and their colleagues at TAPS for making the irradiated capsule baskets available and for helpful discussions. Thanks are also due to K. Balaramamoorthy, director, Materials Group, Bhabha Atomic Research Centre, for his keen interest in this work.

References

[1] Higgins, J. P., "Modified Surveillance Programme for General Electric BWR Pressure Vessel Steels," GE Report APED-5490, General Electric, San Jose, CA, April 1967.

[2] Higgins, J. P. and Brandt, F. A., "Mechanical Property Surveillance of General Electric BWR Vessels," GE Report NEDO-10115, General Electric, San Jose, CA, July 1969.

[3] Chatterjee, S. and Sivaramakrishnan, K. S., "Irradiation Induced Embrittlement of Steels Used as Reactor Pressure Vessel and End Shields," BARC Report-1135, Bhabha Atomic Research Centre, Bombay, 1981, pp. 5, 7, 15–16.

[4] Stahlkopf, K. E. and Martson, T. U., presented at the IAEA Specialists' Meeting on Irradiation Embrittlement, Thermal Annealing and Surveillance of Reactor Pressure Vessel Steels, Vienna, Feb. 1979, IWG-RRPC-79/3, International Atomic Energy Agency, p. 8.

[5] Petrequin, P. and Soulat, P., presented at the IAEA Specialists' Meeting on Irradiation Embrittlement, Thermal Annealing and Surveillance of Reactor Pressure Vessel Steels, Vienna, Feb. 1979, IWG-RRPC-79/3, International Atomic Energy Agency, p. 195.

[6] Peterson, W. R., "Tarapur Material Surveillance Programme," TAPS Report-2884, Tarapur Atomic Power Station, Tarapur, India.

[7] Hogg, C. H. and Weber, L. D., in *Radiation Effects on Metals and Neutron Dosimetry, ASTM STP 341,* American Society for Testing and Materials, Philadelphia, 1963, p. 133.

[8] Dufour, L. B., Lijibrink, E. and Zijp, W. L., presented at the IAEA Specialists' Meeting on Irradiation Embrittlement, Thermal Annealing and Surveillance of Reactor Pressure Vessel Steels, Vienna, Feb. 1979, IWG-RRPC-79/3, International Atomic Energy Agency, p. 97.

[9] NRC Regulatory Guide 1.99, Revision 1, U.S. Nuclear Regulatory Commission, Washington, DC, April 1977.

[10] Steele, L. E., "Neutron Irradiation Embrittlement of Reactor Pressure Vessel Steels," IAEA Technical Report TRS-163, International Atomic Energy Agency, 1975, p. 117.

Ferenc Gillemot,[1] *István Havas,*[2] *and László Szabó*[1]

Static Fracture Criteria Evaluation Using Small Specimens

REFERENCE: Gillemot, F., Havas, I., and Szabó, L., **"Static Fracture Criteria Evaluation Using Small Specimens,"** *Radiation Embrittlement of Nuclear Reactor Pressure Vessel Steels: An International Review (Second Volume), ASTM STP 909*, L. E. Steele, Ed., American Society for Testing and Materials, Philadelphia, 1986, pp. 118–124.

ABSTRACT: The evaluation of valid static fracture criteria in radiation embrittlement research and surveillance measurement is always difficult due to the limited size of the specimens. Test series have been performed to evaluate the optimum side-grooving of the Charpy-size three-point bend (TPB) specimens and a method has been elaborated for using the remnants of broken Charpy specimens for measurements of energy criteria, Absorbed Specific Fracture until Energy (ASFE).

KEY WORDS: radiation effects, pressure vessel steels, energy criterion, irradiation, embrittlement, fracture toughness testing, elastic-plastic fracture mechanics

Surveillance programs and research into radiation embrittlement generally use dynamic fracture tests, most commonly impact energy measurements, on Charpy V-notched specimens. The use of static fracture tests is also advocated but most surveillance programs do not include static fracture mechanical specimens due to their size.

The Charpy-size precracked specimens used for crack-opening displacement (COD) measurements generally do not show unstable crack propagation at room or elevated temperature, which means that the calculation of valid fracture toughness properties is not possible.

To avoid these difficulties, two series of measurements were performed: Absorbed Specific Energy until Fracture (ASFE) measurements on smooth and notched tension specimens cut from pieces of broken Charpy specimens, and J_{Ic} measurements on side-grooved Charpy-size slow-bend specimens.

ASFE Measurements on Used Charpy Specimens

The deformation energy required for crack initiation in a unit volume of material is called Absorbed Specific Energy until Fracture (ASFE) [1,2]. (It has been also

---

[1] Senior research associate and research engineer, respectively, Central Research Institute for Physics, Budapest, Hungary.
[2] Senior research engineer, Technical University of Budapest, Budapest, Hungary.

called ASPEF in the literature.) The ASFE is a simple energy criterion that may be applied to evaluate the embrittlement and fracture properties of low and intermediate strength ductile structure materials. New results show that ASFE measurements enable us, in most cases, to calculate different fracture criteria (J_{Ic}, K_{Ic}), to compare the effects of static and dynamic loading, and to determine the effect of neutron irradiation.

The theoretical basis of ASFE, the fundamental results, and many practical applications have been described elsewhere [1,3–11]. Our principal purpose here is to introduce a new way of using it in surveillance testing.

The ASFE values measured on smooth specimens characterize the fracture properties (W_c) of a material, but the values measured on notched specimens depend not only on the W_c values but also on the volume of the plastic zone at the notch tip. These values (W_m, average ASFE) change with the notch geometry and are sensitive to temperature, that is, average ASFE characterizes the material behavior under certain circumstances only.

In a test series performed by the Technical University of Budapest, static and dynamic ASFE values have been measured on ordinary boiler steel as a function of temperature. Smooth and differently notched tension specimens (diameter = 6 mm) were used for the test. The results are shown in Fig. 1. The energy until fracture measured by static loading on smooth specimens exceeded the absorbed

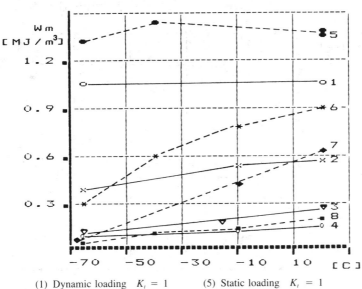

(1) Dynamic loading $K_t = 1$	(5) Static loading $K_t = 1$	
(2) Dynamic loading $K_t = 1.27$	(6) Static loading $K_t = 1.27$	
(3) Dynamic loading $K_t = 2.7$	(7) Static loading $K_t = 2.7$	
(4) Dynamic loading $K_t = 3.2$	(8) Static loading $K_t = 3.2$	

FIG. 1—*Comparison of static and dynamic ASFE values measured on A.45.56 steel* [12] (K_t = *stress concentration factor*).

energy of the dynamically loaded specimens in the whole testing range. However, in the case of the notched specimens, under a specific temperature, this was reversed, showing that dynamic loading is not always the more disadvantageous [12].

On the basis of these results, we developed a method to use the remnants of the tested Charpy and small-size COD specimens for static tension testing. The machining method of the specimens is shown in Fig. 2. As only the middle of the broken Charpy specimens has to be turned, the production of the specimens is simple and cheap. The diameter of each specimen is 4 mm.

To verify the use of these specimens, a test series was performed on unirradiated and irradiated reactor pressure vessel (RPV) steel, type 15H2MFA. The chemical composition and mechanical properties of the tested steels are given in Table 1.

The values measured on smooth specimens (stress concentration factor, $K_t = 1$) show some decrease with decreasing temperature. On the effect of irradiation,

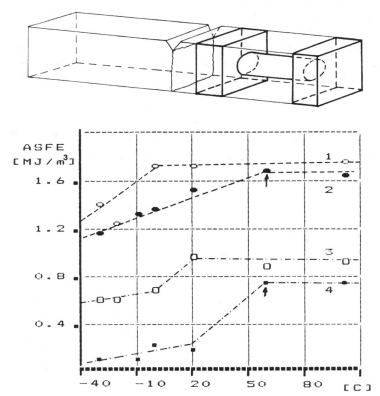

FIG. 2—ASFE results obtained on tension specimens cut from the remnants of broken Charpy specimens (Material 15H2MFA): (1) smooth round tension specimen unirradiated; (2) smooth round tension specimen irradiated with a neutron fluence $3 \cdot 10^{19}$ n/cm² E > 1 MeV; (3) notched round tension specimen, unirradiated; and (4) notched round tension specimen irradiated with a neutron fluence $3 \cdot 10^{19}$ n/cm² E > 1 MeV.

TABLE 1—*Chemical composition (%) of the tested steels.*

Type	C	Si	Mn	Cr	Ni	Mo	V	Yield Stress, MPa
A.45.47.	0.27	0.25	1.46	...	...	...	...	...
15H2MFA	0.15	0.27	0.45	2.8	0.4	0.7	0.3	568
Boiler drum	0.22	0.33	1.23	0.06	...	...	...	266

a small decreasing of the values was experienced, but maximally 10% below the unirradiated values. The W_m values measured on notched specimens ($K_t > 1$) rapidly decrease with decreasing temperature; and the difference between the irradiated and unirradiated values in low temperature increases rapidly (Fig. 2). The temperature where the difference between the two curves starts to increase is suggested to be used as the critical temperature for static loading. If this temperature is below the dynamic transition temperature ($C_v = 68$ J), the latter has to be used as the surveillance criterion otherwise both should be taken into consideration. For comparison, the transition temperatures measured on the Charpy-V specimens in irradiated and unirradiated conditions are shown in Fig. 3.

The tensile data obtained from the remnants of the broken Charpy specimens may be used for other evaluation methods too. Pachur [*13*] suggested a correlation between the shift of the rupture stress and the transition temperature shift caused by irradiation. Czoboly and Havas elaborated methods for the calculation of J_{lc}

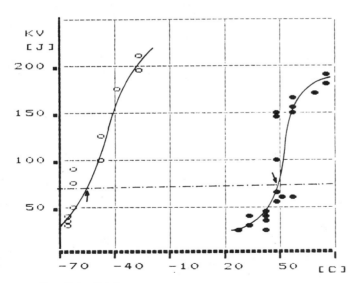

○ = Unirradiated.
● = Irradiated with $3 \cdot 10^{19}$ n/cm² $E > 1$ MeV neutron fluence.

FIG. 3—*Effect of irradiation on the nondestructive testing of 15H2MFA steel.*

[3] Gillemot, L., in *Proceedings*, 1st International Conference on Fracture D-1, Sendai, Japan, 1965, pp. 47–80.

[4] Czoboly, E., Havas, I., and Gillemot, F., in *Proceedings*, International Symposium on Absorbed Specific Energy and/or Strain Energy Density, Martinus Nijhoff, The Hague, 1982, pp. 107–130.

[5] Ivanova, V. S., et al in *Proceedings*, International Symposium on Absorbed Specific Energy and/or Strain Energy Density, Martinus Nijhoff, The Hague, 1982, pp. 101–106.

[6] Radon, J. C. and Czoboly, E., "Specific Fracture Work of Mild Steel," in 7th Symposium on Fracture Mechanics, American Society for Testing and Materials, Philadelphia, 1973.

[7] Gillemot, F. and Kapitány, A., in *Radiation Embrittlement and Surveillance of Nuclear Reactor Pressure Vessels: An International Study, ASTM STP 819*, L. E. Steele, Ed., American Society for Testing and Materials, Philadelphia, 1983, pp. 174–185.

[8] Havas, I., et al, *Materialprüfung*, Vol. 16, 1964, pp. 349–353.

[9] Radon, J. C. and Czoboly, E., in *Proceedings*, International Conference on Mechanical Behaviour of Materials (1), Kyoto, Japan, 1972, pp. 543–557.

[10] Havas, I. and Czoboly, E., *Periodica Polytechnica, Eng.*, Vol. 24, Budapest, 1980, pp. 19–28.

[11] Gillemot, F., "Absorbed Specific Energy of Fracture, a Failure Criteria for Neutron Irradiated Materials," in *Proceedings*, 5th International Conference on Structural Mechanics in Reactor Technology, West Berlin, 1979, Paper G3/2.

[12] Gillemot, F., Czoboly, E., and Havas, I., "Practical Application of ASFE," *Theoretical and Applied Fracture Mechanics*, Vol. 4, 1985, pp. 39–45.

[13] Pachur, D., *Transactions*, Vol. 44, American Nuclear Society, 1983, p. 229.

[14] Soulat, P., Petrequin, P., and Houssin, B., in *Radiation Embrittlement and Surveillance of Nuclear Reactor Pressure Vessels: An International Study, ASTM STP 819*, L. E. Steele, Ed., American Society for Testing and Materials, Philadelphia, 1983, pp. 64–85.

[15] Kobayashi, T., *Engineering Fracture Mechanics*, Vol. 19, 1984, pp. 49–65.

[16] Havas, I., and Czoboly, E., "Comparison of J-integral Estimating Methods and Techniques," in *Proceedings*, International Conference on Application of Fracture Mechanics, Freiburg, 1983.

Pressure Vessel Integrity and Regulatory Considerations

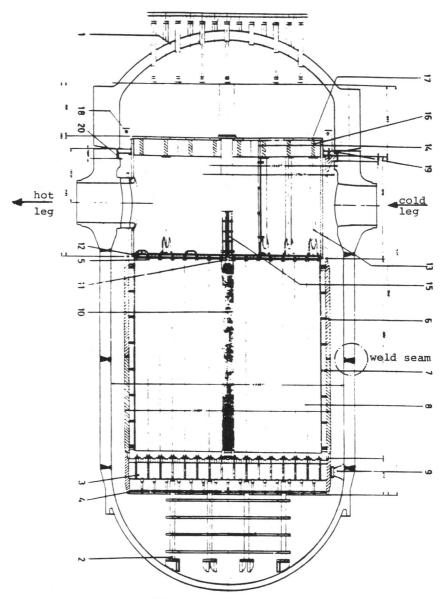

FIG. 1—*Reactor pressure vessel.*

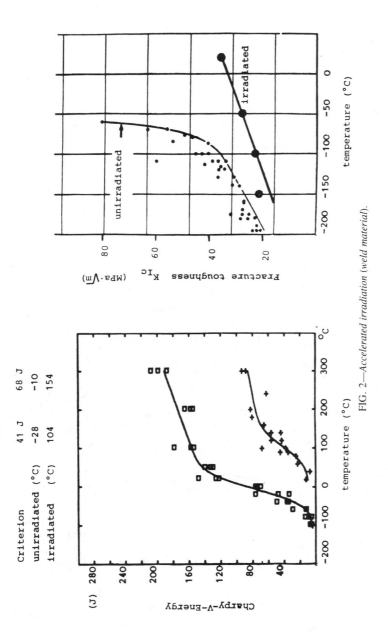

FIG. 2—Accelerated irradiation (weld material).

4). During the sixth and seventh cycles, expired fuel elements were inserted at the core boundary in the principal axle region. From the eighth operation cycle on, the 12 expired fuel elements contained absorber rods in their external positions and, in addition, eight expired fuel elements were inserted in the secondary axles.

This could be done without reducing the nominal power of the reactor. In this way, the neutron exposure of the vessel walls could be reduced by a factor of more than 2.0. Figure 5 shows the expected neutron flux for the EOL state for the individual core charges according to the calculations made then. The present fuel element arrangement results in an EOL neutron fluence of approximately 1.7×10^{19} n/cm^2 ($E \geq 1$ MeV).

Determination of the Neutron Flux

The neutron flux can be determined experimentally and theoretically. In order to evaluate the experimentally determined values, the calculated neutron spectrum at the place of irradiation is generally required.

Neutron measurements can be only performed using the products of neutron reactions with other substances. In this specific case, only methods that permit an evaluation after the samples have been extracted from the reactor can be used. For this purpose, fission and activation detectors that measure the radioactive products of the interaction of neutrons with material are suitable. In determining the neutron flux experimentally, the manufacturer mostly used the activation reactions

$$Fe\text{-}54 \ (n,p) \ Mn\text{-}54$$

$$Nb\text{-}93 \ (n,n') \ Nb\text{-}93m$$

The detector elements were employed in the purest available form. The natural isotope mixture of iron consists of about 5.8% Fe-54, while niobium was 100% Nb-93. Material samples containing the elements substances can simultaneously be used as detectors. For monitoring the neutron flux of the pressure vessel, milling samples were extracted directly from the cladding, and evaluated. In this way, it was possible to determine experimentally the maximum flux, the azimuthal distribution of flux in the pressure vessel, and the increase flux as a function of time.

The theoretical determination of neutron flux was done by the manufacturer and us in one and two-dimensional space using the computer program ANISN [1] and DOT [2], which are based on the S_N-method.

In the range of the maximum flux, a very good agreement between calculated and experimental results was found.

Change of Material Properties Under Neutron Irradiation

In order to predict the condition of the material of the vessel wall that would be caused by neutron irradiation in the course of operation, an extensive program

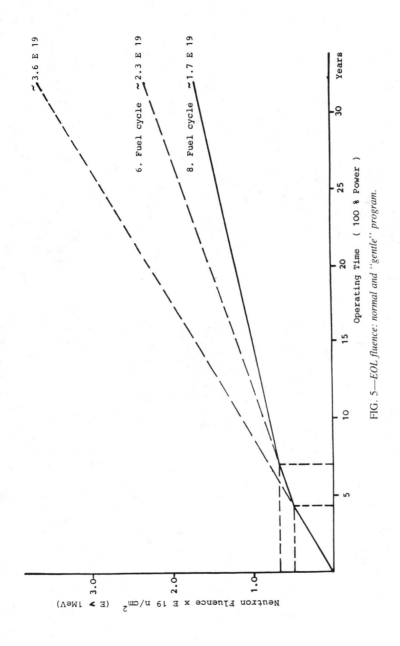

FIG. 5—EOL fluence: normal and "gentle" program.

pressure of the secondary safety valves. In this situation, it is no longer certain that the natural convection by means of the steam generators can be maintained. For this reason, it is conservatively assumed that only cold water with a temperature of 30°C enters the annulus of the pressure vessel without mixing processes occurring. Figure 7 shows the temperature and pressure curves that were determined with our simplified calculation for this critical load (pressurized thermal shock).

Further extensive analysis on the thermohydraulic behavior of the primary circuit without consideration of mixture processes does not lead to an essential improvement of the fracture safety [3]. This fact led to the conclusion that the nozzles for the emergency coolant injection have to be transferred to the "hot leg" so that the cold water cannot reach the wall of the reactor pressure vessel as long as there is high pressure.

After this, the LOCA with medium and large leaks in the primary system will determine the design, because the "cold leg" injection of the pressure accumulators will be retained. The maximum occurring pressure, in this case, is the system pressure of the pressure accumulators of $p = 20$ bar. The worst case with respect to the brittle fracture is the thermal shock from 288 to 20°C with constant internal pressure of 20 bar (depressurized thermal shock).

Further transients possible in the plant have been investigated, for example, primary pressure increase due to erroneous injection or secondary-induced undercooling. As a main result, the pressure and temperature-curves shown in Fig. 8 cover all these transients in a conservative manner. A comparison showed that in the range where brittle fracture is of concern, the load path (see Fig. 12) of this transient is covered by the depressurized thermal shock (see Fig. 11).

Integrity Proof for the Pressure Vessel

At this stage, we restrict ourselves to the proof of the pressure vessel's integrity under the loads of depressurized thermal shock, which now determines the vulnerability to brittle fracture. The proof is done using linear fracture mechanics. For the fracture mechanics analysis (Fig. 9), the following are required:

1. stress intensity factors, $K_{I,tot}$, as a consequence of the postulated crack geometries in the vessel walls;
2. fracture toughness values, K_{Ic}, dependent on the temperature, T, and the neutron fluence, ϕ; and
3. determination of the initiation and arresting values from the conditions $K_{I,tot} = K_{Ic}$ and $K_{I,tot} = K_{Ia}$, respectively.

In the model, the austenitic cladding was regarded as bearing no load.

Surface cracks on the inside of the critical weld seam in axial and circumferential direction were presumed to be the worst crack geometries (Fig. 10). The interior pressure load alone causes stress intensities in axial cracks that are a

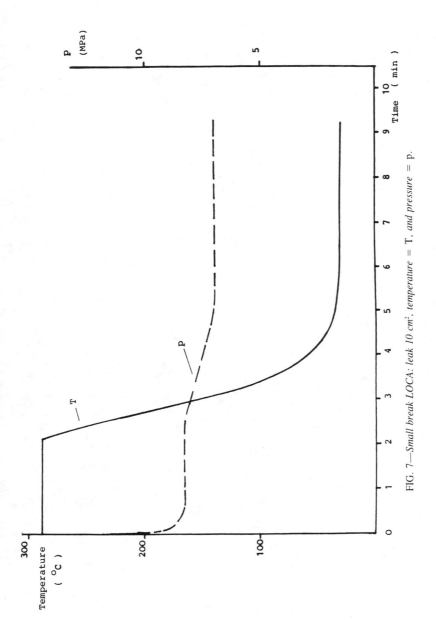

FIG. 7—*Small break LOCA: leak 10 cm², temperature = T, and pressure = p.*

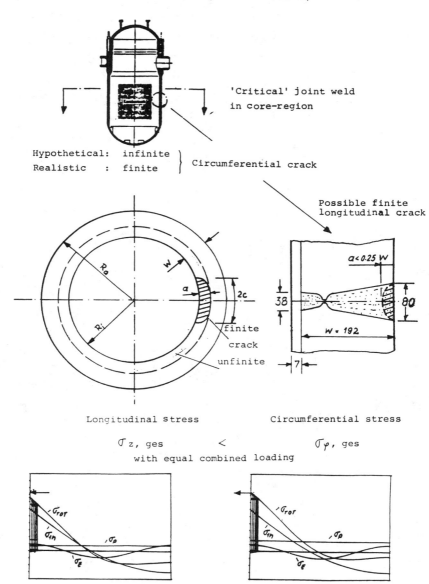

FIG. 10—*Geometry and stresses.*

factor of two larger than in circumferential cracks, so that these crack configurations are generally to be regarded as being more critical. However, due to the irradiation results, a failure due to embrittlement needs only to be assumed in the region of the weld seam. In the fracture-mechanics analysis [4], it was shown that such axial crack geometries cannot spread beyond the weld seam and are arrested within 25% of the wall thickness. The following investigations are therefore restricted to circumferential crack configurations.

For the thermal shock from 288 to 20°C, the nonstationary temperature distributions throughout the thickness of the walls were determined from the thermal diffusion equation using the finite difference method. The cladding's influence was taken into consideration by using modified heat transfer coefficients.

Modified heat transfer coefficients result in lower base material temperatures compared to explicit cladding simulation. A steep temperature gradient is calculated, especially within the first phase of the transient, resulting in increased stress intensity. So, the stress increase due to different cladding and base material thermal strain coefficients is regarded implicitly by neglecting the cladding in the analysis model.

The thermal stress distribution is calculated based on the differential equation for stresses in a cylinder of infinite length [5]. Use of the relationship between stress and strain, including thermal expansion [5], leads to the differential equation for axial displacement

$$u_{,rr} + \left(\frac{E_{,r}}{E} + \frac{1}{r} \right) u_{,r} + \left(\frac{m}{1-m} \frac{E_{,r}}{E} \frac{1}{r} - \frac{1}{r^2} \right) u = \frac{1+m}{E(1-m)} (Ee_T - me_z)_{,r}$$

where

$$e_T = \int_{T_0}^{T(r)} \alpha\,(T)\,dT = \text{thermal strain,}$$
$$e_z = \text{constant axial strain,}$$
$$m = \text{Poisson's ratio,}$$
$$E(T) = \text{temperature dependent modulus of elasticity, and}$$
$$T = \text{thermal strain coefficients.}$$

Three particular solutions are found by the Runge-Kutta technique, and superimposed to match the boundary conditions.

Residual stresses are regarded by a cosine-shaped stress distribution, chosen in such a way that experimental results from Ref 6 are included conservatively.

The stress intensity factors, K_I, for complete circumferential cracks were calculated using the approximation method of weighted functions as mentioned in Ref 7. The results for the consequent load and several crack depths depending on the temperature at the front of the crack are shown for the depressurized thermal shock in Fig. 11 and for the envelope of secondary-induced undercooling and erroneous injection, in Fig. 12.

For the fracture mechanics analysis, the flux-dependent fracture toughness values, K_{Ic}, determined from the research reactor's irradiation programs using

the temperature shifts in Fig. 6, were used, providing lower bound values for the EOL of the critical weld seam.

The crack arrest toughnesses, K_{Ia}, were assumed to be the initiation toughnesses, K_{Ic}, translated 43 K towards higher temperatures. This shifting has been performed according to the initiation and arrest curves of the ASME Code that are based on experimental data [8]. In this way, safe arresting toughnesses, K_{Ia}, for a static crack arrest analysis were determined, as the results of the ASTM test program [9] have shown.

The results of the fracture mechanics analysis for the EOL situation of the pressure vessel under an integrated neutron fluence of 1.7×10^{19} n/cm^2 for postulated circumferential cracks are shown in Fig. 13. They take into account the increase in toughness that is due to the shielding effect of the vessel walls in the lateral direction.

The representation for the worst case in Fig. 13 characterizes the following

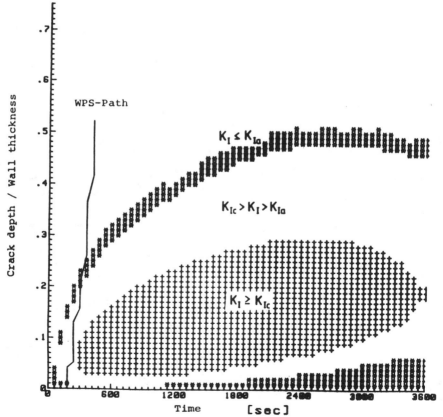

FIG. 13—*Initiation and arrest diagram (thermal shock 288/20°C + 20 bar + residual stress).*

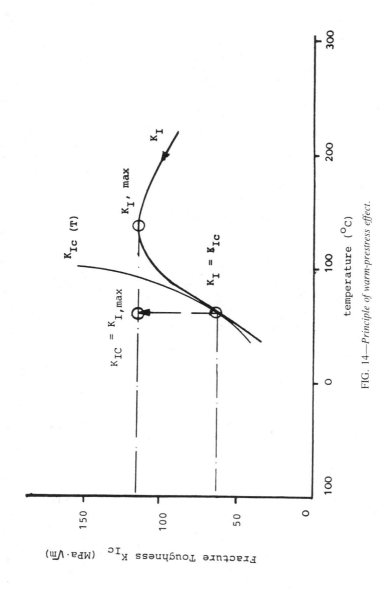

FIG. 14—*Principle of warm-prestress effect.*

Conclusion

In this paper, the procedures and investigations that have been and are being performed as a result of the neutron-induced embrittlement of the weld seam in the core region of a reactor pressure vessel are reported. Because of the combined schools of knowledge, such as neutron physics, thermohydraulics, material and structural mechanics, and nondestructive testing, a high degree of safety can be demonstrated for the EOL conditions of a nuclear power plant.

References

[1] Engle, W. W., *A Users Manual for A One-Dimensional Discrete Ordinates Transport Code With Anisotropic Scattering*, Union Carbide Corporation K-1693, Oak Ridge, 1967.

[2] Rhoades, W. A. and Mynatt, F. R., *The DOT-III Two-Dimensional Discrete Ordinates Transport Code*, ORNL-TM-4280, Oak Ridge National Laboratory, 1973.

[3] TÜV Norddeutschland, "Zwischenbericht zur Sicherheit des Kernkraftwerkes Stade—Sprödbruchsicherheit des Reaktordruckbehälters," Hamburg, Nov. 1981.

[4] Peters, W. H. and Blauel, J. G., "Bruchmechanische Analyse des Verhaltens von Axialrissen in einem RDB bei Kühlmittelverlust-Störfällen (KMV)," IWM-Bericht V7/79, July 1979.

[5] Melan, E. and Parkus, H., *Wärmespannungen infolge Stationärer Temperaturfelder*, Springer-Verlag, 1953.

[6] Ferril, D. A., Jul, P. B., and Miller, D. R., "Measurements of Residual Stresses in a Heavy Weldment," Welding Research Supplement No, 1966.

[7] Labbens, R., Pellissier-Tanon, A., and Heliot, J. in *Mechanics of Crack Growth, ASTM STP 590*, American Society for Testing and Materials, Philadelphia, 1976, pp. 368–384.

[8] ASME-Code, Section XI, Appendix A 4200-1.

[9] Hahn, G. T., Hoagland, R. G., Rosenfield, A. R., and Barnes, C. R. in *Crack Arrest Methodology and Applications, ASTM STP 711*, Hahn and Kanninen, Eds., American Society for Testing and Materials, Philadelphia, 1980, pp. 248–269.

[10] TÜV Norddeutschland, "Stellungnahme zur Nachweisempfindlichkeit der Ultraschallprüfung für Risse unter der Plattierung," 587-Dr.Jt/Ric, 18 Jan. 1984.

[11] TÜV Norddeutschland, "Kernkraftwerk Stade—Reaktordruckbehälter Ultraschalluntersuchungen an einem Prüfkörper mit einem *1,8 mm Riss unter der Plattierung*," 587-Dr.Jt/Ric, 12 Mar. 1984.

[12] Loss, J. J., Gray, R. A., and Hawthorne, J. R., "Significance of Warm Prestress to Crack Initiation during Thermoshock," NRL/NUREG Report 8165, Nuclear Regulatory Commission, 1977.

[13] Beremin, I. M., "Study of Instability of Growing Cracks Using Damage Function. Application to Warm Prestress Effect," *Proceedings*, CNSI Specialist Meeting on Plastic Tearing Instability, St. Louis, Sept. 1979, NUREG Report CP0010.

[14] Cheverton, R. D. and Iskander, S. K., *HSST-Program Quarterly Progress Report*, Nuclear Regulatory Commission Report NUREG/CR-1941, Oct.–Dec. 1980, pp. 37–54.

Pryor N. Randall[1]

Basis for Revision 2 of the U. S. Nuclear Regulatory Commission's Regulatory Guide 1.99

REFERENCE: Randall, P. N., **"Basis for Revision 2 of the U. S. Nuclear Regulatory Commission's Regulatory Guide 1.99,"** *Radiation Embrittlement of Nuclear Reactor Pressure Vessel Steels: An International Review (Second Volume), ASTM STP 909,* L. E. Steele, Ed., American Society for Testing and Materials, Philadelphia, 1986, pp. 149–162.

ABSTRACT: Regulatory Guide 1.99, "Radiation Damage to Reactor Vessel Materials," is being updated to reflect recent studies of the physical basis for neutron radiation damage and efforts to correlate damage to chemical composition and fluence. Revision 2 of the Guide contains several significant changes. Welds and base metal are treated separately. Nickel content is added as a variable and phosphorus removed. The exponent in the fluence factor is reduced, especially at high fluences. And, guidance is given for calculating attenuation of damage through the vessel wall. This paper describes the basis for these changes in the Guide.

KEY WORDS: radiation effects, pressure vessel steels, neutron irradiation, nuclear reactor materials, low alloy steels, fluence, copper, nickel, fracture toughness

Revision 2 of U. S. Nuclear Regulatory Commission's (NRC) Regulatory Guide 1.99 "Radiation Damage to Reactor Vessel Materials" (the Guide), is an outgrowth of many activities: (1) experience with the application of Revision 1 in licensing work since 1977; (2) technical contacts at meetings of the American Society for Testing and Materials (ASTM) Committee E-10 on Nuclear Technology and Applications and Metal Properties Council Subcommittee 6 Task Groups on radiation damage plus an American Nuclear Society seminar in 1983; (3) accumulation of surveillance data from commercial power reactors; (4) resolution of the pressurized thermal shock issue, which required best-estimate calculative procedures and careful attention to uncertainties; (5) extensive help in data analysis by G. L. Guthrie[2]; and (6) interaction with G. R. Odette.[3]

---

[1] Senior materials engineer, U. S. Nuclear Regulatory Commission, Washington, DC 20555.
[2] From Hanford Engineering and Development Laboratories, a contractor to the U. S. Nuclear Regulatory Commission.
[3] From the University of California, Santa Barbara, CA, a contractor to the Electric Power Research Institute.

nickel, and the average of their normalized shift values was 43°C (77°F). To get a feel for the task of developing correlations, it is instructive to attempt to draw isoshift "contour" lines on Figs. 1 and 2 for several values of shift. Two characterisics of the data base will become obvious from this exercise: the degree of scatter is significant, and there are clumps of data and sizeable blank areas where there are no data.

In Revision 2 of the Guide, it was necessary to give values of the chemistry factor for copper content ranging from 0 to 0.40% and for nickel ranging from 0 to 1.2% to provide guidance over the full range of expected compositions. Admittedly, these values somewhat exceed the ranges of the data base; hence, the Guide violates a restriction placed on the correlation functions by Guthrie. The most likely occurrence is for welds having copper content less than 0.12% and nickel in the 0.6% range. Clearly, application of the Guide at the fringes of the data base should be made with caution and supported by additional data. Unfortunately, these will likely be test reactor data, and their applicability to a correlation useful for operating reactors is still in doubt.

There is also a dearth of surveillance data for materials having low copper and higher than normal phosphorus contents. The upper limit on phosphorus in the data base is 0.020% for welds and 0.017% for base metal. Application of the Guide to cases where the phosphorus content is significantly higher should not be made without supporting data, which again brings up the question of the applicability of test reactor data.

To observe the distribution of fluence values in the data base, refer to Fig. 11, which will be described in the discussion of residuals (measured minus calculated values) as a function of fluence. The range of fluence values was from 7.3×10^{17} to 7.8×10^{19} n/cm^2 ($E > 1$ MeV), and the distribution within that range was reasonably uniform.

The Odette Data Base

The data base used by Odette et al [4] was the Electric Power Research Institute (EPRI) data base [5], which contained 65 weld data and 151 base metal data. It overlapped the Guthrie data base almost completely and the ranges of copper, nickel, and fluence were about the same. There are more data from boiling water reactors in the Odette data base. The principle difference is in the derivation of shift values. In the EPRI data base, the plots of Charpy energy as a function of temperature were refitted using a hyperbolic tangent function and the 41-J (30-ft·lb) shift values were then recalculated. A spot check showed the results are about the same as those in the Guthrie data base.

Derivation of the Chemistry Factor from the Guthrie and Odette Correlation Functions

Guthrie and Odette reached similar conclusions in several areas: (1) separate correlations are needed for welds and base metal, (2) the expression should be

the product of a chemistry factor and a fluence factor, (3) the elements in the chemistry factor should be copper and nickel, and (4) the fluence factor should provide a trend curve slope when plotted on log-log paper of about 0.25 to 0.30 at 10^{19} n/cm^2, and it should be steeper at lower fluences and flatter at higher fluences.

For welds, their correlation functions for ΔRT_{NDT} are as follows:

Guthrie: $\Delta RT_{NDT} = [624 \text{ Cu} - 331\sqrt{\text{CuNi}} + 251 \text{ Ni}][f^{0.282 - 0.0409 \ln f}]$

1 Standard Deviation = 16°C (28°F)

Odette: $\Delta RT_{NDT} = 360 \text{ Cu}\left[1 + 1.38\left(\text{erf}\left\{\dfrac{0.3 \text{ Ni-Cu}}{\text{Cu}}\right\} + 1\right)\right]$

$$\times \left[1 - \exp\left(\dfrac{-f}{0.11}\right)\right]^{1.36} [f^{0.18}]$$

1 Standard Deviation = 15°C (27°F)

For base metal, their correlation functions for ΔRT_{NDT} are as follows:

Guthrie: $\Delta RT_{NDT} = \left[-38 + 556 \text{ Cu} + 480 \text{ Cu} \tan h \, 0.353 \dfrac{\text{Ni}}{\text{Cu}}\right]$

$$\times [f^{0.266 - 0.0449 \ln f}]$$

1 Standard Deviation = 10°C (17°F)

Odette: $\Delta RT_{NDT} = 389 \text{ Cu}\left[1 + 0.33\left(\text{erf}\left\{\dfrac{0.77 \text{ Ni-Cu}}{\text{Cu}}\right\} + 1\right)\right][f^{0.28}]$

1 Standard Deviation = 13°C (23°F)

The units of ΔRT_{NDT} are degrees Fahrenheit. (The equations by Odette have been converted from degrees Centigrade.) Copper and nickel are given in percent by weight, and fluence, f, is in units of 10^{19} n/cm^2 ($E > 1$ MeV). Values for the error function, erf, are given in Table A-3 of Ref 4.

To compare the correlation functions given by Guthrie and Odette, the first step is to compare the chemistry factors, the expressions obtained by setting the fluence equal to 1×10^{19} n/cm^2. Figures 3 and 4 compare the Guthrie and Odette chemistry factors for welds for two nickel contents. There is remarkable agreement at the higher copper levels. However, the function chosen by Odette passes

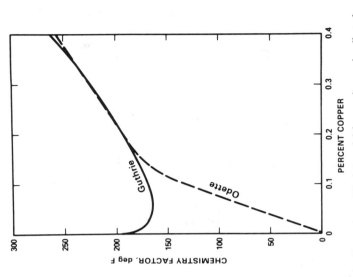

FIG. 4—Comparison of Guthrie and Odette studies on the effect of copper on the chemistry factor—welds with 0.8% nickel.

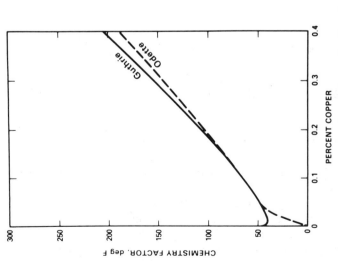

FIG. 3—Comparison of Guthrie and Odette studies on the effect of copper on the chemistry factor—welds with 0.2% nickel.

through zero at zero copper whereas that by Guthrie intercepts the zero-copper ordinate at increasingly higher values as nickel increases. This difference is understandable in view of the lack of weld data below 0.10% copper. Because it has been generally accepted that the effect of nickel is a synergistic copper-nickel effect, it follows that ΔRT_{NDT} should be low when the copper content is low, regardless of the nickel content. Therefore, the Odette curves were used throughout for welds with the exception of the cutoff at the lower end, discussed later.

For base metal, Figs. 5 and 6 compare the Guthrie and Odette chemistry factors with regard to the effects of copper. In this case, the curves cross. Those by Guthrie are higher at high copper levels, but those by Odette are higher at low copper levels. For the Guide, the higher curve was used, with two exceptions. First, when the Guthrie curves for base metal exceeded those for welds, which they did at high copper levels (see Fig. 6), the latter were used, the justification being that there were no base metal data for copper above 0.25% and there is no basis to believe that base metal should be more sensitive to radiation than welds. Second, at very low copper levels, the curves for both welds and base metal were leveled off at $CF = 11°C$ (20°F). Again, the weld data is lacking in the range 0 to 0.10% copper, but some guidance is needed in this range because newer plants will have low copper. Therefore, test reactor data were used as described later to assist in setting the CF function for very low copper values.

Test reactor data [6,7] for low copper, high nickel (0.7%, nominal) materials were normalized to a fluence of 10^{19} n/cm^2 by dividing the measured shift by the quantity: $(f)^{0.5}$, the fluence function favored by the authors of the reports. Most test fluences were in the range 2 to 8 $\times$ 10^{19} n/cm^2, hence, the normalized values of shift were felt to be as low as one could justify. The results are plotted in Fig. 7 for welds and Fig. 8 for base metal, superimposed on the chemistry factor data as given in the Guide. For base metal, there is adequate surveillance data to support the Odette and Guthrie work, but for welds, the data are sparse. Nevertheless, in the light of the test reactor data plotted in Figs. 7 and 8, it seemed prudent to establish a minimum at 11°C (20°F) for the chemistry factor. In addition, for base metal, the curves in Fig. 8 were faired in to the minimum at 0.05% copper, which meant raising the curves for 0 and 0.2% nickel about 8°C (15°F).

A comparison of the chemistry factors for welds and base metal is given in Fig. 9. The fact that the differences disappear at copper levels above about 0.25% is an artifact of the procedure used to draw the curves, just described.

Derivation of the Fluence Factor

Guthrie found only small differences in the constants of the fluence factors for welds and base metal. (See the correlation functions given earlier.) In Fig. 10, the two factors are plotted over the range 2 $\times$ 10^{17} to 10^{20}. They differ by less than 4%. Consequently, in the interests of simplicity, the fluence factor used

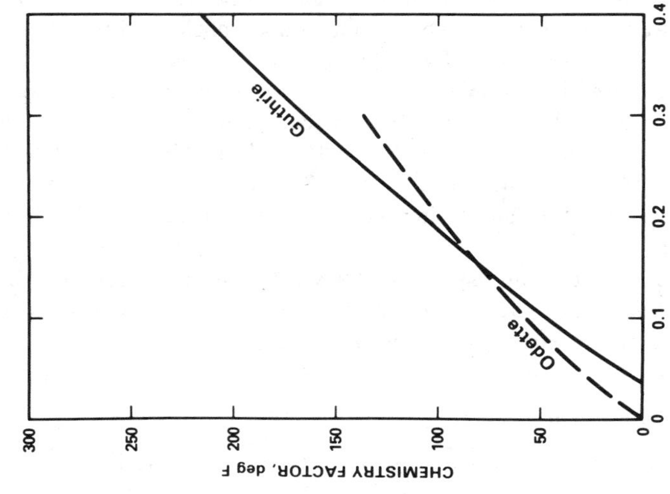

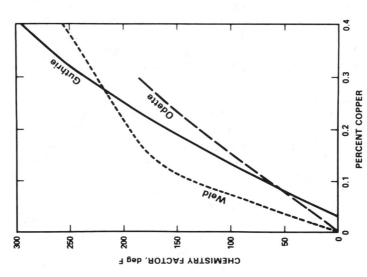

FIG. 6—*Comparison of Guthrie and Odette studies on the effect of copper on the chemistry factor—base metal with 0.8% nickel.*

FIG. 5—*Comparison of Guthrie and Odette studies on the effect of copper on the chemistry factor—base metal with 0.2% nickel.*

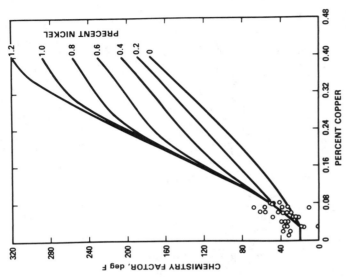

FIG. 8—Test reactor data for low copper base metal, normalized to 10^{19} n/cm^2, compared to the curves for chemistry factor versus copper from Revision 2.

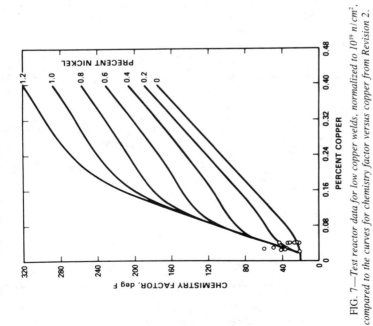

FIG. 7—Test reactor data for low copper welds, normalized to 10^{19} n/cm^2, compared to the curves for chemistry factor versus copper from Revision 2.

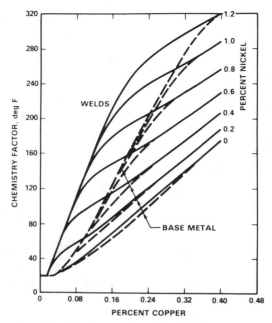

FIG. 9—*Comparison of chemistry factors for welds and base metal, given in Revision 2.*

for both was: $f \exp (0.28 - 0.0434 \ln f)$ or $f \exp (0.28 - 0.10 \log f)$ as it is given in the Guide. For clarity, this curve is not shown in Fig. 10. It would fall between the Guthrie curves for weld and base metal. The fluence factor for welds derived by Odette, also shown in Fig. 10, gives good agreement with that obtained by Guthrie except at fluences below 1.5×10^{18}, where the Odette fluence factor drops off sharply. For base metal, Odette used a uniform slope 0.28, which

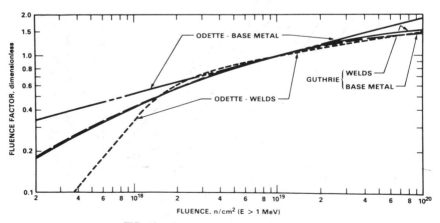

FIG. 10—*Comparison of fluence factors.*

(happily) agrees with that found by Guthrie at 10^{19} n/cm^2. Therefore, it was an easy decision to use Guthrie's fluence factor with the constants just given.

Justification for the Calculative Procedures Given in the Guide

To show that the calculative procedures given in the Guide are faithful to the data base, they were used to calculate a shift value based on the copper, nickel, and fluence values for each line of data in the Guthrie data base. The residual (observed minus calculated value) is plotted versus fluence, copper, and nickel content in Figs. 11, 12, and 13, respectively. Scatter about the zero residual axis is fairly well balanced between overprediction and underprediction. One exception is seen in Fig. 12 where for base metal the perturbation seen at low copper values is a reflection of the adjustment of chemistry factors made to reflect test reactor data and provide a conservative minimum.

Another purpose in showing these plots of residuals is to demonstrate that the blending of Guthrie's and Odette's results to get the calculative procedures for the Guide has not invalidated the use of twice the standard deviation from Guthrie's regression analysis to provide suitable margin. The "two-sigma" limits, $\pm 31°C$ ($\pm 56°F$) for welds and $\pm 19°C$ ($\pm 34°F$) for base metal, plotted on the figures, do indeed show that only one weld and two base metal data points will be underpredicted if the margin on ΔRT_{NDT} is made twice the standard deviation.

In considering the requirement for the amount of margin to be added, there was a question about the choice of margin for very low values of calculated shift. A more general question was: should the margin be some function of the shift? To answer this question, the residuals were plotted against the calculated value of shift as shown in Fig. 14. There is no clear evidence of a relationship of the residuals to the calculated value. Consequently, it was decided to add twice the

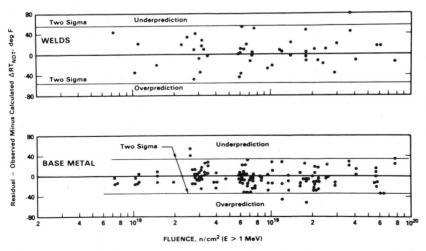

FIG. 11—*Plots of residuals versus fluence for 51 weld and 126 base metal data points.*

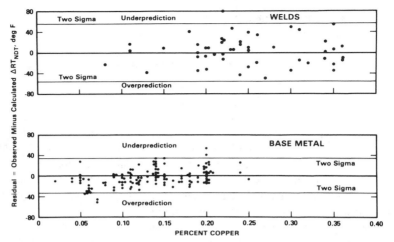

FIG. 12—*Plots of residuals versus copper content for 51 weld and 126 base metal data points.*

standard deviation across the board except at low values where it was arbitrarily decided to add 100% of the calculated value, as shown in Fig. 14.

As given in the Guide, the margin to be added in calculating conservative values of RT_{NDT} for use in Appendix G (10 CFR Part 50) evaluations includes margin on initial RT_{NDT} as well as margin on ΔRT_{NDT}. Following the precedent set in the analyses for the pressurized thermal shock problem, the two are combined in the expression

$$\text{margin} = 2\sqrt{\sigma_0^2 + \sigma_\Delta^2}$$

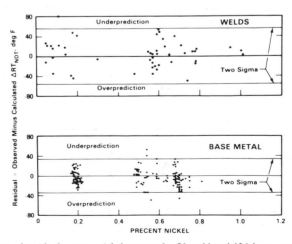

FIG. 13—*Plots of residuals versus nickel content for 51 weld and 126 base metal data points.*

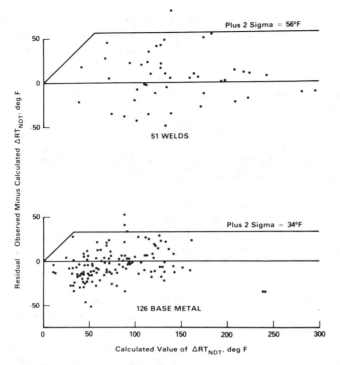

FIG. 14—*Plots of residuals versus calculated value of* RT$_{NDT}$ *for both welds and base metal.*

where σ_0 is the standard deviation on initial RT_{NDT} when a generic mean value is used, and σ_Δ is the standard deviation on ΔRT_{NDT}.

Attenuation of Radiation Damage Within the Vessel Wall

The changes in neutron energy spectra with depth of penetration in the wall are significant; and to take this into consideration, it was decided to use a "dpa equivalent" (displacements per atom) attenuation formula. This is one change in the method used previously. Another change is brought about by the change in the fluence factor from a simple power law with an exponent of 0.50 to one with an exponent of $(0.28 - 0.10 \log f)$. In the face of considerable uncertainty about the various elements in this calculation, we elected to use the following simplified procedure.

The starting point was the attenuation formula used for a number of years

$$ f = (f_{\text{surface}})e^{-0.33x} $$

where f is the fluence in units of n/cm^2 ($E >$ MeV) and x is depth in the wall, in inches, measured from the inside surface. This formula came from a staff

review of surveillance reports made several years ago. To convert to a "dpa equivalent" formula, we used some calculations reported at the 4th ASTM—Euratom Symposium [*8*], which showed that dpa attenuation through an 8.0 in. vessel wall is less than the attenuation of fluence, n/cm^2 ($E > 1$ MeV) by a factor of 2.06, the average of six calculations made for different reactor vessels. To achieve this reduction in attentuation, the equation for fluence attenuation becomes:

$$f = (f_{surface})e^{-0.24x}$$

For simplicity, the relationship of ΔRT_{NDT} to fluence is taken to be a simple power function with an exponent of 0.28 with the result:

$$\Delta RT_{NDT} = [\Delta RT_{NDTsurface}]e^{-0.067x}$$

This is a best-estimate expression. The uncertainty is assumed to be accounted for in the margin term described earlier.

Conclusion

The work of two independent investigators, working from separate data bases, yet coming to very similar conclusions, has provided a sound basis for the calculative procedures for adjustment of reference temperature given in Revision 2 of Regulatory Guide 1.99. The Guide will receive peer review when published for public comment and will be reviewed again within the NRC in response to those comments.

References

[*1*] Guthrie, G. L., "Charpy Trend Curves Based on 177 PWR Data Points," LWR Pressure Vessel Surveillance Dosimetry Improvement Program, Quarterly Progress Report April 1983–June 1983, Hanford Engineering Development Laboratory, NUREG/CR-3391, Vol. 2, HEDL-TME 83-22, April 1984.
[2] LWR Pressure Vessel Surveillance Dosimetry Improvement Program, W. N. McElroy, Ed., 1983 Annual Report, Hanford Engineering Development Laboratory, NUREG/CR-3391, Vol. 3, HEDL-TME 83-23, June 1984.
[*3*] Moore, K. E. and Heller, A. S., "B&W 177FA Reactor Vessel Beltline Weld Chemistry Study," Babcock and Wilcox Co., BAW-1799, July 1983.
[*4*] Odette, G. R., Lombrozo, P. M., Perrin, J. F., and Wullaert, R. A., "Physically Based Regression Correlations of Embrittlement Data From Reactor Pressure Vessel Surveillance Programs," Electric Power Research Institute, EPRI NP-3319, Jan. 1984.
[5] Oldfield, W., McConnell, P., Server, W., and Oldfield, F., "Irradiated Nuclear Pressure Vessel Steel Data Base," Electric Power Research Institute, EPRI NP2428, June 1982.
[6] Guionnet, C., Houssin, B., Brasseur, D., Lefort, A., Gros, D., and Perdreau, R., in *Effects of Radiation on Materials—11th International Symposium, ASTM STP 782*, H. R. Brager and J. S. Perrin, Eds., American Society for Testing and Materials, Philadelphia, 1982, pp. 392–411.
[7] Petrequin, P., "A Review on Activities in France on Irradiation Embrittlement Pressure Vessel Steels," presented at IAEA Specialists Meeting on Irradiation Embrittlement, Vienna, International Atomic Energy Agency, Oct. 1981.
[8] Guthrie, G. L., McElroy, W. N., and Anderson, S. L., "A Preliminary Study of the Use of Fuel Management Techniques for Slowing Pressure Vessel Embrittlement," paper presented at 4th ASTM-Euratom Symposium, American Society for Testing and Materials, March 1982.

Shafik K. Iskander,[1] Arthur W. Sauter,[2] and Jürgen Föhl[2]

Reactor Pressure Vessel Structural Implications of Embrittlement to the Pressurized-Thermal-Shock Scenario

REFERENCE: Iskander, S. K., Sauter, A. W., and Föhl, J., "**Reactor Pressure Vessel Structural Implications of Embrittlement to the Pressurized-Thermal-Shock Scenario**," *Radiation Embrittlement of Nuclear Reactor Pressure Vessel Steels: An International Review (Second Volume), ASTM STP 909*, L. E. Steele, Ed., American Society for Testing and Materials, Philadelphia, 1986, pp. 163–176.

ABSTRACT: A deterministic fracture-mechanics parametric-type analysis of a generic pressurized-water reactor pressure vessel has been conducted for loading conditions imposed by a specific category of hypothetical pressurized-thermal-shock transients. The time in the life of the vessel for which the calculations were made corresponds to attainment of the limiting nil-ductility transition reference temperature specified by the U. S. Nuclear Regulatory Commission's pressurized thermal-shock-issue-related screening criteria.

The transients considered were characterized by a constant pressure and an exponential decay of the downcomer coolant temperature. The decay constant, the final temperature of the coolant, and the fluid-film heat-transfer coefficient were the variable parameters. A search was performed to determine the critical pressure corresponding to incipient crack initiation for a range of crack depths up to 20% of the wall thickness. Results indicate that the critical pressure is greater than the normal operating pressure, if the coolant final temperature is greater than 150°C.

The fracture mechanics model used in the study tends to be conservative in the sense that it ignores possible beneficial effects of warm prestressing and cladding.

KEY WORDS: pressure vessel steels, radiation effects, screening criteria, reactor pressure vessels, over-cooling accident, pressurized thermal shock, neutron embrittlement, linear elastic fracture mechanics, crack initiation, reference temperature, flaws (materials), stress intensity factor

Nomenclature

a Crack depth, or depth in wall
b Crack length
F Fluence

[1] Resident engineer, U. S. Nuclear Regulatory Commission, on assignment from Oak Ridge National Laboratory. Present address at Staatliche Materialpruefungsanstalt, Universitaet Stuttgart (MPA), 7000 Stuttgart 80, West Germany.
[2] Staff members, Staatliche Materialpruefungsanstalt, Universitaet Stuttgart (MPA), 7000 Stuttgart 80, West Germany.

F_s Fluence at inside surface of vessel
FM   Fracture mechanics
h Convective surface heat transfer coefficient
HSST   Heavy-Section Steel Technology
K_1 Stress intensity factor
$\dot{K}_1$ Rate of variation of K with respect to time
K_{Ic} Plane-strain fracture toughness
LEFM   Linear elastic fracture mechanics
M Margin to account for twice the standard deviation
n Decay constant
NRC   U. S. Nuclear Regulatory Commission
OCA   Over-cooling accident
PTS   Pressurized thermal-shock
PWR   Pressurized-water reactor
RPV   Reactor pressure vessel
RT_{NDT} Reference temperature (nil-ductility transition)
RT^0_{NDT} Unirradiated reference temperature
ΔRT_{NDT} Transition temperature shift
ΔRT^s_{NDT} Transition temperature shift at the surface
SC   Screening criteria
t Time
T_c Coolant temperature
T_i, T_f Initial and final (or asymptotic) temperature, respectively
w Wall thickness
WPS   Warm prestressing

The possible threat to the integrity of pressurized water reactor (PWR) pressure vessels, when subjected to postulated over-cooling accidents (OCAs), has been recognized for some time [1–4]. The early studies were concerned with loss-of-cooling-accident conditions, which are characterized by the absence of any significant internal pressure, while more recent studies have been concerned with the pressurized-thermal-shock (PTS) issue.

As a result of a PTS transient, which is characterized by both thermal and pressure loading of the beltline region of the reactor pressure vessel (RPV), the thermal loading may cause shallow surface flaws to propagate, and as they get deeper, the pressure loading may drive them through the wall. Several PTS transients have already occurred [5], and preliminary studies have indicated that had these transients occurred much later in the life of the vessel, and if appropriate flaws existed, propagation of the flaws might occur [6].

The concern about PTS transients has become the subject of much investigation by both industry and regulatory bodies in the United States [7–9] and in Europe [10–12]. It was designated by the NRC as Unresolved Safety Issue A-49 in December 1981. Since that time, the NRC staff has issued a report on the matter [13], and their recommendations are in the review process [14].

One of the recommendations of the NRC has been submitted in the form of screening criteria (SC), which define limiting values of the material nil-ductility transition reference temperature, RT_{NDT}, and specify the methods by which these limiting values are to be computed.

This paper, which is based on a more extensive study [15], evaluates, in a limited generic sense, the integrity of pressurized-water RPVs, that have reached the limiting values of RT_{NDT} set forth in the NRC SC, when subjected to PTS loading conditions.

Objectives of a Limited Parametric Study

The objective of this study was to determine, for a range of transient-related parameters, the minimum pressure required to cause crack initiation when the NRC SC are reached. The parameters included were thermal transients of varying severity, two initial values of RT_{NDT}, and two-dimensional circumferential and axial flaws of different depths.

Model and Method of Analysis

The factors that influence the fracture mechanics (FM) behavior of a flaw in an RPV during PTS transients have been described elsewhere [6]. The FM model used in this study is based on two-dimensional linear elastic fracture mechanics (LEFM), and the size of the RPV is representative of a 1000 MW(e) PWR (inside diameter of 4.37 m, and wall thickness of 216 mm).

For a particular thermal transient and set of material properties, the pressure was increased in increments of 1 MPa until a crack initiated; that is, until the stress-intensity factor (K_1) became equal to or greater than the plane-strain fracture toughness (K_{Ic}). The maximum pressure included was 20 MPa, which is just above the usual pressure-relief-valve setting of 17 MPa.

The maximum crack depth considered was 20% of the wall thickness. It seemed reasonable to assume that deeper cracks could be readily detected.

The critical pressure corresponding to incipient crack initiation is also sensitive to the duration of the transient. A value of 1 h was assumed to be a reasonable value for most transients and was used in this study.

The analysis has been performed using the OCA-I code [16]. For values of the material properties not specifically mentioned here, those built into the OCA-I code were used (typical for A508 steel). Temperature independent material properties were used because previous limited studies have shown that the error involved in the calculation of K_1 is less than 10% [17,18].

Applicability of Linear Elastic Fracture Mechanics

The only restriction of LEFM is that the size of the plastic zone surrounding the crack tip is small compared to the remaining ligament of the wall. For the shallow inner-surface flaws considered in this study, LEFM is appropriate, as has been demonstrated by the Heavy-Section Steel Technology (HSST) program

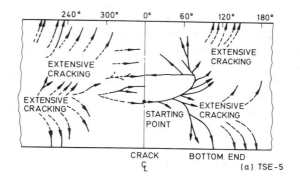

(a) TSE-5

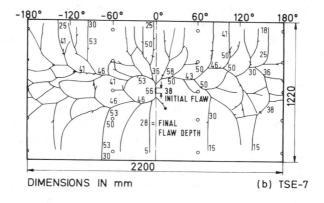

DIMENSIONS IN mm   (b) TSE-7

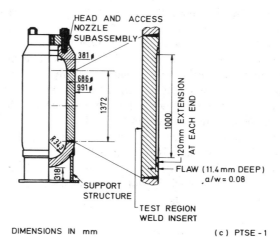

DIMENSIONS IN mm   (c) PTSE-1

FIG. 1—*Finite length flaws tend to become long* [21,22,20].

for thermal-shock loading [19], and more recently for pressurized-thermal-shock loading [20].

Infinitely Long Flaws are not Excessively Conservative

A frequently raised concern about the use of infinitely long flaws is that such flaws are unlikely to exist in real pressure vessels, and that they are overly conservative. Certainly, finite length flaws are more credible. However, in the absence of cladding and in the presence of a steep toughness gradient, a finite length flaw tends to become a long flaw. Figures 1a and b show the "crazed" pattern of cracks that propagated from a single finite length flaw during thermal-shock experiments TSE-5 [21] and TSE-7 [22]. In Fig. 1c, the long axial flaw in the PTSE-1 test cylinder bifurcated and grew axially at each end by 120 mm, concurrently with the first crack jump [20]. It is likely that further extension of this flaw was prevented by the restraint of the ends.

Analysis of finite length flaws is more complex, and at present only qualitative-type predictions are possible about the propagation behavior of such flaws. More-over, for crack depths under consideration in this study, the K_1 value at the bottom of a finite length 6/1 semi-elliptic flaw is very close to the K_1 of an infinitely long flaw, as indicated in Fig. 2 [23]. It has been shown that the benefits of considering finite length flaws are considerable under certain conditions. How-ever, above a certain pressure there may be no benefit, depending on the duration of the transient and the limit on crack arrest toughness [24].

Effects of Cladding

Cladding has been neglected in the model used for this study. It has been demonstrated analytically that if both the thermal and stress effects of cladding are excluded, nearly the same potential for crack initiation exists as estimated by the inclusion of the cladding as a discrete region [25].

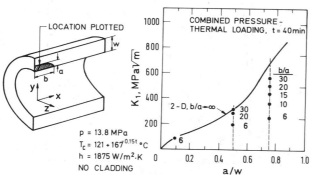

FIG. 2—K_1 for shallow finite length flaws is close to K_1 for infinitely long flaws [23].

Warm Prestressing

The behavior of a flaw is influenced by a phenomena known as warm prestressing (WPS) [26]. An essential characteristic of one type of WPS, relevant to a PTS FM analysis, is that K_1 first increases and then *monotonically* decreases with time, as shown in Fig. 3. For some postulated PTS transients, K_1 does not exceed K_{Ic} until $\dot{K}_1 < 0$. Under these conditions a flaw will not propagate even if $K_1 \gg K_{Ic}$ [19,26].

Following a period of $\dot{K}_1 < 0$, K_1 may once again increase. The effect of this load history on the subsequent FM behavior is still under study. In several transients relevant to the PTS issue, repressurizations have been recorded [13]. Preliminary indications of the pressure and thermal transients from one of these PTS transients is shown in Fig. 4. In PTSE-1, crack initiation occurred when K_1 exceeded by about 13% the maximum K_1 value attained during a prior transient [20]. It is also possible that cyclic variations in K_1 negate the beneficial effects of WPS by a mechanism similar to that operative during low-cycle fatigue.

It is therefore prudent not to rely on WPS as a means of preventing crack initiation. It is a well-established phenomena only for monotonically decreasing K_1, which is not possible to ensure under most accident conditions.

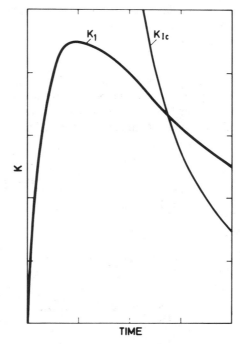

FIG. 3—*The WPS-effect cracks will not initiate while* K_1 *is decreasing.* K *values are for one value of* a/w.

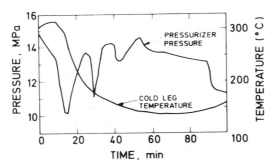

FIG. 4—*Pressure and temperature variations during the 1978 accident at Rancho Seco* [13].

Failure Criterion Utilized

In this study, if crack initiation was predicited, failure of the RPV was assumed. Implicit in this approach is the neglect of the possibility of crack arrest. There are several reasons for neglecting crack arrest in this study. Inside cracks initiating in a brittle mode and running deeper into the wall are most likely to encounter material that is on the upper-transition or upper-shelf region of the material toughness. The behavior of such flaws is still under investigation. Furthermore, previous studies [6,15] have shown that crack arrest is effective only for rather-low pressure transients. Also, a recent probabilistic FM study [27] showed that inclusion of crack arrest does not substantially influence the calculated frequency of vessel failure. Thus, crack arrest was not considered in this study.

Wall Temperature Cool-Down Rates

In order to study the effect of the severity of the thermal transient, both the convective surface heat transfer coefficient, (h), and the coolant temperature were varied. Two values of h were used: 1000 and 6000 W/m$^2 \cdot K$. The lower value was assumed to represent natural convection, while the larger value represents the state with the main circulating pumps running. The variation of coolant temperature with time was represented by an exponential expression

$$T_c = T_f + (T_i - T_f) \exp(-nt) \tag{1}$$

where

$$T_c = \text{coolant temperature,}$$
$$T_i, T_f = \text{initial and final (or asymptotic) temperatures, respectively,}$$
$$n = \text{decay constant, and}$$
$$t = \text{time.}$$

The values used for the preceding parameters are shown in Table 1. A value of ∞ for n represents a step change of the coolant temperature from its initial

TABLE 1—*Data used in parametric analysis.*

Vessel dimensions	
Inside diameter, m	4.37
Wall Thickness, mm	216
Flaw orientations	axial, circumferential
T_i, °C	288
T_f, °C	50, 100, 150
n, min^{-1}	0.015, 0.045, 0.15, ∞
h, W/m$^2 \cdot$ K	1000, 6000
Pressure, MPa	0 to 20, in 1 MPa increments

value, the condition usually assumed for a loss-of-coolant accident. The variation of coolant temperature with time for $T_f = 50°C$ and for different values of n is shown in Fig. 5.

Material Toughness Used

The K_{Ic} versus $T - RT_{NDT}$ function was that given in Section XI of the ASME Code (T is the temperature at the tip of the crack). In Ref *14*, the method of calculating RT_{NDT} is given as follows

$$RT_{NDT} = RT^0_{NDT} + \Delta RT_{NDT} + M \tag{2}$$

where

RT^0_{NDT} = initial RT_{NDT} of the material (in the unirradiated state),
ΔRT_{NDT} = shift in RT_{NDT} due to radiation damage, and
M = margin equal to twice the standard deviation of both RT_{NDT} and ΔRT_{NDT}.

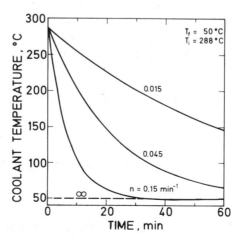

FIG. 5—*Variation of coolant temperature with time.*

TABLE 2—*Material parameters used in this study with the Guthrie mean trend curve, and SC of 132°C for axial cracks, 149°C for circumferential ones.*

Initial RT_{NDT}, °C (°F)	Margin, K (°R)	Residual Shift RT_{NDT}, K (°R)	
		Axial	Circumferential
	MATERIAL 1		
−49	33	148	165
(−56)	(59)	(267)	(297)
	MATERIAL 2		
−18	33	117	134
(0)	(59)	(211)	(241)

The SC defines limiting values of RT_{NDT} of 132°C (270°F) for axially oriented flaws, and 149°C (300°F) for circumferential flaws.

At the time of construction of many of the older RPV, there were no requirements for the determination of the RT_{NDT} of the RPV material. For such cases, the NRC has defined a generic mean value and a standard deviation. It appears that the weld metal for many of these older vessels falls into two groups for purposes of defining the mean value for RT_{NDT}: −49°C (−56°F) and −18°C (0°F) [14]. Both these values have been used in this study. The standard deviation for both these two groups is 9.44 K (17°R).

Reference 14 also defines the method of computing the ΔRT_{NDT}

$$\Delta RT_{\mathrm{NDT}} = \text{chemistry factor} \times F^{0.27} \tag{3}$$

and

$$\Delta RT_{\mathrm{NDT}} = C \times F^{0.194}, K \tag{4}$$

whichever is smaller, where F = fluence (>1 MeV), in units of 10^{19} n/cm², and C = a constant independent of chemistry.

The standard deviation associated with Eq 3 is 13.33 K (24°R).

TABLE 3—*Material parameters associated with Regulatory Guide 1.99 Rev. 1, upper bound trend curve, for SC of 132°C for axial cracks, 149°C for circumferential ones.*

Initial RT_{NDT}, °C (°F)	Margin, K (°R)	Residual Shift RT_{NDT}, K (°R)	
		Axial	Circumferential
	MATERIAL 1		
−49	19	162	179
(−56)	(34)	(292)	(322)
	MATERIAL 2		
−18	19	131	148
(0)	(34)	(236)	(266)

The value M in Eq 2 is obtained by taking twice the square root of the sum of the squares of the standard deviations associated with RT^0_{NDT} and ΔRT_{NDT} [13]. For the cases considered here, this is 33 K (59°R).

The attenuation of the fluence in the vessel wall was calculated as follows [13]

$$F = F_s \exp(-9.45 \, a) \tag{5}$$

where

F_s = fluence on the inner surface of the vessel, and
a = depth in the wall, m.

Equation 4 usually comes into play only at rather high values of F, and thus for the purposes of this study was ignored. Then, Eqs 3 and 5 can be combined to obtain

$$\Delta RT_{NDT} = \Delta RT^s_{NDT} \exp(-2.55 \, a) \tag{6}$$

where ΔRT^s_{NDT} = shift in RT_{NDT} at the inner surface.

Since both RT_{NDT} and RT^0_{NDT} have been prescribed, ΔRT_{NDT} is defined. Some of the values just mentioned have been summarized in Tables 2 and 3.

Discussion of the Results

The critical pressure as a function of T_f for each of the cases analyzed is shown in Fig. 6 and in Table 4. The symbols on Fig. 6 correspond to the numbers in the first column of Table 4. Symbols with an arrow through them are used to

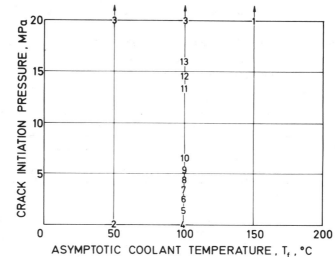

FIG. 6—Results of parametric analysis.

TABLE 4—*Results of parametric analysis. Numbers in the first column refer to the symbols on Fig. 6.*

Symbol	T_f, °C	Pressure, MPa	n, min^{-1}	h, W/m$^2 \cdot$ K	Materials	Crack Orientation
1	150	>20	0.015, 0.045, 0.15, ∞	1000, 6000	1, 2	both
2	50	0	0.045, 0.15, ∞	1000, 6000	1, 2	both
3	50 or 100	>20	0.015	1000, 6000	1, 2	both
4	100	0	0.15, ∞	6000	2	both
5		1–2	∞	1000	2	circ
6		2–3	∞	1000	1	circ
7		3–4	0.15	1000	2	circ
		3–4	0.045	6000	2	circ
8		4–5	0.15	1000	1	circ
		: :	0.045	6000	1	circ
9		: :	∞, 0.15	6000	2	axial
		5–6	0.045	1000	2	axial
10		: :	∞, 0.15	6000	1	axial
		6–7	0.045	1000	1	axial
11		13–14	0.045	1000	2	axial
12		14–15	0.045	1000	1	axial
		: :	0.045	1000	2	circ
13	↓	16–17	0.045	1000	1	circ

show that at the maximum pressure of 20 MPa no crack initiation had yet occurred. Note that the pressures were increased by increments of 1 MPa (150 psi), so there is an error of about that amount in the results.

The K_1 values at which incipient crack initiation occurred are in the range of 45 to 115 MPa$\sqrt{m}$, well within the range of validity of LEFM.

The crack depths that resulted in initiation range from 5 to 20% of the wall thickness ($a/w = 0.2$ was the maximum crack depth considered).

In the cases in which a failure pressure was determined, that pressure was relatively insensitive to $RT^0{}_{NDT}$, in the range -49 to $-18°C$. In a previous study [6], a similar result was found for $RT^0{}_{NDT}$ in the range -29 to $4°C$.

As may be seen from the results, no crack initiation would occur if $T_f > 150°C$, for all values of n and h considered. Also, no failure would occur in the case of the smallest value of n ($n = 0.015$ min^{-1}) for $T_f \geq 50°C$, which is the lowest value of T_f considered. For T_f of $100°C$, the critical pressure is dependent upon the severity of the transient. For $T_f = 50°C$, crack initiation could occur without any pressure in the vessel (except for $n = 0.015$ min^{-1}), but the flaw could not actually penetrate the wall.

In the NRC recommendation, the SC has been established as a means of requiring: (a) early analyses and implementation of plans to reduce the fast neutron flux in order to avoid reaching the SC; and (b) plant-specific OCA analyses before the plant is within three calendar years of reaching the SC. As can be seen from the analyses presented, PTS transients may be a concern for RPV whose RT_{NDT} is equal to the SC, provided, of course, that the postulated transients are severe enough. This study indicates how severe a transient must be for crack initiation to be of concern.

In a preliminary effort to determine what transients might be of concern, the NRC fitted an exponential curve (similar to Eq 1) to "actual" recorded coolant temperatures associated with the limited available data base (consists of eight severe OCA events within 350 reactor years). The values of parameters so obtained are termed the stylized representation of the event. The values of the stylized T_f are in the range 107 to 177°C. Thus, if one of these OCAs were to occur in a RPV whose RT_{NDT} had reached the SC, crack initiation could occur, if n was greater than 0.015 min^{-1}, the critical pressure depending upon the severity of the transient.

Summary

A somewhat simplified two-dimensional linear elastic fracture mechanics analysis of the beltline of a generic PWR pressure vessel subjected to idealized PTS transients indicates the severity of the transients required to result in the propagation of initially shallow surface flaws at the time the NRC PTS-issue-related screening criteria are attained.

Results indicate that the critical pressure is greater than the normal operating pressure, if the coolant final temperature is greater than 150°C.

The fracture mechanics model used in the study tends to be conservative in the sense that it ignores possible beneficial effects of warm prestressing and cladding.

Acknowledgments

The support and encouragement of K. Kussmaul of the Universitaet Stuttgart (MPA), C. Z. Serpan, and M. Vagins of the NRC are gratefully acknowledged. The calculations were performed by U. Weber of MPA. Very helpful discussions with R. D. Cheverton of Oak Ridge National Laboratory over many years (including the review of this paper) are also gratefully acknowledged.

This research was sponsored by the Office of Nuclear Regulatory Research, U. S. Nuclear Regulatory Commission under Interagency Agreements 40-551-75 and 40-552-75 with the U. S. Department of Energy under Contract DE-AC05-840R-21400 with Martin Marietta Energy Systems, Inc.

References

[1] Tuppeny, W. H., Jr., Siddall, W. F., Jr., and Hsu, L. C., "Thermal Shock Analysis of Reactor Vessels Due to Emergency Core Cooling System Operation," Combustion Engineering, Inc., Report A-68-9-1, 15 March 1968.
[2] Hutto, R. C., Morgan, C. D., and Van De Sluys, W. A., "Analysis of the Structural Integrity of a Reactor Vessel Subjected to Thermal Shock," Babcock and Wilcox Power Generation Division, Topical Report BAW10018, May 1969.
[3] Ayres, D. J. and Siddall, W. F., Jr., "Finite Element Analysis of Structural Integrity of a Reactor Pressure Vessel During Emergency Core Cooling," Combustion Engineering Report A-70-19-2, Jan. 1970; also presented at Petroleum Mechanical Engineering Pressure Vessel and Piping Conference, Denver, CO, Sept. 1970.
[4] Cheverton, R. D., Iskander, S. K., and Bolt, S. E., "Applicability of LEFM to the Analysis of PWR Vessels under LOCA-ECC Thermal Shock Conditions," ORNL/NUREG-40, Oak Ridge National Laboratory, Oct. 1978.
[5] Phung, D. L. and Cotrell, W. B., "Analyzing Precursors to Severe Thermal Shock," Journal of Nuclear Engineering International, Feb. 1983.
[6] Cheverton, R. D., Iskander, S. K., and Whitman, G. D., "Integrity of PWR Pressure Vessels During Overcooling Transients," Nuclear Safety, Vol. 24, No. 2, March–April 1983.
[7] Chexal, V. K., Marston, T. U., and Sun, B. K. H., "EPRI's Efforts to Resolve Pressurized Thermal Shock Issue," Journal of Nuclear Engineering International, May 1982.
[8] Pugh, C. E., HSST Program Semiannual Progress Report, Oct. 1983–Mar. 1984," NUREG/CR-3744 (ORNL/TM-9154/V1), Oak Ridge National Laboratory, May 1984.
[9] Kryter, R. C., et al, "Evaluation of Pressurized Thermal Shock—Initial Phase of Study," NUREG/CR-2083 (ORNL/TM-8072), Oak Ridge National Laboratory, Oct. 1981.
[10] Kussmaul, K., et al, "The Consequence of the Coincidence of Irradiation Embrittlement, Surface Cracking and Pressurized Thermal Shock in RPVs of LWRs," NUREG/CP-0027, Proceedings, International Meeting on Thermal Nuclear Reactor Safety, Aug.–Sept. 1982, Chicago.
[11] Lucia, A. C., "An Experimental and Theoretical Study for the Evaluation of Residual Life of the Primary Circuit of LWR's," NUREG/CP-0027, Proceedings, International Meeting on Thermal Nuclear Reactor Safety, Aug.–Sept. 1982, Chicago.
[12] Pellisier-Tanon, A., Sollogoub, P., and Houssin, B., "Crack Initiation and Arrest in an SA 508, Class-3 Cylinder under Liquid Nitrogen Thermal-Shock Experiment," Transactions, 7th SMIRT, Vol. G/H, Aug. 1983, G/F 1/8, pp. 137–142.
[13] "NRC Staff Evaluation of Pressurized Thermal Shock," U. S. Nuclear Regulatory Commission, Washington, DC, 17 Nov. 1982.

176 RADIATION EMBRITTLEMENT (SECOND VOLUME)

[14] "Proposed Pressurized Thermal Shock (PTS) Rule," U. S. Nuclear Regulatory Commission, Washington, DC, Secy-83-283.

[15] Cheverton, R. D., Iskander, S. K., and Ball, D. G., "PWR Pressure Vessel Integrity During Overcooling Accidents: A Parametric Analysis," NUREG/CR-2895, (ORNL/TM-7931), Oak Ridge National Laboratory, Feb. 1983.

[16] Iskander, S. K., Cheverton, R. D., and Ball, D. G., "OCA-I, A Code for Calculating the Behavior of Flaws on the Inner Surface of a Pressure Vessel Subjected to Temperature and Pressure Transients," NUREG/CR-2113, (ORNL/NUREG-84), Oak Ridge National Laboratory, Aug. 1981.

[17] Cheverton, R. D., et al, "Effect of the Temperature Dependence of Material Properties on the Calculated Values of K_1," HSST Quarterly Progress Report for Oct.–Dec. 1981, NUREG/CR-2141, Vol. 4, (ORNL/TM-8252), Oak Ridge National Laboratory, April 1982, pp. 84–87.

[18] Cheverton, R. D., et al, "The Effect of the Temperature Dependence of Material Properties on K^* Values for Two Dimensional Flaws," HSST Quarterly Progress Report Oct.–Dec. 1982, NUREG/CR-2751, Vol. 4, (ORNL/TM-8369/V4), Oak Ridge National Laboratory, May 1983, p. 68.

[19] Cheverton, R. D., et al, "Fracture Mechanics Data Deduced from Thermal-Shock and Related Experiments with LWR Pressure Vessel Material," *Transactions,* American Society of Mechanical Engineers, Vol. 105, *Journal of Pressure Vessel Technology,* May 1983.

[20] Bryan, R. H., "Pressurized-Thermal-Shock Technology," HSST Program Semiannual Progress Report for October 1983–March 1984, NUREG/CR-3744, Vol. 1, (ORNL/TM-9154/VI), Oak Ridge National Laboratory, June 1984, pp. 142–173.

[21] Cheverton, R. D., Bolt, S. E., and Iskander, S. K., "Experimental Verification of the Behavior of Surface Flaws in Thick-Walled Steel Cylinders During Severe Thermal Shock," *Transactions,* 6th SMIRT, Vol. G/H, G9/1, Aug. 1981.

[22] Cheverton, R. D., Ball, D. G., and Bolt, S. E., "Thermal-Shock Experiment TSE-7," HSST Program Quarterly Progress Report April–June 1983, NUREG/CR-3334. Vol. 2, (ORNL/TM-8787/V2), Oak Ridge National Laboratory, Dec. 1983.

[23] Merkle, J. G., et al, "Comparison of 3-D and 2-D Computed K Values of Long, Inside Surface Flaws in a PWR for Combined Pressure-Thermal Loading," HSST Program Quarterly Progress Report July–Sept. 1982, NUREG/CR-2751, Vol. 3, (ORNL/TM-8369/V3), Oak Ridge National Laboratory, Dec. 1983.

[24] Cheverton, R. D. and Ball, D. G., "A Reassessment of PWR Pressure Vessel Integrity During Overcooling Accidents, Considering 3-D Flaws," *Transactions,* American Society of Mechanical Engineers, Vol. 106, *Journal of Pressure Vessel Technology,* Nov. 1984.

[25] Sauter, A. W., Cheverton, R. D., and Iskander, S. K., "Modification of OCA-I for Application to a Reactor Pressure Vessel with Cladding on the Inner Surface," Report NUREG/CR-3155, ORNL/TM-8649, Oak Ridge National Laboratory, May 1983.

[26] Loss, F. J., Gray, R. A., Jr., and Hawthorne, J. R., "Significance of Warm Prestress to Crack Initiation During Thermal Shock," Naval Research Laboratory, NRL/NUREG 8165, Washington, DC, Sept. 1977.

[27] Cheverton, R. D. and Ball, D. G., "The Role of Crack Arrest in the Evaluation of PWR Pressure Vessel Integrity During PTS Transients," CSNI Workshop on Application of Crack Arrest Concepts, Fraunhofer-Institut für Werkstoffmechanik, Freiburg, Federal Republic of Germany, 4–5 June, 1984.

Karl-Robert Ernst,[1] *Egon N. Klausnitzer,*[2] *and Christof Leitz*[2]

Safety Standard KTA 3203: Monitoring Radiation Embrittlement of Reactor Pressure Vessels of Light-Water Reactors

REFERENCE: Ernst, K.-R., Klausnitzer, E. N., and Leitz, C., **"Safety Standard KTA 3203: Monitoring Radiation Embrittlement of Reactor Pressure Vessels of Light-Water Reactors,"** *Radiation Embrittlement of Nuclear Reactor Pressure Vessel Steels: An International Review (Second Volume), ASTM STP 909*, L. E. Steele, Ed., American Society for Testing and Materials, Philadelphia, 1986, pp. 177–183.

ABSTRACT: The paper presents a survey of the recently published German safety standard on surveillance programs for light-water reactor pressure vessels. The Kerntechnischer Ausschuss (KTA) safety standard is based on the new design of reactor pressure vessels with limited end-of-life neutron fluence and optimized steel quality. The program and the specimens required are outlined. Provisions are made for possible extension of the program in the event that the results are not as expected. Furthermore, careful program planning and documentation is required.

KEY WORDS: radiation effects, pressure vessel steels, light-water reactors, embrittlement, safety standards

The Nuclear Safety Standards Commission, "Kerntechnischer Ausschuss," (KTA), in the Federal Republic of Germany has recently published the Safety Standard KTA 3203 [1].

The KTA, which has the task of establishing and promoting the use of nuclear safety standards, set up a working group[3] responsible for developing a safety standard on reactor pressure vessel (RPV) irradiation surveillance programs, and this has now been completed.

---

[1] Section manager, Mechanical Engineering, KERNTECHNISCHER AUSSCHUSS (KTA)-Geschäftsstelle, Cologne, West Germany.

[2] Senior scientific advisor and department manager, Materials Testing; and department manager, Irradiation Programs; respectively, KRAFTWERK UNION AG (KWU), Erlangen, West Germany.

[3] The working groups of the KTA are constituted by representatives of the manufacturers, the suppliers, the utilities, the licensing and supervisory authorities, and other organizations involved in licensing procedures in West Germany. The authors of this article are chairman (E. N. K.) and members, respectively, of the working group KTA 3203. Every KTA standard must be reviewed at five-year intervals to establish whether it still complies with the state of the art, or should be revised.

The most important features of the new safety standard are described in the following sections.

Requirements for the Surveillance Program

With respect to the irradiation-induced property changes of the materials used for reactor pressure vessels, it is common practice:

1. to allow for embrittlement in the design of the reactor pressure vessel, and
2. to verify the design assumptions experimentally.

A predicted fracture toughness (K_{Ic}) curve is used for the purposes of verifying prevention crack instabilities in the beltline region of the reactor pressure vessel. This curve is based on the adjusted reference temperature according to ASTM

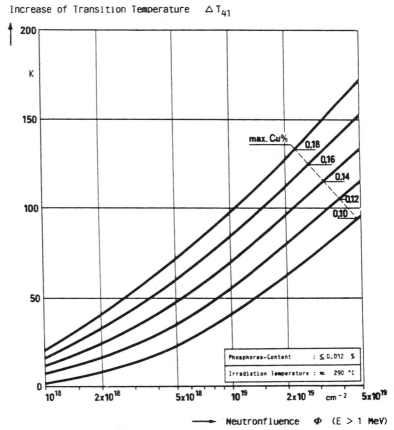

FIG. 1—*Design curves for the predetermination of embrittlement, dependent on copper and phosphorus content, according to KTA 3203.*

Practice for Conducting Surveillance Tests for Light Water-Cooled Nuclear Power Reactor Vessels (E 185-82) being defined as the sum of $RT_{NDT} + \Delta T_{41}$. The specified value of the pre-irradiation reference temperature, RT_{NDT}, and a predicted ΔT_{41} are used for the design calculations. This prediction is based on the design curves in Fig. 1 and on the specified copper and phosphorus contents.

These curves, which are quite similar to the curves given in NRC Regulatory Guide 1.99 [2], were developed [3] as an upper bound using data obtained for the steels 20 MnMoNi 5 5, 22 NiMoCr 3 7, and welding materials such as NiCrMo 1 and S3 NiMo 1. This data base largely overlaps with that of the Regulatory Guide but does not contain the older non-nickel-alloyed steels such as A302 B and A212 B. In the light of more recent surveillance data, the curves seem to be over-conservative at high fluences. As is the case with the safety standard as a whole, the curves are also subject to periodic review and revision as necessary.

It is assumed that embrittlement need not be allowed for in design where neutron fluences are lower than 1×10^{17} cm^{-2} ($E > 1$ MeV).

Outline of the Surveillance Program

Experimental verification is performed by accelerated irradiation of specimens removed from the original material of that welded joint in the beltline region of the pressure vessel that is expected to have sustained the highest degree of embrittlement by end of life (EOL).

In limiting the neutron fluence on the inside surface of the reactor pressure vessel at EOL to 1×10^{19} cm^{-2} ($E > 1$ MeV), as is German licensing practice, in reducing the content of copper, phosphorus, and sulfur in the chemical composition of the steel used and by implementing the toughness concept, a high standard has been attained in solving the embrittlement problem. Consequently, the following testing program is required.

The number of specimens, materials, and sets of specimens required for EOL neutron fluences between 1×10^{18} and 1×10^{19} cm^{-2} ($E > 1$ MeV) is shown in Table 1.

TABLE 1—*Number of specimens for fluences* $>1 \times 10^{18}$ cm^{-2} *up to* 1×10^{19} cm^{-2} (E > 1 MeV).

Specimen Set Number	Charpy V-Notch Specimens				Tension Test Specimens			Time of Removal
	BM1[a]	BM2	HAZ[b]	WM[c]	BM1	BM2	WM	
1	12	12	12	12	3	3	3	unirradiated
2	12	12	12	12	3	3	3	50% EOL[d]
3	12	12	12	12	3	3	3	100% EOL

[a]BM = base metal.
[b]HAZ = heat-affected zone.
[c]WM = weld metal.
[d]EOL = End of life; removal of the specimen set when its mean fast neutron fluence corresponds to approximately 50 and 100% of the peak EOL vessel fluence.

TABLE 2—*Number of specimens for fluences $\leq 1 \times 10^{18}$ cm^{-2} (E > 1 MeV).*

Specimen Set Number	Charpy V-Notch Specimens		Time of Removal
	BM[a]	WM[b]	
1	12	12	unirradiated
2	12	12	50% EOL[c]
3	12	12	100% EOL

[a]BM = base metal.
[b]WM = weld metal.
[c]EOL = End of life; removal of the specimen set when its mean fast neutron fluence corresponds to approximately 50 and 100% of the peak EOL vessel fluence.

For neutron fluences between 1×10^{17} and 1×10^{18} cm^{-2} ($E > 1$ MeV) at EOL, the adjusted reference temperature does not exceed the scatter range. Therefore, the reduced testing program of Table 2 is applicable.

Specimens are to be removed from a weld coupon manufactured for the surveillance program from original materials and using original welding parameters. The locations and orientations of the specimens in weld metals and heat-affected zones (HAZ) are shown in Fig. 2. Base metal specimens are removed from the one-fourth thickness location in the transverse direction.

The coupon is fabricated such that after removal of specimens an approximately 1.5-m-long section is available for any additional investigations that may be required if the results obtained for the irradiated specimens are not as expected.

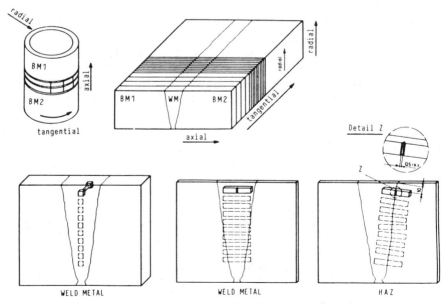

FIG. 2—*Location and orientation of specimens in weld metals and the heat-affected zone.*

Plan of Surveillance Program

Before the surveillance program is conducted, a plan is to be established that is subject to approval by the authorized expert according to Article 20 of the German Atomic Energy Act (Atomgesetz). This plan contains the following information:

1. description and selection of materials including the manufacturing plan for the welds,
2. sampling plan,
3. position of the capsules inside the reactor pressure vessel,
4. calculations of the neutron fluence,
5. lead factor,
6. number and type of neutron dosimeters and temperature monitors, and
7. capsule assembly plan with specimens, dosimeters, and monitors.

Lead Factor

The KTA Safety Standard stipulates a lead factor of at least 3. This ensures that the results for the first set of irradiated specimens withdrawn at approximately 50% of the fluence predetermined for the vessel at EOL are available prior to the first in-service pressure test of the reactor pressure vessel. If results are not as expected, there is therefore enough time to decide on supplementary actions. Consequently, it is not necessary to include optional specimens (for example, for fracture mechanics tests) in the standard program.

However, limitation of the lead factor to low values is deemed unnecessary since the formerly postulated dose-rate effect is negligible [4,5] and the entire reactor operation history can be best followed by continuous recording of cooling water temperature, core loading patterns, fuel burnup and reactor power history, and by including all this information in the fluence recalculation.

TABLE 3—*Types of dosimeters for selection.*

Dosimeter	Reaction
Iron	$^{54}\text{Fe}(n,p)^{54}\text{Mn}$
Niobium	$^{93}\text{Nb}(n,n')^{93}\text{Nb}^{m}$
Thorium	$^{232}\text{Th}(n,f)^{137}\text{Cs}$
Neptunium	$^{237}\text{Np}(n,f)^{137}\text{Cs}$
Uranium	$^{238}\text{U}(n,f)^{137}\text{Cs}$
Nickel	$^{58}\text{Ni}(n,p)^{58}\text{Co}$
Copper	$^{63}\text{Cu}(n,\alpha)^{60}\text{Co}$
Cobalt[a]	$^{59}\text{Co}(n,\gamma)^{60}\text{Co}$

[a]Cobalt is used for determination of the thermal neutron fluence. This can be employed, if necessary, for correction of the fast neutron fluence determined by means of other detectors.

TABLE 4—*List of possible temperature monitors.*

Monitor	Melting Point (minimum),[a] °C
Pb Ag 1.7 Sb 6	263
Bi	271
Pb Ag 1.9 Sb 5	272
Pb Ag 1.9 Sb 4.5	273
Pb Ag 1.9 Sb 4.3	278
Pb Ag 2 Sb 4	280
Pb Ag 2 Sb 3.5	284
Pb Ag 2 Sb 3	288
Pb Pt 5	290
Pb Ag 2 Sb 2	293
Pb Ag 2.5	304
Pb Ag 1.75 Sn 0.75	308
Pb In 5	314
Pb Zn 0.5	318
Pb	327

[a]At these temperatures, there is a defined change in the shape of the specimen.

Neutron Dosimetry

The determination of the neutron fluence is based on both theoretical calculations and dosimetry. The calculation makes use of the transport theory. The neutron spectrum, the fast neutron fluence, and the lead factor for energies $E > 1$ MeV are evaluated. Experimental verification of the calculated fast neutron fluence is conducted by means of neutron dosimeters. The types of dosimeters are selected from those proposed in Table 3 according to the suppliers' qualified methods. The axial fluence distribution is monitored by means of identical dosimeters inserted at three positions along the capsule axis.

Temperature Monitoring

Monitors are inserted into the capsule to determine an upper temperature limit. Low melting point metals and alloys are used as proposed in Table 4.

The time-dependent irradiation temperature is derived from the continuously recorded cooling water temperature. A temperature increase of more than 5 K, as a result of γ-irradiation, has to be considered in the evaluation of the changes in the materials' properties.

Evaluation

The effect of irradiation on the materials used in the beltline region is demonstrated by comparing the materials' characteristics measured by tension and instrumented impact tests before and after irradiation.

The transition temperature increase, ΔT_{41}, is the prime factor needed for the safety analysis of the pressure vessel based on the reference-temperature concept.

This temperature increase is determined from the best fit Charpy V-energy absorbed versus temperature curves. If the value of ΔT_{41} evaluated for the vessels' EOL fluence does not exceed that used in the design safety analysis and the upper-shelf energy remains above 68 J, the safety analysis is considered to be conservative. For the plants presently under construction, it may be assumed that this criterion will not be violated on account of the strict requirements placed on materials quality.

The performance of testing and evaluation of results for each set are controlled and carefully documented. This documentation is part of the quality assurance of the surveillance programs of the reactor pressure vessel.

Conclusions

By complying with the requirements for limiting the RPV neutron fluence at EOL to 1×10^{19} cm^{-2} ($E > 1$ MeV) and by optimizing the composition of the materials used, the degree of embrittlement can be kept within predetermined limits. In consideration of this, the numbers of sets and specimens are sufficient to be regarded as conservative with respect to the design postulates. Nevertheless, provision for reserve materials ensures that additional investigations are possible.

It may be stated that the surveillance program in West Germany is a redundant measure for validation of the design of reactor pressure vessels and may be seen as a "go/no go check."

The differences between the surveillance programs required by ASTM E 185-82 and KTA 3203 (3/84), such as the number of specimen sets and removal schedule, reserve material (instead of optional specimens in the standard capsules), and magnitude of the lead factor, are justified by the fact that the predicted transition temperature increase does not exceed 40 K, and that the pre-irradiation nil-ductility transition temperature of $\leq -12°C$ is required for the steels used in the beltline regions of reactor pressure vessels.

References

[1] Safety Standard KTA 3203: "Monitoring Radiation Embrittlement of the Reactor Pressure Vessel of LWRs," Carl Heymanns-Verlag KG, Cologne, West Germany, March 1984.
[2] Regulatory Guide 1.99, Revision 1, "Effects of Residual Elements on Predicted Radiation Damage to Reactor Vessel Materials," Nuclear Regulatory Commission, Washington, DC, April 1977.
[3] Leitz, C., Atomkernenergie, Vol. 29, 1977, p. 75.
[4] Buswell, J. T., "A Comparison of Reactor Surveillance and Material Test Reactor Data on the Radiation Embrittlement of Water Reactor Pressure Vessel Steels," Central Electricity Generating Board (UK), Report TPRD/B/0351/N83, Oct. 1983.
[5] Perrin, J. P., Wullaert, R. A., Odette, G. R., and Lombrozo, P. M., "Physically Based Regression Correlations of Embrittlement Data from Reactor Pressure Vessel Surveillance Programs," Electric Power Research Institute (USA), Report EPRI-NP-3319, Jan. 1984.

Mechanisms of Irradiation Embrittlement

Colin A. English[1]

Microanalytical Studies of Pressure Vessel Weld Materials

REFERENCE: English, C. A., **"Microanalytical Studies of Pressure Vessel Weld Materials,"** *Radiation Embrittlement of Nuclear Reactor Pressure Vessel Steels: An International Review (Second Volume), ASTM STP 909,* L. E. Steele, Ed., American Society for Testing and Materials, Philadelphia, 1986, pp. 187–205.

ABSTRACT: In this paper, the results from microanalytical studies of four quenched, tempered, and stress-relieved A533 B welds are reported. Emphasis has been placed on determining the micro-distribution of copper and nickel; elements known to cause or enhance irradiation embrittlement of pressure vessel steels. Copper contents varied from 0.15 to 0.6% by weight and both high (1.6%) and low nickel (0.1%) welds were examined. Specimens have been studied using transmission electron microscope (TEM) techniques whereby chemical information can be acquired of the scale of ≥ 10 nm. In the high copper welds, copper precipitation was observed on both grain boundaries and dislocations. However, the form and extent of the precipitation has been found to be affected by the nickel level. Preliminary results from unirradiated welds on the composition of small regions (10 by 10 by 100 nm) of the ferrite, free of second-phase particles, indicate the following. First, the manganese levels in all materials and the nickel levels in the high nickel welds were in good agreement with the bulk levels. Second, in the high copper welds, the levels of copper were significantly lower than the bulk (0.5 to 0.6% by weight) and were influenced by heat treatment. The last aspect to be reported is the observation of copper sulfide particles in all the welds studied, particularly in association with large manganese silicate inclusions. The implications of this work to the irradiation embrittlement phenomenon are discussed.

KEY WORDS: radiation effects, pressure vessel steels, embrittlement, welded joints, irradiation, microanalysis

Embrittlement of light-water reactor pressure vessel (RPV) materials due to neutron irradiation at elevated temperatures is a well known, but not well understood phenomenon. Experimentally, residual levels of elements such as copper, nickel, or phosphorous have been found to be detrimental. As a result, there has been a considerable interest in establishing empirical relationships that allow a prediction of the magnitude of the irradiation embrittlement from a knowledge of the bulk material chemistry and neutron dose (for a review see Ref *1*). Relatively little attention has been given to the micro-distribution of these elements in ferrite, both before and after irradiation. Previous transmission electron microscope (TEM) studies of the microstructure of irradiated RPV steels have

---

[1] Group leader, Materials Development Division, AERE Harwell, Didcot, Oxfordshire, UK.

concentrated on characterizing the dislocation structure [2,3], density [3], and composition [3,4] of the second-phase particles. Further, at doses $<4 \times 10^{23}$ nm^{-2} ($E > 1$ MeV), no irradiation-produced microstructure was observed in material irradiated at 250 and 288°C. Both Buswell [3] and Thomas [4] considered that any small defect clusters produced during irradiation were not detectable in the presence of surface oxide particles left by electropolishing.

In this paper, the initial results from microanalytical studies of both unirradiated and irradiated weldments will be described. Specimens have been examined using TEM techniques whereby chemical information can be acquired on the scale of ≥ 10 nm from both the ferrite and second-phase particles. The detailed aims of the work are threefold:

1. To develop the experimental techniques necessary to precisely characterize the spatial distribution of known embrittling species.
2. To characterize the unirradiated microstructure with particular emphasis on the distribution of copper and nickel. In particular to attempt to measure the level of copper and nickel in regions of the ferrite, free of second-phase particles.
3. To characterize the irradiated microstructure with emphasis on the distribution of copper and nickel.

This paper is concerned primarily with Aims 1 and 2 although some comparison with irradiated specimens has been made. It is to be stressed that the microstructure of these welds exhibits considerable spatial variation. Some attempt has been made to study this spatial variation, although the results presented here have been obtained from sampling a restricted number to TEM samples. It is to be noted that Buswell [3] made a detailed study of the uniformity of precipitate and dislocation structures of similar welds.

The organization of the paper is as follows. In the next section, the experimental procedure is detailed and materials fabrication, heat treatment, and composition are given. The results of the microanalytical studies are then presented and, in the last section, the implications of these to the mechanical property response of these weldments are discussed.

Experimental Procedure

Materials

The details of the composition of the weldments studied are given in Table 1. It can be seen that the bulk copper content varied from 0.17% by weight in 1W to ~0.6% in SH and WV; further 1W and SH are low nickel while 2W and WV are high nickel.

The fabrication procedures and heat treatment conditions have been fully described by Williams et al [5]. Briefly, the welds were taken from submerged-arc-weld runs. Originally, runs were stress relieved (12 h at 600°C and 6 h at

TABLE 1—*Chemical composition of the welds.*

Heat Code	Cu	Ni	Mn	Mo	Si	C	Cr	V	Co	S	P
1W	0.17	0.10	1.66	0.52	0.61	0.06	0.04	...	...	0.024	0.017
2W	0.265	1.61	1.62	0.33	0.30	0.047	0.11	0.003	0.009	0.003	0.007
SH	0.53	0.1	1.61	0.45	0.40	0.069	0.04	0.001	...	0.015	0.015
WV	0.6	1.7	1.41	0.38	0.4	0.05	0.05	...	0.046	0.010	0.012

650°C) and subsequently were given an additional quench and temper and stress-relief treatment (42 h at 600°C and 6 h at 650°C).

In the laboratory, 1-mm slices cut transversely from broken Charpy specimens of WV and SH were given an additional heat treatment in argon in order to study different distributions of copper. The conditions employed were 50 h at 600°C, or 5 h at 650°C or 700°C or 750°C, and the samples were quenched in brine.

Metallographic Techniques

Specimens for metallography were prepared from slices cut transversely from broken Charpy specimens. For optical metallography, slices were mounted and mechanically polished to the required surface finish. They were imaged in either the as-polished condition where the inclusions alone produced visible contrast or after potentiostatic etching in 2% nital at −300 mV that revealed the precipitate and grain structure. The 3-mm disks for electron microscopy were spark-cut from slices and electropolished in a solution of 5% perchloric acid in butoxyethelene at room temperature in a Struers Tenupol jet polishing machine.

The thin electron transparent regions of disks were examined in either a Philips EM400 electron microscope at Harwell or a modified Vacuum Generator HB5 scanning transmission electron microscope (STEM) at the University of Glasgow. Both microscopes were operated at 100 keV and are fitted with X-ray energy dispersive detectors (EDX). The chemical composition of small regions could be determined by placing a finely focused electron probe on the desired feature. On the EM400, a spatial resolution of a few tens of nanometres is possible; the high brightness field emission gun on the HB5 enables smaller, intense probes to be formed, which improves the spatial resolution to ~1 nm. Thus, the Philips EM400 was used to determine the composition of relatively coarse features (≥50 nm), whereas on the HB5, the high X-ray count rate and low background count made it possible to precisely measure low concentrations of elements (<1 atomic %) in regions ~10 nm in diameter. The foil thickness of the regions analyzed were generally between 10 and 100-nm thick.

Clearly, in attempting to determine the copper content of these small regions, where the copper levels may be as low as 0.1 atomic %, it is necessary to ensure that no artifacts have been introduced, such as surface deposition of copper or

other elements, during electropolishing. Two such artifacts were found in the present work. The first is illustrated in Fig. 1. The very small islands arrowed were found to be copper rich, and gave every appearance of lying on the foil surface. They are most probably ε-Cu that has been polished out of the material and deposited on the surface during the final stages of electropolishing. Similar effects have been seen by other workers.[2,3] This gave rise to a concern that even in foils that did not show this effect copper might have been plated on the surface

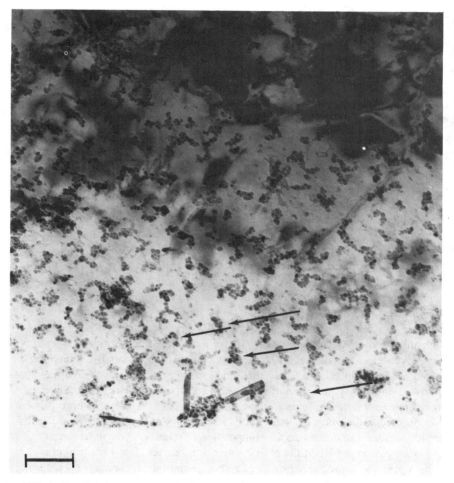

FIG. 1—*Bright field micrograph showing the copper-rich islands (arrowed) deposited on the foil during electropolishing. Scale marker is 200 nm.*

[2] Bushwell, private communication.
[3] Jostons, private communication.

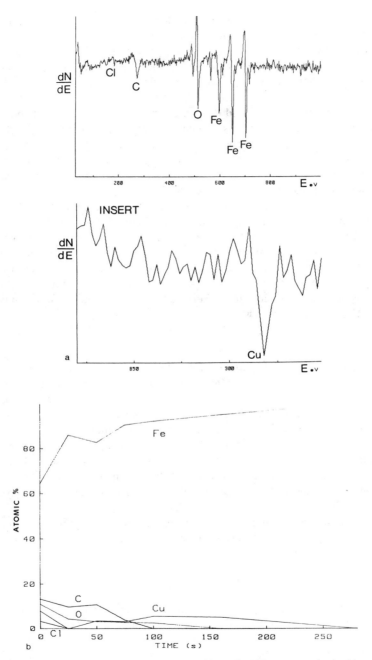

FIG. 2—(a) *Auger* dN/dE *versus* E *curves for a 100 μm by 100 μm area of a freshly polished SH material. (b) Dependence of surface composition versus time for ion-beam sputtered SH. Approximately five monolayers were eroded every 25 s.*

during electropolishing. This was investigated using Auger electron spectroscopy that enables the surface composition to be analyzed with a spatial resolution of ~1 μm. Figure 2a shows the spectrum obtained from the surface of an electro-polished SH specimen that was examined immediately after polishing. Peaks due to chlorine, carbon, and oxygen are clearly visible, and on the expanded insert evidence of copper can be seen. After 20 monolayers had been removed by sputter erosion, the chlorine and oxygen disappeared and the carbon and copper fell to very low levels. The precise dependence of surface composition with depth is presented in Fig. 2b. The copper concentration at the surface is clearly very much in excess of the bulk level. In a WV specimen that had been stored in absolute alcohol for 17 h before examination, similar effects were observed. However, in this case, the oxygen was only removed after 70 to 80 monolayers had been removed. It was also found that copper was enriched and nickel depleted in the near-surface regions of the as-received foil. Thus, it was regarded as essential to ion-beam clean the surface before any measurements of the composition of the ferrite were attempted on the HB5 at Glasgow. Usually ~100 to 200 nm was removed, considerably in excess of the thickest oxide layer measured of ~30 nm. The disadvantage of this ion-beam "wipe" is that it may introduce small dislocation loops close to the surface. These would give rise to contrast in the TEM identical to any radiation-produced clusters.

Results

The general structural features of the low nickel welds were similar with extensive areas of equi-axed ferrite grains, individual grains varied in size from ~0.5 to ~30 μm (Figs. 3a and c). A tempered bainitic structure was found in the high nickel welds, Figs. 3b and d. Copious precipitation was found both on the grain boundaries and within the grains, primarily cementite (M_3C) and Mo_2C. There was also a distribution of large spherical inclusions 0.5 to 1 μm in diameter in all the welds, although the density and precise size range varied from weld to weld; these inclusions contained primarily silicon, manganese, and oxygen and were presumed to be manganese silicates. Smaller manganese-silicon-rich particles were also found on grain boundaries.

In the subsequent sections, results are presented on the copper precipitation in the high copper welds, analysis of the composition of small regions of the ferrite, and the formation of copper sulfide particles.

Copper Precipitation in High Copper Welds SH and WV

The visible copper precipitation was studied on the EM400. In the low nickel material, SH, ε-Cu precipitates were found both on the grain boundary and within the grains. The former is illustrated in Fig. 4a where the composition of the particles has been identified from their X-ray spectra. It can be seen that, although the majority of precipitates are carbides, ε-Cu particles are present. These were identified from the copper X-ray peak superimposed on the matrix spectra, Fig.

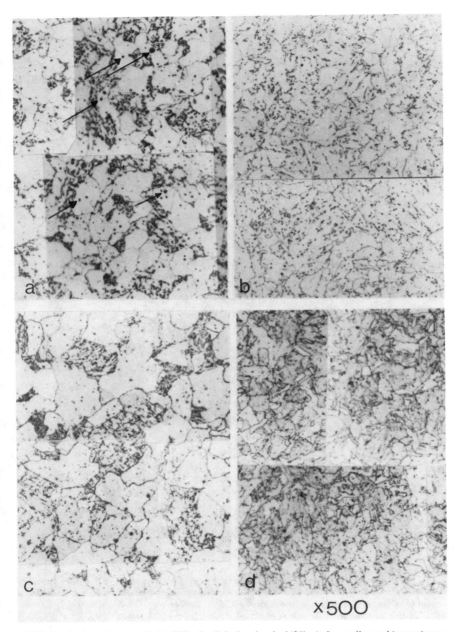

×500

FIG. 3—*Optical micrographs (×500) of polished and etched (2% nital) metallographic specimens of* (a) *1W,* (b) *2W,* (c) *SH, and* (d) *WV. For clarity, the manganese-silicate inclusions have only been arrowed in* (a). *Similar features are apparent in* (b) *through* (d).

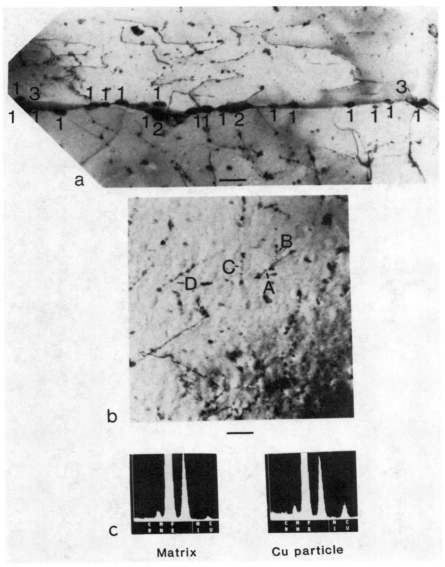

FIG. 4—*Bright field micrographs of SH material. In (a), the composition of the grain boundary precipitates is as follows: 1 are Mo₂C, 2 are manganese-silicon rich, and 3 are ε-Cu. In (b), a region is imaged in g = 011, and the Particles A, B, C, and D are ε-Cu. Scale marker is 200 nm. (c) EDX spectra taken from the matrix and a ε-Cu particle on a dislocation.*

$4c$, and by the analysis of convergent beam diffraction patterns. As yet, no quantitative measurements have been made of the distribution of grain boundary precipitates between the various types. However, in the region from which Fig. $4a$ was taken, 9 out of 69 boundary precipitates were found to be ϵ-Cu. The copper particles observed within the grains were considerably smaller, up to ~15 nm, and were usually associated with dislocation lines. A typical area is presented in Fig. $4b$. The precipitates arrowed were found to be copper rich, indicating that the great majority of particles on dislocations were ϵ-Cu. Occasionally, small molybdenum-rich particles were observed on dislocation lines. Copper precipitation was found to be present on the dislocations of all the grains examined. In the high nickel material, ϵ-Cu precipitates were also present on the grain boundaries. For example, on the boundary shown in Figs. $5a$ and b, 8 out of 26 precipitates were found to be ϵ-Cu, the remainder being molybdenum-carbide or manganese-silicon rich. Clearly, there is insufficient data, as yet, to determine if the grain boundary precipitation was different or similar to the SH material. Frequently, in both materials, copper-rich particles were associated with Mo_2C, an example is shown marked X in Fig. $5a$. As the molybdenum L line, and sulfur K_α lines occur at the same energy position on an EDX spectrum, the possibility of copper sulfide (see the section on Formation of Copper Sulfide) cannot be ruled out. The copper-rich particles illustrated are larger than the copper-sulfide particles identified in other regions (see the section on Formation of Copper Sulfide). In contrast, the precipitation within the grain in WV was very different to the SH material. In some regions, a very low density of small copper-rich particles were observed on dislocations (Region A, Fig. $5c$), more commonly no decoration was observed (Region B, Fig. $5c$), and on the EM400 no copper-rich particles were found. This was further investigated using the greater spatial resolution of the HB5 at Glasgow University. The results of a very limited number of analyses indicate that copper-rich regions can be detected on apparently precipitate-free dislocation lines. Such an analysis is illustrated in Fig. $5d$. An electron probe was placed at nine equally spaced points (60 nm apart) along the dislocation line (contained in a specimen that had been ion-beam wiped); at five points, copper levels above the matrix level were detected. On other dislocation lines studied, copper-rich regions were less frequent. A most significant aspect of this copper precipitation is that although nickel has influenced the form the precipitation takes, there was no evidence for the formation of copper-nickel particles. The nickel levels in regions containing copper particles was always similar or less than the levels found in the matrix.

In order to further investigate the effect of nickel on copper precipitation in these alloys, samples were studied after a further anneal for either 50 h at 600°C or 5 h at 650 or 700 or 750°C. At 700 and 750°C, no visible copper precipitation was observed on dislocations in either material (at the higher temperature, the WV material had clearly transformed during the anneal). The straight precipitate-free dislocations observed at 750°C in SH are shown in Fig. $6a$. After 5 h at 650°C, copper particles were more frequently observed on dislocation lines in

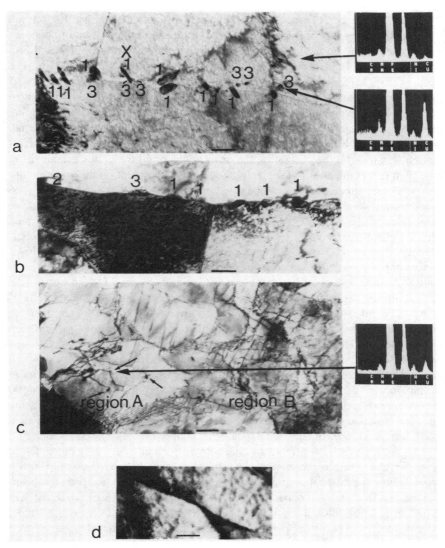

FIG. 5—*Bright field micrographs of WV material. In* (a) *and* (b), *the composition of the grain boundary particles as in Fig. 4. In* (c), *in Region A, copper-rich particles on the dislocations are arrowed; in Region B, no such particles were found. Scale marker is 200 nm. EDX spectra taken from the matrix, a grain boundary ε-Cu particle, and a copper particle on a dislocation are illustrated.* (d) *Precipitate free dislocation analyzed on the modified HB5. The scale marker is 60 nm.*

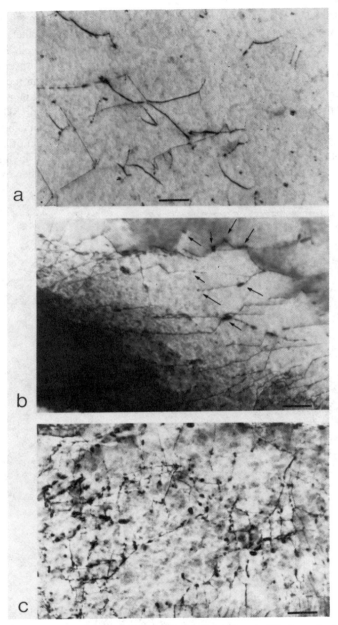

FIG. 6—*Bright field micrographs of SH and WV: (a) dislocations in SH after a further 5 h at 750°C, (b) copper precipitates arrowed on dislocations in WV after 5 h at 650°C, and (c) copper-rich precipitates on dislocations in WV aged 5 h at 600°C. Scale marker is 200 nm.*

the high nickel WV material, Fig. 6b. This may be due to growth during the anneal or variability in precipitation from one 3-mm disk to another. At 600°C, precipitation on dislocations in WV material was very pronounced, Fig. 6c.

Similar structures to those illustrated in Figs. 4 and 5 were observed in SH and WV material irradiated to ~5 × 10²² n/m² ($E > 1$ MeV) in the HERALD reactor at 250°C. (The full irradiation procedure is given in Williams et al [5].) Copper precipitates were present after irradiation on dislocations in SH (Fig. 7a). In some regions of irradiated WV, small precipitates were associated with dislocations (Fig. 7b). These precipitates have not as yet been identified or measurements made to determine if their density is greater than in unirradiated material. No irradiation-produced clusters were detected in either material. In

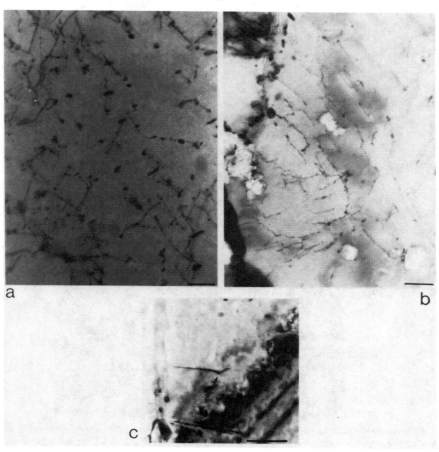

FIG. 7—*Bright field micrographs of material irradiated to* ~5 × 10²² *n/m² at 250°C in the HERALD reactor at Aldermaston:* (a) *SH,* (b) *WV, and* (c) *example of a pinned dislocation in SH. Scale marker is 200 nm.*

agreement with Buswell [3], dislocations were observed in both irradiated and unirradiated WV and SH that appeared to be pinned by obstacles, an example is shown in Fig. 7c. The region where the dislocation was pinned contained more copper than the matrix.

Composition of Small Regions of the Ferrite

Measurements were made on foils of 1W, 2W, SH, and WV that had been ion-beam cleaned immediately before loading into the HB5. Featureless regions of the ferrite where no second-phase particles were visible were studied either by placing a static probe on the region of interest or by scanning over an area ~13 by 10 nm. Foil thickness was estimated to be <100 nm and data were collected for ~300 s with count rates of 500 to 2000 counts/s, depending on thickness. The general features of the spectrum were similar to the matrix spectra presented in Fig. 4, with the majority of the X-rays arising from iron but with characteristic peaks from silicon, molybdenum, manganese, nickel, and copper clearly visible. The size of the copper peak increased on going from the low copper 1W material to the high copper SH and WV welds, although the magnitude of the increase on going from 1W to WV and SH was less than that expected from the bulk levels.

These trends can be examined in greater detail from the following analysis of the K_α intensities of manganese, iron, nickel, and copper. For a foil containing Elements A and B in a known ratio C_A/C_B, the ratio of the X-ray intensities I_A/I_B is

$$I_A/I_B = \frac{C_A}{C_B} \cdot \frac{\sigma_A}{\sigma_B} \cdot \frac{w_A}{w_B} \cdot \frac{f_A}{f_B} \cdot \frac{\epsilon_A}{\epsilon_B} \cdot \frac{A_B}{A_A}$$

where σ, w, f, ϵ, and A are, respectively, the K-shell ionization cross-section, the fluorescence yield, the fraction of K_α to total emitted K radiation, detector efficiency at the energy of the K_α X-ray, and the atomic weight. In the present case, to determine, say, I_{Cu}/I_{Fe}, it is first necessary to subtract the background contribution from the K_α peaks, and then to evaluate the number of counts within the peak. The former was done by using a Modified Bethe Heitler (MBH)

TABLE 2—*Parameters employed in estimating C_{elem}/C_{Fe}.*

Element	A	$\sigma_{elem}/\sigma_{Fe}{}^a$	w^b	f	$\epsilon_{elem}/\epsilon_{Fe}$
Mn	54.9	1.15	0.315	0.865	1.0
Fe	55.85	1.0	0.345	0.865	1.0
Ni	58.71	0.79	0.414	0.865	1.0
Cu	63.55	0.71	0.445	0.865	1.0

^{a} Taken from Bethe-Powell calculations in Ref 6.
^{b} Taken from Ref 7.

background model fitted to the experimental spectra. The fitting procedure was as follows. An MBH background was calculated for the approximate composition and corrected for detector efficiency and self-absorption (if any). This spectrum was convoluted for with the gaussian detector response function and scaled and fitted to the experimental spectrum in two regions above and below the peaks of interest (manganese to copper). The copper peak integral was determined by fitting gaussian peak to the observed experimental K_α peaks; the manganese, iron, and nickel were determined from the counts in windows set on the peaks. The values of σ, w, f and A employed to convert I_A/I_B to C_A/C_B are given in Table 2. The uncertainties in the quoted weight fractions C_A/C_B arise from the systematic errors of the parameters in Table 2, the counting statistics, and the uncertainty in the background fitting. In these preliminary measurements, the error of individual readings for manganese and high nickel was estimated at 10%, while for copper, the error was ±25% for SH, WV, and 2W, and ±35% for 1W. The larger error for 1W is due to the low copper levels that approached the detection limit of ~0.1% by weight for this technique.

The results for the low nickel materials, 1W and SH, and the high nickel materials, 2W and WV, are given in Tables 3 and 4, respectively. It can be seen that in both sets of data the mean manganese levels are close to the bulk levels; indeed, the lower bulk level in WV is reflected in the values quoted. This is perhaps surprising as some manganese is incorporated in second-phase particles and thus the levels in the ferrite should be lower than the bulk. It may be due to either errors in the analysis or variation in manganese levels within the weld block. In the high nickel alloys, the nickel levels determined for 2W and WV are in good agreement with the values in Table 1. This is to be expected as no nickel-rich second-phase particles or nickel segregation has been observed. The copper contents of the ferrite 1W and 2W are close to the bulk values. However,

TABLE 3—*Weight fraction (C_{elem}/C_{Fe}) (%) for low nickel welds estimated from the average of ten measurements.*

	Mn	Cu
1W MATERIAL		
Mean standard deviation	1.67 ± 0.07	0.18 ± 0.03
min	1.62	0.13
max	1.82	0.21
% error in individual readings	10%	35%
SH MATERIAL		
Mean standard deviation	1.54 ± 0.06	0.39 ± 0.04
min	1.45	0.36
max	1.61	0.45
SH MATERIAL (5 H AT 750°C)		
Mean standard deviation	1.66 ± 0.08	0.49 ± 0.05
min	1.47	0.42
max	2.16	0.53
% error in individual readings	10%	25%

TABLE 4—*Weight fraction (C_{elem}/C_{Fe}) (%) for the high nickel welds estimated from ten measurements.*

	Mn	Ni	Cu
2W MATERIAL			
Mean standard deviation	1.58 ± 0.12	1.66 ± 0.08	0.32 ± 0.05
min	1.36	1.56	0.25
max	1.77	1.79	0.38
WV MATERIAL			
Mean standard deviation	1.44 ± 0.08	1.75 ± 0.05	0.36 ± 0.09
min	1.32	1.66	0.29
max	1.60	1.82	0.47
% error in individual readings	10%	10%	25%

even within the uncertainties of the analysis, it is clear that the copper levels in WV and SH are less than the bulk. Further, the mean copper level of SH is clearly dependent on heat treatment with, as expected, more being retained in solution after the 750°C anneal. The spatial variation of manganese and nickel was not pronounced, and the large uncertainty in determining the copper level precluded any assessment of the variation of the level of this element with sampling position.

Formation of Copper Sulfide

Fisher and co-workers [8,9] have observed copper sulfide in both plate and weld of the type used in Magnox pressure vessels, frequently in association with large aluminum nitride particles. In this work, copper sulfide has been detected associated with manganese-silicate inclusions and also as very small particles (<10 nm) within the matrix. This is illustrated in Figs. 8a and b. In Fig. 8a, copper-sulfide particles have been identified on the surface of a large manganese-silicate inclusion. The frequency with which this association can occur may be judged from Fig. 8b. This shows a ductile fracture surface of 1W where the inclusions are clearly visible, and of the 20 inclusions studied, 17 had associated copper and sulfur. In a detailed study of the composition of particles in 1W and 2W, employing both SEM of ductile fracture surfaces and TEM of disks and extraction replica specimens, sulfur has only been detected unambiguously when copper was also present in the X-ray spectrum. The small size and the fact that the copper-sulfide precipitates are obscured by the bulk of the manganese-silicate inclusions makes it difficult to determine the volume fraction. However, no evidence of large manganese-sulfide inclusions has been found and it must be concluded that potentially a high proportion of the sulfur in these materials may form copper sulfide. A further important question is the crystallographic phase. Convergent beam diffraction patterns obtained from sulfides in 1W were consistent with diginite, $Cu_{1.8}S$, the phase observed by Harbottle et al [8].

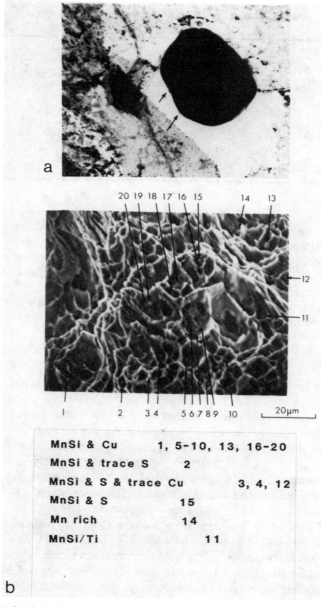

FIG. 8—(a) *Bright field micrograph of manganese-silicate inclusion decorated with small copper sulfide particles (arrowed). The scale marker represents 20 μm. (b) Ductile fracture surface of 1W. The inclusions numbered were analyzed, and their elemental composition is indicated below the figure.*

Discussion and Conclusions

The microstructural observations presented in the previous section have established the following for the quench-tempered and stress-relieved welds:

(a) ϵ-Cu precipitation occurs in high copper welds particularly along dislocation lines.

(b) In high and low nickel welds, with otherwise very similar composition and copper content, the scale and extent of the precipitation is very different. Less precipitation was visible in the high nickel weld where the ϵ-Cu precipitates did not contain high nickel levels.

(c) Preliminary results of measuring the composition of the ferrite have shown good agreement with the bulk manganese in all the welds and the nickel levels of 2W and WV. The copper levels exhibited considerable spatial variation, particularly in the high nickel weld WV. Further, in WV and SH, the mean copper levels were significantly less than the bulk levels. In SH, the level of copper in the ferrite was found to increase after an additional anneal for 5 h at 750°C followed by a brine quench.

(d) Copper sulfide precipitates have been observed in all the welds, particularly on the surface of manganese-silicate inclusions.

The observation of ϵ-Cu precipitates in SH and WV is to be expected as the bulk level exceeds the copper solubility limits at the tempering temperature, 600°C, and the stress relief temperature, 650°C, 0.15% and 0.3% by weight, respectively. Comparison with other workers is difficult because of the two-stage heat treatment. Fisher et al [9] did not report copper precipitation in a Magnox plate material containing 0.4% by weight copper after stress relief for 6 h at 600°C but did after the material had been aged for 19 600 h at 350°C.

It is known that nickel augments the embrittling effects of copper and, further, there is now increasing evidence that the embrittlement due to irradiation is a direct consequence of precipitation hardening due to copper (for a review see Ref 1). The observation presented here that the ϵ-Cu particles and copper-rich regions on dislocations in WV did not contain high nickel levels suggests that its role is not simply to increase the volume fraction of hardening centers through the formation of copper-nickel precipitates. The results of this study have not ruled out that nickel may be in the coherent body centered cubic (bcc) phase. A possible effect of nickel is suggested from this study of copper distribution in WV and SH. Nickel has clearly influenced the copper distribution and precipitation along dislocation lines. If copper precipitation along dislocation lines occurs during irradiation and is influenced in a similar manner, then the flow properties of the material may be affected.

Turning to the measurements of copper level in the ferrite, the most important implication is that for high copper material the amount of copper available may be less than the bulk level, and that this will depend on the precise heat treatment

conditions. In comparing impact data from high copper material, it is clearly necessary to take account of different post-weld heat treatment procedures. Further, ideally, it is the average copper content of the ferrite that should be employed in determining empirical relationships linking the composition to the magnitude of the irradiation embrittlement. It is interesting to note that in spite of the different levels of precipitation visible in WV and SH, the mean copper levels from ten readings are not dissimiliar. This may be due to errors introduced because of the small sample size, or to copper precipitates on dislocation lines in WV being in the form of coherent particles that are not visible in the TEM.

The implications of copper-sulfide formation to radiation embrittlement have been fully discussed by Fisher et al [9]. The results presented here establish that copper sulfide is also formed in these submerged-arc welds. Buswell has also observed copper sulfide in the UK weld of the IAEA program detailed in Ref 3. In the present work, it is not feasible to establish the volume fraction because of the association with the silicate inclusions. Fisher et al [9] found evidence for other sulfides and also a mixed copper-iron sulfide phase, whereas in the present work no evidence for this has been obtained. However, in agreement with Fisher and co-workers, we conclude that copper-sulfide formation represents a potentially important factor in determining the amount of free copper in the ferrite.

Acknowledgments

The author wishes to thank Dr. J. N. Chapman for making time available on the modified HB5 at the Department of Natural Philosophy, The University of Glasgow. It is also a pleasure to thank Drs. J. N. Chapman, W. A. P. Nicholson, and G. R. Morrison for their very considerable assistance and patience in operating the machine and Mr. J. K. Jenkins for his reliable and skillful preparation of specimens. Further thanks are due to Messrs. Adams and Paterson for their careful analysis of the X-ray spectra. Stimulating discussions with Drs. E. A. Little, T. J. Williams, and J. T. Buswell are gratefully acknowledged.

References

[1] Little, E. A., *Proceedings,* BNES Conference on Dimensional Stability and Mechanical Behaviour of Irradiated Metals and Alloys, Brighton, April 1983, Vol. 2, British Nuclear Energy Society, p. 141.
[2] Smidt, F. A. and Sprague, J. A. in *Effects of Radiation on Substructure and Mechanical Properties of Metals and Alloys, ASTM STP 529,* American Society for Testing and Materials, Philadelphia, 1973, p. 78.
[3] Buswell, J. T., "Examination of Materials by Electron Microscopy," in Report of the UK contribution to the IAEA Co-ordinated Programme on the Analysis of the Behaviour of Advanced Reactor Pressure Vessel Steels under Neutron Irradiation, L. M. Davies, Ed., UK Atomic Energy Agency, 1983.
[4] Thomas, L. E., "Microstructural Examination of Neutron-Irradiated Pressure Vessel Steels," NUREG/CR-1241, Vol. I, U.S. Nuclear Regulatory Commission, Washington, DC, Jan–March 1980.
[5] Williams, T. J., Thomas, A. F., Berrisford, R. A., Austin, M., Squires, R. L., and Venables, J. H. in *Effects of Radiation on Materials, 11th Conference, ASTM STP 782,* H. R. Brager and

J. S. Perrin, Eds., American Society for Testing and Materials, Philadelphia, 1982, pp. 343–374.
[6] Chapman, J. N., Nicholson, W. A. P., and Crozier, P., "Understanding Thin Film Spectra," *Journal of Microscopy,* in press.
[7] Langenberg, A. and van Eck, J., *Journal of Physics B,* Vol. 12, 1979, p. 1331.
[8] Harbottle, J. E. and Fisher, S. B., *Nature,* Vol. 299, 1982, p. 139.
[9] Fisher, S. B., Harbottle, J. E., and Aldridge, N. B. in *Proceedings,* BNES Conference on Dimensional Stability and Mechanical Behaviour of Irradiated Metals and Alloys, Brighton, April 1983, Vol. 2, British Nuclear Energy Society, p. 87.

G. Robert Odette[1] and Glenn E. Lucas[1]

Irradiation Embrittlement of Reactor Pressure Vessel Steels: Mechanisms, Models, and Data Correlations

REFERENCE: Odette, G. R. and Lucas, G. E., "**Irradiation Embrittlement of Reactor Pressure Vessel Steels: Mechanisms, Models, and Data Correlations,**" *Radiation Embrittlement of Nuclear Reactor Pressure Vessel Steels: An International Review (Second Volume), ASTM STP 909*, L. E. Steele, Ed., American Society for Testing and Materials, Philadelphia, 1986, pp. 206–241.

ABSTRACT: A model of irradiation embrittlement is described for predicting the 41-J Charpy V-notch temperature shifts (ΔT) as a function of metallurgical variables and neutron exposure conditions. This forecasting procedure combines semi-empirical physical models with statistical analyses of test and power reactor data, and calibration against data from fundamental experiments in which both mechanical property and microstructural changes are evaluated. The models are based on the evolution of a damage microstructure, which includes both copper precipitates and a radiation damage component enhanced by nickel. The precipitate volume is also increased by nickel and impurity phosphorus. Predicted hardening and shifts associated with these extended defects are based on empirically validated models. The model is able to self-consistently rationalize a wide array of microstructural and mechanical property data for commercial pressure vessel steels as well as model alloys.

KEY WORDS: radiation effects, pressure vessel steels, embrittlement, irradiation, Charpy V-notch, temperature shifts, neutron exposure

Accurate characterization of reductions in the fracture toughness of reactor pressure vessel (RPV) steels due to in-service neutron exposure is very important to the safe and reliable operation of nuclear power plants. Irradiation embrittlement is usually characterized by the shift in the temperature at which Charpy V-notch (CVN) specimens absorb 41 J of energy during an impact test; hence, such shifts will be the focus of this paper.

Historically, forecasting procedures have been based on simple empirical correlations of CVN data from reactor surveillance programs and test reactor experiments [1]. Recently, statistical analyses of surveillance data have been applied to developing correlations [2–5]. These correlations suffer the inherent problems

[1] Professor of Nuclear Engineering and associate professor, respectively, Department of Chemical and Nuclear Engineering, University of California, Santa Barbara, CA 93106.

associated with their largely empirical bases and the limited range of available data; the data base is also subject to significant uncertainties and less than optimal variable characterization.

The objective of this work is to develop better embrittlement forecasting methods through a synthesis of various sources of information including: physical models; fundamental experiments; test and power reactor CVN and other mechanical property data; and statistical regressions.

Analysis of CVN Data Trends

The Surveillance Data Base [3]

The original data base in this analysis was composed of 65 weld and 151 plate shifts. Regression functions were motivated by the physical models of embrittlement. However, a wide variety of phenomenological functions were tried. The final choices for the recommended "best fit" correlations were based on the following criteria: minimum residual sum-of-the-squares standard errors; conservatism on the edges and outside the data base; agreement with higher quality subsets of data, particularly individual heats with shifts at more than one fluence, and for more irradiation sensitive alloys; consistency with physical models; and simplicity. Further, an effort was made to account for the inherent uncertainties in both the data base and particular data points to avoid overcorrelation and to define regimes of reliable application.

The temperature shifts (ΔT) can be reasonably represented by a product of a chemistry factor (CF) and a fluence (ϕt) function. The correlation for the weld is[2]

$$\Delta T = 200 \text{ Cu } \{1 + 1.38 \text{ (erf } [(0.3 \text{ Ni } - \text{ Cu})/\text{Cu}] + 1)\} \times \{1 - \exp (\phi t/0.11)\}^{1.38} \phi t^{0.18} \quad (1)$$

Figure 1a shows weld CF plotted as a function of copper (Cu) and nickel (Ni), and Fig. 1b shows the fluence function; Fig. 1c shows a plot of predicted versus measured shifts for the weld. Corresponding plots for base metal can be found elsewhere [3]. Figure 2 compares the correlation predictions to data for individual welds with data at more than one fluence. The results of this study can be summarized as follows:

1. The prime variables controlling shifts are fluence, copper and nickel content. Flux (ϕ), irradiation temperature (T_i) in the range from about 270 to 310°C, phosphorus (P) content, and thermomechanical treatment (TMT) and related metallurgical factors were found to be weak or hidden variables within the limited range and scatter in the data base.

---

[2] The units used in this paper are: fluence (ϕt — n/m^2 × 10^{23}, E_n > 1 MeV); flux (ϕ — n/m^2 — s × 10^{16}, E > 1 MeV); copper (Cu), nickel (Ni), and phosphorus (P) content in percent by weight; temperature and temperature shifts = °C; stress = MPa; hardness = VHN at 500 g; all others are SI units.

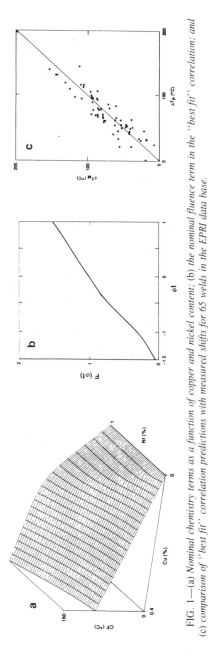

FIG. 1—(a) Nominal chemistry terms as a function of copper and nickel content; (b) the nominal fluence term in the "best fit" correlation; and (c) comparison of "best fit" correlation predictions with measured shifts for 65 welds in the EPRI data base.

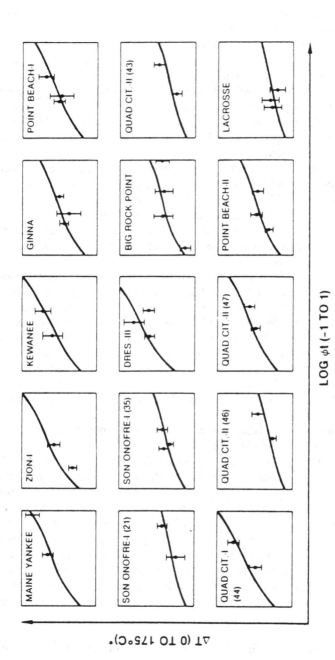

FIG. 2—*Comparison of the "best fit" correlation predictions of shift as a function of fluence with results for surveillance welds with data at more than one exposure.*

2. Significant differences beween alloy types were not found; however, variations between base and weld at nominally similar compositions are possible, and use of separate correlations was found to be more conservative for the welds. It is noted, however, that the range of compositional overlap between plate and weld is limited.

3. The chemistry factor is nonlinear in copper; smaller incremental increases occur at higher copper levels. A synergistic effect of nickel was found with an increasing chemistry factor at higher nickel. The effect of nickel increases with increasing copper content; at low copper levels the effect of high nickel was found to be minimal.

4. For welds, the fluence function had a complex low exposure transient followed by a simple power law fluence dependence, for example, ΔT proportional to ϕt^p, with p about equal to 0.18 above intermediate fluences. The same type of fluence function gave a good fit for the base, but a simpler pure power law form with p about equal to 0.28 was found to be comparable and somewhat more conservative. No compositional dependence of the fluence function could be identified.

5. The residual errors were found to be from about 12 to 15°C, which is close to the measurement uncertainties. The reasonably reliable application ranges for the weld correlations are: fluence between 0.2 and 6; nickel between about 0.1 to 1.2; and copper between about 0.1 to 0.4. The weld correlations are not well established at low copper ($Cu \leq 0.1$) by the surveillance data, which is an important regime for modern steels. The appropriate composition range for the base correlation is copper less than 0.25 and nickel less than 0.7. Even within these limits, the data are sparse in some variable regimes. An upper bound uncertainty at the 90% confidence level is estimated to be about 24°C for both base and weld.

6. The recommended correlations are neither statistically nor physically unique. However, within the range of the data, they are broadly consistent with predictions of the physical models, and, outside the data base, they generally tend to be conservative. Further, tests of the weld correlation on 32 data points not in the original EPRI analysis showed only two data points, both for the same weld, which were in excess of the upper bound shift estimate [6]. Overall, 94 out of 97 points fall below the estimated upper bound. One of the three "deviant" points is at low fluence ($\phi t < 0.1$) and comes close to falling in the prediction band when corrected chemistry values are used. The remaining two deviant shifts were found to be inconsistent with other data for welds with nominally similar composition. The source of this inconsistency is not known, although some combination of fluence and temperature errors may be the cause.

It can be anticipated that additional surveillance data will result in modifications in the correlations and absolute shift estimates; and it is likely that some new data will fall outside the estimated uncertainty bounds. Nevertheless, neither the

magnitude of the revisions nor the number of additional deviant points are expected to be large within the range of the data base. Hence, near-term efforts to improve the shift predictions can usefully focus on making use of test reactor data to extend the variable range of the correlations and to evaluate the effects of variables that cannot be discriminated in the surveillance data base.

The Test Reactor Data Base

Many experimental studies of embrittlement based on accelerated irradiations in materials test reactors (MTR) have been reported in the literature. The major advantage of this data field is that it covers a much wider range of known or potentially significant irradiation variables than the surveillance data base. However, there are questions about the direct applicability of the MTR data to predict in-service behavior due to large differences in flux levels and corresponding irradiation times. Power reactors reach end-of-life fluences after about 30 full power years of operation; MTR irradiations rarely exceed periods of several months to reach similar exposures.

Theoretical considerations suggest such large differences in damage rate may have a strong effect on the development of embrittling microstructures by a variety of mechanisms. Further, it has been noted for some time that there appear to be some systematic differences in the fluence dependence observed in MTR compared to power reactor irradiations, although the absolute magnitude of the shifts are comparable at intermediate fluences [7].

Therefore, an analysis of a large number of data sets from MTR irradiations has been carried out to evaluate broad trends and to develop semiquantitative relationships between shifts and variables such as nickel, copper, phosphorous, fluence, flux, and irradiation temperature. The effects of TMT reported in a few studies are noted, but they do not yet constitute a sufficient data base to analyze. The analysis can be summarized in the following paragraphs.

1. Although the detailed behavior varies from heat to heat, the trends show that ΔT is roughly proportional to ϕt^p, where p is about 0.5 for high flux, compared to a p of about 0.25 for low flux irradiations. Figure 3 illustrates this for nine pressure vessel base plates, forgings, and welds irradiated at both low and high fluxes [3,8–15]. The shift data are plotted in terms of estimated millidisplacements[3] per atom because of considerable spectral variations for the in-wall capsules in one experiment [8]. In eight out of nine cases, the slopes are larger for the high flux irradiations. Only one (MY) weld shows comparable data trends; unfortunately, the data overlap only at high fluences in this case.

2. There is also limited evidence that the compositional dependence of the shifts is relatively insensitive to flux levels, at least in restricted fluence ranges

---

[3] For data points without an associated spectrum, the displacement cross section σ_{dpa} ($E > 1$ MeV) was assumed to be $1.5 \times 10^{-25} m^2$. For the PSF experiment, the exposures are preliminary estimates [16].

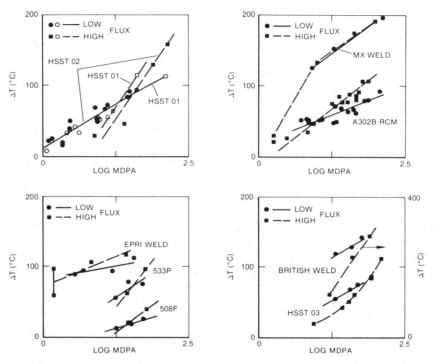

FIG. 3—*Comparison of the fluence dependence of shift for several plates and welds for irradiations in high versus low flux ranges.*

[16]. The approximate fluence at which there is a crossover of high and low flux shifts is about 2 (~30 mdpa), although this point clearly varies somewhat as seen in Fig. 3.

3. The MTR shift data do not appear to be sensitive to variations in copper content below levels of about copper (Cu) $\lesssim$ 0.1. In this composition regime, the embrittlement can be attributed to other impurities (for example, phosphorus) and alloying elements (for example, nickel) or inherent radiation damage or both. This also suggests that the surveillance correlations for welds, which have little supporting data in this regime, may not be valid for modern clean steels; MTR data may be a better basis for predicting embrittlement at low copper levels, at least at intermediate fluences.

4. Above the apparent threshold copper content of Cu_0, the shift varies roughly as

$$\Delta T \simeq C\sqrt{Cu - Cu_0} \qquad (2)$$

where C is approximately equal to 200 ± 25°C and Cu_0 is about 0.1

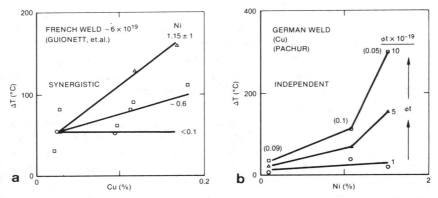

FIG. 4—*MTR data illustrating both* (a) *synergistic and* (b) *independent enhancement of shift by nickel.*

5. Test reactor data [*17,18*] show evidence of both synergistic (with copper) and independent nickel enhancement of shifts as shown in Fig. 4. Figure 4*b* suggests that the independent effect of nickel increases with fluence. This is shown even more clearly in Fig. 5 where data at various nickel levels are plotted as a function of the square root of fluence for low copper welds. Approximately linear increases in both yield stress change ($\Delta\sigma$) and shift (ΔT) data [*18,19*] are observed with a low fluence threshold (ϕt_0). This behavior can be represented by an independent nickel-enhanced contribution to the shift in the form

$$\Delta T_i = (A + B\mathrm{Ni}) \sqrt{\phi t - \phi t_0} \qquad (3)$$

Estimated values for A and B are about $10 \pm 5°C$ and $25 \pm 10°C$ up to intermediate nickel levels (<1.2) and fluences (<10). Values of the threshold fluence

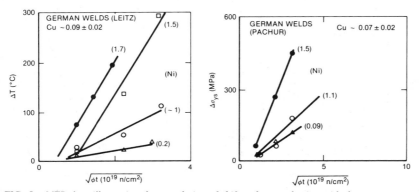

FIG. 5—*MTR data illustrating the correlation of shift and strengthening with the square root of fluence above a threshold and the nickel enhancement of embrittlement for low copper welds.*

(ϕt_0) are estimated to be on the order of 0.5. At higher nickel levels (>1.2), the effect of this element appears to increase, particularly at high fluences, and values of B on the order of 40 ± 10°C are indicated by the data.

6. At higher copper levels, there appears to be a low-to-intermediate fluence regime that saturates, which is primarily related to copper content, followed by a high fluence regime in which the shifts again increase at a rate enhanced by nickel. Such behavior is illustrated in Fig. 6 [11,18–20].

7. Figure 7 shows the combined effects of nickel and copper; here shifts interpolated or extrapolated to a fluence of five are plotted against nickel for various ranges of low to high copper contents. In addition to showing both synergistic and independent effects, these results suggest a linear superposition of the independent nickel plus the nickel-dependent copper (synergistic) contribution to the shifts.

8. Hawthorne has reported an enhanced embrittlement due to phosphorus [21,22] for MTR irradiations to a fluence of 2.5 in steels with low copper levels. This data set was analyzed as follows [6]: the low copper data were used to approximately establish an independent shift contribution due to phosphorous as

$$\Delta T_p = D\sqrt{P - P_0} \qquad (4)$$

where D is less than or about equal to 500 and P_0 is about 0.002.

Low phosphorous data were used to establish a nickel-dependent copper contribution. The data suggest that the individual contributions should be combined by a root-sum-square (RSS) superposition as

$$\Delta T \sim \sqrt{\Delta T_p^2 + \Delta T_c^2} \qquad (5)$$

The RSS superposition explains the small contribution of phosphorus at higher copper levels, and it may rationalize the failure to observe its effect in the

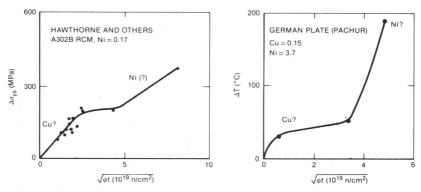

FIG. 6—*MTR data illustrating how the dependence of strengthening and shift might be decomposed into a low fluence, copper-dominated saturating term, and a high fluence nickel-dominated term.*

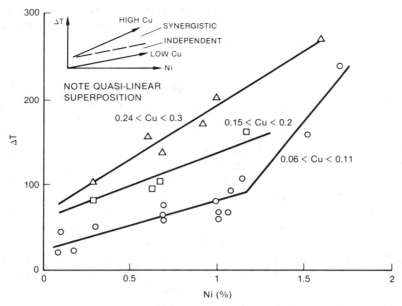

FIG. 7—*MTR shift data extrapolated or interpolated to a fluence of 5 plotted against nickel content for three ranges of copper content.*

surveillance data base. The net phosphorous contributions to the total shift range from about 10 to 40°C.

In this analysis, an independent contribution from nickel was neglected. Indeed, Hawthorne's data at low copper and phosphorous show small shifts up to intermediate nickel levels. However, some contribution from radiation damage of up to 10 to 40°C, depending on the nickel content, is expected. Hence, Eq 4 probably overestimates the effect of phosphorous. Similarly, Eq 3 probably overestimates the effect of the radiation damage component. A self-consistent compositional model for the MTR data cannot be derived, in part, due to confounding effects of other variables. Hence, Eqs 2 to 5 should be viewed as indicative of trends, rather than absolute formulas for predicting embrittlement.

9. Finally, we note that we have analyzed a number of MTR data sets to evaluate irradiation temperature dependence of damage [6]. Considerable variability is observed; shift decreases with increasing irradiation temperature in the range 0.4 to 2°C/°C for irradiation temperatures 250 to 310°C; however, the majority of data sets cluster around the average value of 1 ± 0.2 °C/C.

Models and Fundamental Experiments

Models and Mechanisms

Models of embrittlement must account for: (*a*) the microstructural features induced by irradiation; (*b*) the effect of the microstructural changes on funda-

mental structure-sensitive properties; and (C) the relationship between these properties and the shift in the CVN temperature at the 41-J energy level. Each of these has been discussed elsewhere [3,7,23–25]; hence, they will only be briefly summarized here.

Microstructure—There are a number of plausible candidates for embrittling microstructures, including: small vacancy clusters in the form of microvoids, depleted zones, or dislocation loops; interstitial clusters (dislocation loops); point defect cluster-solute atom complexes; and precipitates. Indeed, there is evidence that all of these occur in irradiated pressure vessel steels [23–36]. Detailed characterization has been hampered by their small size, typically on the order of a few nanometers or less. However, there is now considerable evidence that copper precipitates are one important, and perhaps often the dominant, embrittling feature in high-sensitivity steels [23]. Unfortunately, the exact character of these precipitates is not known. For example, they may be alloyed with iron, other solute atoms like nickel, or vacancies. Precipitates can be expected to form under irradiation for two reasons: the copper is far above the solubility limit of about 0.002% at 300°C; and, while normal thermal diffusion processes would be very sluggish at these temperatures, radiation enhanced diffusion accelerates the precipitation kinetics by several orders of magnitude [23,24].

The precipitate evolution is based on the following model assumptions [23,24]: (a) precipitates form rapidly at low fluences saturating prior to copper depletion at number densities dictated by the copper content; (b) precipitate growth is controlled by diffusion limited kinetics; and (c) copper diffusion rates under irradiation can be estimated by calculating the excess vacancy concentration using simple rate theory, coupled with measurements of dislocation densities that are taken as the dominant point defect sink. While it is broadly supported by the analysis of the experimental results discussed later, this model is only approximate.[4]

The possibility that microvoids are an important source of embrittlement has also been considered in some detail [7,24–27,32]. It is expected that such defects might form as a consequence of the high vacancy concentration in a cascade [25]. Such microvoids would be small ($\bar{r}_{mv}$ < 0.5 nm) and most would be thermally unstable, dissolving with a characteristic lifetime, τ_{mv}. Theoretical considerations suggest that the microvoid stability would be increased by some impurities and minor alloying elements such as copper [25].

Other potentially important microstructural features include stable or growing microvoids [24,26], interstitial loops [26,32], and other precipitates [33] such as phosphides and nickel/silicon-rich phases [6]. At high concentrations, some

---

[4] For example, nucleation and coarsening are not accounted for and may be important even in various stages of precipitate development. Establishing the precise balance of kinetic factors controlling precipitate nucleation and growth and coarsening kinetics, and corresponding hardening and embrittlement will require a significant amount of additional fundamental research.

of these features may be important point defect sinks, which must be considered in rate theory calculations of excess vacancy concentrations.

Structure-Property Relationships—The microstructures just described act as obstacles to dislocation slip, thereby increasing the yield stress. The most likely interaction mechanism for microvoids and copper precipitates appears to be associated with the lower local elastic modulus of these features, which lowers the dislocation line energy. Russell and Brown [37] have proposed a model based on this concept and have applied it to copper precipitate-strengthened alloys with some success. Model predictions for iron/copper alloys are in reasonable agreement with some field ion microscopy (FIM) [32,35,36] and transmission electron microscopy (TEM) [38,39] data from the literature. Peak hardening is expected at a size of about 1.2 nm, with a rapid decrease at smaller radii. However, there is no rigorous empirical verification of the Russell-Brown model, particularly at very small sizes.

Mechanical Property-CVN Parameter Relationships—CVN parameters such as the 41-J temperature are not fundamental mechanical properties. However, it has been shown that there is a close correlation between yield stress changes ($\Delta\sigma$) and temperature shifts (ΔT) at 41 J [40]. The proportionality between shifts and yield strength changes depends on the unirradiated CVN properties of the steel and the change in yield stress. Temperature shifts at the 41-J level were shown to have two contributions. The most important is due to increases in the maximum temperature of elastic fracture (T_e, which is approximately the temperature at 10 J). These shifts can be modeled using stress-controlled cleavage fracture theory. Irradiation does not change either the microcleavage fracture stress (which is also independent of temperature, alloy type, and condition) or the slope of the yield stress versus temperature curve. Therefore, the ratio of the shift in elastic fracture temperature to yield stress change can be uniquely calculated.

A second contribution to the shift is due to a reduction in the upper-shelf energy (USE) and a corresponding lowering of the slope of the CVN curve in the transition regime. The fractional reduction in upper-shelf energy could also be correlated empirically with the changes in the yield stress; and that the transition regime occurred over a relatively constant temperature interval. These observations allow the shift increment, ΔT_t, in the transition regime to be estimated from the initial upper-shelf-energy, USE°, T_e^0, and $\Delta\sigma$. The total shift at 41 J is given approximately by

$$\Delta T = C_e(T_e^0, \Delta\sigma)\Delta\sigma + \Delta T_t \, (\text{USE}^0, \Delta\sigma) \tag{6}$$

Prescriptions for calculating C_e and ΔT_t are given elsewhere [40]. The average overall coefficient relating shift to yield stress increases is about 0.65 ± 0.25°C/MPa [3,41].

Composite Models—Most trends predicted by a model combining the elements just outlined are in good agreement with observation, including [3,23,24]: the magnitude of shifts in low nickel alloys; the nonlinear dependence on copper content; the modest temperature and flux sensitivity for the surveillance data base; and the fluence dependence. The flux-dependent microvoid component coupled with the effects of damage rate on precipitation also partly rationalizes differences between surveillance and MTR irradiations [3,7,24,25]. However, many components of the model are qualitative and have not been verified experimentally. Further, the effects of nickel and the increase in shift at high fluences for surveillance data are not accounted for. Therefore, a set of experiments to address fundamental mechanisms and to evaluate the effect of undefined embrittlement variables has been carried out.

Fundamental Experiments

An experimental program to evaluate the combined effects of irradiation temperature, fluence, flux, composition, and microstructure has been described previously along with some preliminary results [24]. Compositions of the 10 model and 13 commercial-type alloys studied are given elsewhere [24]. Irradiations were performed in the University of Virginia Reactor. Nominal irradiation conditions were: $\phi = 0.5, 3; T_i = 270, 288, 307, 325;$ and $\phi t - 0.25, 0.7, 1.0$. Note, not all combinations of these variables were included in the experimental matrix. Thermal controls were included for all irradiation matrix points. Mechanical properties were characterized by measured changes (irradiated minus thermal control) in Vickers microhardness that are assumed to track corresponding changes in yield stress [41]. The unirradiated microstructures have been characterized by TEM. Limited TEM and small-angle neutron scattering (SANS) studies have been conducted on irradiated alloys as well as corresponding controls.

The data must be considered preliminary for a number of reasons, including: (a) dosimetry results are yet to be finalized; (b) an overall statistical analysis of the hardness change data base for the initial, thermally aged, and irradiated specimens has not been completed to indicate the optimal way to represent the effects of irradiation and to establish uncertainty levels (the estimated average hardness standard deviation is ±7 DPH); (c) additional data are needed to resolve questions raised in the analysis of the TEM and SANS observations; and (d) measurements for a number of matrix points have not yet been completed. Nevertheless, the available data show a number of consistent trends that are not greatly influenced by these qualifying factors; these results are summarized in the following paragraphs, along with appropriate caveats where needed.

Hardness Changes—Most of the hardness data have been obtained at an intermediate (nominal) fluence of about 0.7 at a flux of 3 for the four temperatures. No significant effect of nickel on hardening is observed in this fluence range at most temperatures. Possible exceptions include commercial plate, if estimated

corrections are made for differences in copper contents, and for some low (<0.03) copper plate and welds. In these cases, an increase in nickel (about 0.2 to 0.6 for plate with Cu = 0.16 to 0.2 and 0.6 to 0.9 for plate and weld with low copper) may result in increased irradiation hardening at 270°C, with a smaller effect apparent at 288°C, and no effect at even higher temperatures. Of course, other variables may account for the differences in hardness.

Figure 8 shows changes in hardness as a function of copper at the irradiation temperature of 288°C, fluence of 0.7, and flux of 3. The nonlinear behavior discussed previously is clearly observed in both model and commercial alloys. There is an indication of a threshold copper concentration at about 0.1, and with a small amount of hardening that is not dependent on copper at lower levels.

A great deal of data on the temperature dependence of hardening has been obtained at a flux of 3 and fluence level of 0.7, as shown in Fig. 9. Data for individual curves shows a considerable variability. Possible trends include: (1) a steeper decrease in hardness with increasing temperatures in the lower temperature regime (less than about 288°C), and (2) a decrease in the temperature dependence at the higher copper levels at temperatures greater than about 288°C. However, considering potential uncertainties in individual data points, a fairly consistent behavior is observed for all the steels containing copper, as shown in Fig. 9 by the dashed line with a slope of about 0.4 DPH/°C. When translated to nominal average increases in yield stress and shift, this is equivalent to about a 0.9°C/°C shift sensitivity that is generally consistent with embrittlement trends. The threshold/low copper residual hardening appears to vary with irradiation temperature as shown in Fig. 10 where data at 270 and 327°C are shown. The extrapolated copper intercept decreases with decreasing temperature, and the low copper hardening increases.

Additional data have been obtained for the nominal fluence of 0.25 at 2 fluxes of 0.5 and 3 and temperatures of 288 and 307°C. The dosimetry uncertainties are particularly significant when cross-comparing the low fluence results at different temperatures and fluxes, and in comparisons with the high fluence data.

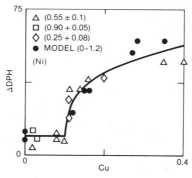

FIG. 8—*Hardness changes as a function of copper content in both model and commercial alloys after irradiation at 288°C, a fluence of 0.7 and a flux of 3.*

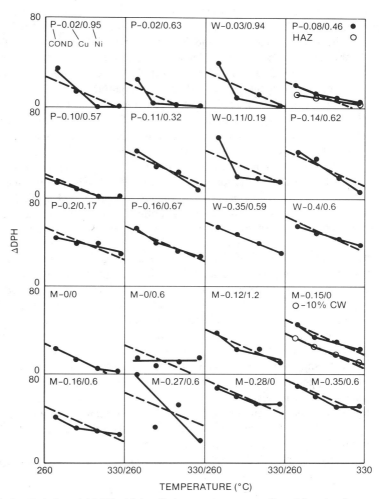

FIG. 9—*Variation of ΔDPH with irradiation temperature at a flux of 3 and a fluence of 0.7 (P = plate, W = weld, M = model alloy). Note the reduction in hardness change in 10% cold-worked material.*

Tentatively assuming the nominal values for flux and fluence are correct, a number of trends can be identified. Figure 11 shows the temperature dependence of the hardening at the fluence of 0.25 at the two flux levels. The overall behavior is similar to that at higher fluences; however, the data may indicate that there is a slightly lower temperature dependence at the intermediate flux of 3 and a slightly stronger temperature dependence at a lower flux of 0.5.

The fluence dependence in the range of 0.25 to 0.7 is shown in Fig. 12 for the irradiation temperature of 288°C. The lines are for averaged data in low,

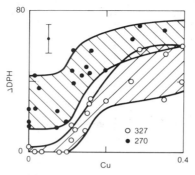

FIG. 10—*Trend bands showing hardness changes as function of copper at two irradiation temperatures at a fluence of 0.7 and a flux of 3.*

intermediate, and high copper categories for both commercial and model alloys. The low copper alloys generally have little hardness increase at either fluence. The commercial alloys with an intermediate and high copper content both have a large increase in hardening (~26) in the nominal fluence range from 0.25 to 0.7. The corresponding model alloys have a larger hardening at low fluence, but a smaller increase (~18) in going to the higher fluence. Within the scatter in the data, the fluence dependence of each of the alloys fits into one of these three categories. Generally, similar behavior is observed for the 307°C data. It appears that the main effect of the copper content and microstructure (that is, commercial versus model alloys) is on the incubation fluence, rather than the slope of the hardening increase with fluence.

There also appears to be a systematic effect of microstructure that is also shown in Fig. 9 for intermediate flux and fluence irradiations. A 10% cold-work treatment on an alloy containing about 0.15 copper results in hardening about 13 DPH lower than the same alloy in a solution-annealed condition at all temperatures. The dislocation density (ρ) measured by TEM is about $2 \times 10^{13}/m^2$ for solution-annealed and aged alloys, and about $2 \times 10^{14}/m^2$ for the cold-worked and aged alloy.

Finally, there appears to be a moderate but systematic effect of flux at a temperature of 288°C and fluence of 0.25 in steels containing significant copper, as shown in Fig. 11. For model and commercial steels containing greater than 0.15 copper, the average hardening is about 10 DPH (or about 50%) for the low flux (0.5) compared to the intermediate flux (3) irradiations. At the temperature of 307°C, little difference is observed.

Because of uncertainties in the fluences, scatter in the data (particularly at low copper levels) and potential confounding factors, the temperature, microstructure, flux, and fluence trends in hardening should be considered tentative. Nevertheless, they are consistent with many of the embrittlement data trends discussed previously, as well as predictions of irradiation-enhanced precipitation models.

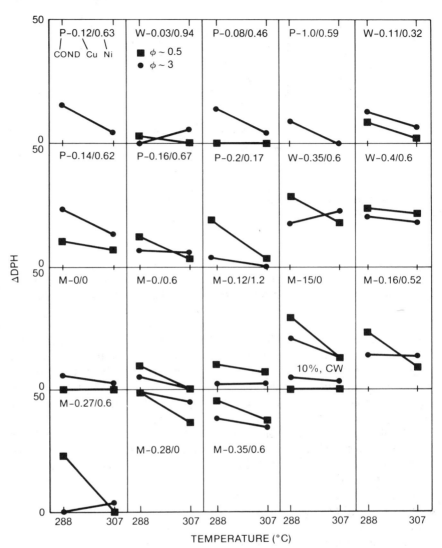

FIG. 11—*Variation of hardness change with irradiation temperature at two flux levels, 0.5 and 3, and a fluence of 0.25.*

Specifically, the data can be interpreted to suggest:

1. A hardening microstructure composed of a temperature-sensitive vacancy damage component plus a relatively temperature-insensitive precipitation component.
2. A copper precipitation mechanism that can be modeled based on simple

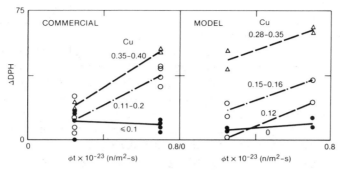

FIG. 12—*Normalized hardness changes as a function of fluence for different copper level ranges in commercial and model alloys.*

irradiation-enhanced precipitate growth kinetics. This interpretation rationalizes: the nonlinear hardening dependence on copper; apparent thresholds in fluences and copper contents; flux dependence (due to an irradiation-induced sink); and microstructure and copper dependence of the incubation fluence.

3. A weak independent effect of nickel at low fluences, and a small synergistic effect of nickel with copper in alloys with a simple thermal history (for example, model alloys and plate).

Microstructural Studies—Optical metallography and TEM were used to characterize the relatively coarse scale microstructure of the steels used in this study. The model alloys were ferrite (ASTM Grain Size Number 6–8) mixed with fine pearlite and acicular carbides. Some ε-carbides formed during solution-annealing and quench treatments of the copper-bearing model alloys, but they decomposed to acicular carbides rapidly during aging. Model steels without copper, which were not subject to the solution annealing treatment, had qualitatively similar carbide morphology both prior to and after aging or irradiation. Thermal aging resulted in a transient, temperature-dependent evolution in the microstructure and hardness; this was followed by an approximately time-independent quasi-equilibrium microstructure and hardness. All but one of the solution annealed and aged model alloys had dislocation densities of about $2 \times 10^{13}/m^2$; after aging, alloy J had a dislocation density about a factor of 2 higher and appears to have been subject to inadvertent cold work during part of its processing history. The cold-worked and aged alloy had a dislocation density about an order of magnitude higher than its solution-annealed counterpart. Due to these variations in microstructure as well as carbon contents and carbide structures, there was considerable variation in the initial hardness of the model alloys.

The commercial alloys had a more complex and predominantly bainitic microstructure. Carbide morphologies and sizes were typical of previously reported microstructures [42]. The dislocation structure was less homogeneous than in the

model alloys and, on average, had a much higher density of about $2 \times 10^{14}/m^2$ in weld and about $5 \times 10^{14}/m^2$ in plate. No significant microstructural changes in the commercial alloys were observed after thermal aging.

Neither the model nor commercial steels showed a significant difference in the microstructure after irradiation compared to thermal controls on the size scale >10 nm. Hence, the hardening observed must be attributed to smaller features. One promising technique available to characterize microstructures on this scale is small-angle neutron scattering (SANS). Briefly, discrete microstructural features embedded in a matrix scatter a well-collimated beam of cold neutrons in a manner that characterizes the scattering center: the angular scattering distribution (characterized by the scattering vector $q = 2\pi \sin(\theta)/\lambda$) is dependent on the size distribution and composition of the scattering centers; and the intensity scale is related to the volume fraction of precipitates and their composition relative to the matrix [43–44]. Unfortunately, it is not possible to independently specify the composition and number density (or volume fraction) of the scattering centers. Further, many practical complications exist, including the possibility of: multiple scattering centers; complex multimodal size distributions; shape differences; background due to room and sample radiation and incoherent scattering; statistical counting and scattering calibration uncertainties; and limited q ranges and resolution.

Hence, in analyzing SANS data, other sources of information must be sought; and the inherent nonuniqueness of results derived from scattering curves, particularly in complex alloys, must be recognized. One additional source of SANS information can be found by measuring both the nuclear and magnetic scattering. If small precipitates and microvoids have different saturation magnetization than iron, an extra component of scattering is added that varies as $\sin^2(\phi)$, where ϕ is the angle with respect to the strong applied magnetic field. The magnetic scattering for a simple paramagnetic hole is independent of the composition. In this case, the ratio (R_{pp}) of perpendicular to parallel scattering varies with the identity of the scattering center: for microvoids in iron, R_{pp} is about 1.4. For parametric pure copper precipitates, the ratio is about 11.5. If the scattering center is alloyed with iron and is ferromagnetic but with a lower saturation magnetization than iron, the ratio may still be close to that for a pure copper precipitate. However, in general (and in particular if the scattering center is paramagnetic), the ratio varies with the composition of the precipitate.

An initial SANS study of two model steels irradiated in this experiment was carried out.[5] Table 1 summarizes the alloys and irradiation conditions characterized by SANS. The following assumptions were used in the analysis of the data: (a) thermal control scattering was substracted from sample background-corrected as-irradiated measurements; (b) the minimum q for data analysis was set at

---

[5] The SANS experiments were conducted at the National Bureau of Standards (NBS) in Gaithersburg, MD, under a guest user program with the cooperation of the NBS Reactor staff. The invaluable assistance of Dr. C. Glinka is particularly noted.

TABLE 1—*Summary of SANS studies.*

Cu	Ni	φt	φ	T
		ALLOY J		
0	0	0.7	3	288
		ALLOY S		
0.35	0.6	0.7	3	270
. . .	. . .	. . .	. . .	307
. . .	. . .	. . .	. . .	307[a]
. . .	. . .	. . .	. . .	326
. . .	. . .	0.25	0.5	288
		ALLOY D		
0.4	0.6	0.7	3	288[b]

[a] Plus post-irradiation annealing at 500°C for 20 h.
[b] Only preliminary results are available.

$q = 0.05$ to avoid the effects of small changes in the large (>10 nm) scattering centers and magnetic diffraction; (c) only data perpendicular to the magnetic field were quantitatively analyzed and only up to q values with signals above an average of about 10 net counts per channel to avoid uncertainties introduced by counting statistics; (d) based on analysis of the curvature of the scattering data a single particle size (r_p) and number density (N_p) scattering curve was least squares fit to the data (the data suggests a narrow size distribution); and (e) the particles were assumed to be 50% iron and 50% copper and to have a proportional magnetic scattering length half that of pure iron.

A typical analysis sequence is illustrated in Fig. 13 for a model alloy (S) containing 0.6 Ni and 0.35 Cu irradiated at a flux of 3, fluence of 0.7, and temperature of 307°C. The other model alloys were analyzed in a similar fashion. Notably, model alloy J without copper or nickel, shows very little scattering, with only a weak indication of a possible vacancy-type defect.

Figure 14 summarizes the effects of temperature, fluence, and flux on the precipitate parameters for alloy S. These results qualitatively support many of the assumptions in the previous model, including: rapid nucleation of a high density of precipitates; growth of the precipitates in this fluence range by irradiation-enhanced diffusion; an increase in the precipitate size and volume fraction with decreasing flux; a decrease in the precipitate number density with increasing temperature; and indications of a damage component due to microvoids at high number densities and small sizes ($N_{mv} > 10^{23}/m^3$, $r_{mv} < 0.7$ nm). Note, the latter conclusion derives from an analysis of the residual nuclear scattering signal left after subtraction of the nominal precipitate component; however, due to the counting statistics, these results must be considered qualitative.

Figure 15 shows the scattering results for alloy S ($\phi = 3$, $\phi t = 7$, $T_i = 307$) after the post-irradiation anneal (PIA) of 500°C for 20 h. The results clearly indicate a coarsening of a component of the precipitates to a larger size and a

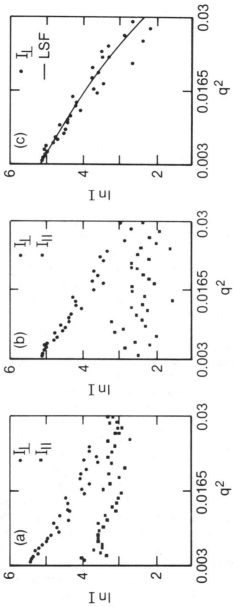

FIG. 13—*Sequence illustrating SANS data analysis for Alloy S. Average counts per channel as a function of q^2 (a) background subtracted and (b) background plus thermal control subtracted from the irradiated sample for scattering parallel ($I_\parallel$) and perpendicular ($I_\perp$) to the applied magnetic field; (c) LSF fit to the data in (b) for $I_\perp$.*

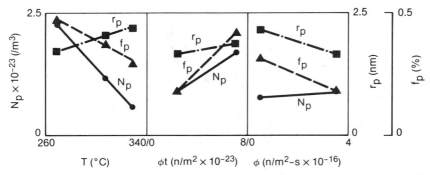

FIG. 14—*Summary of precipitate number density, size, and volume fraction derived from SANS data for model alloy S as a function of temperature, fluence, and flux.*

lower number density. The magnetic-to-nuclear scattering increases approaching the theoretical value for precipitates, and the residual vacancy signal is essentially eliminated. The positive curvature in the signal indicates a very broad distribution of sizes. However, the data can be fit crudely by assuming two precipitate sizes; the larger size category has a low number density of about $6.7 \times 10^{21}/\mathrm{m}^3$ and a characteristic radius of about 3.8 nm, while the other component has a higher density of about $8 \times 10^{22}/\mathrm{m}^3$ and smaller radius of about 1.8 nm. The precipitate volume fraction is approximately constant. Preliminary TEM studies of the PIA alloys and controls using a weak-beam dark-field technique have tentatively confirmed the larger component of the precipitate distribution.

Finally, we note that a very preliminary SANS study of a commercial weld

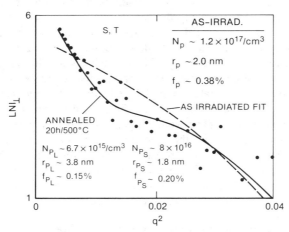

FIG. 15—*SANS scattering curves perpendicular to the applied magnetic field for model Alloy S irradiated at 288°C at a flux of 3 to a fluence of 0.7 and post-irradiation annealed 20 h at 500°C. LSF curves for the as-irradiated and annealed specimens are also shown, indicating significant coarsening of a component of the precipitate distribution.*

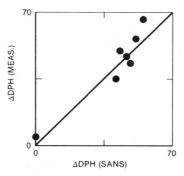

FIG. 16—*Measured changes in hardness versus predicted changes due to copper precipitation based on the modified Russell-Brown model and the SANS results.*

containing 0.4 copper, 0.6 nickel irradiated at a flux of 3 at 307°C indicated a much stronger vacancy component of damage and a higher density of smaller defects.

Even if the analysis assumptions are correct, the absolute values are uncertain by significant factors (that is, about 2) for the volume fractions and number densities; precipitate sizes are accurate to about ±0.2 nm. Further, the assumption of a 50% iron-50% copper particle composition is questionable. It is based primarily on the results of early FIM measurements [35]. The hardness measurements are also consistent with this composition, as shown in Fig. 16. Here, calculated changes in hardness based on the SANS results coupled with the Russell-Brown hardening model are compared to measured changes. If the precipitates were pure copper, the predicted hardening would be about half that measured. However, the early FIM measurements are subject to considerable uncertainties; and even assuming the hardening model is completely valid, microvoids, which were neglected, might account for the hardness increment not predicted for pure precipitates. Indeed, the observed decrease in the ratio of perpendicular-to-parallel scattering with increasing scattering angle indicates a smaller vacancy-type defect component. The estimated number of densities and volume fractions of precipitates are high by a factor of 4, if the scattering centers are actually predominantly pure copper. Further, accounting for the possible vacancy component of damage would slightly increase the size and further decrease the volume fraction of the precipitate component. Hence, these results may be modified with additional research. Indeed, future research will attempt to resolve these compositional ambiguities by use of isotopic contrast techniques (alloys with varying ratios of $^{63}Cu/^{65}Cu$) and temperature-dependent magnetic contrast (to assess the curie temperature of the particles).

Analysis and Synthesis of the CVN Data Trends and Fundamental Studies

The objective of this work is to combine the insights gained from the fundamental experiments and models with the phenomenological trends found in the

analysis of the CVN data to refine correlations of the power reactor surveillance data base. Ultimately, such correlations should cover the entire range of metallurgical and irradiation variables of interest and should be based on rigorous treatment of all the important physical mechanisms. A more realistic near-term objective is the preservation of the broad trends in all the data sets (surveillance, MTR, and fundamental) based on a combination of physical and phenomenological models. Since physical correlation models compete with other approaches in confronting the engineering data base, it is critical that good indices of statistical fit and reasonable values for the model parameters be obtained.

A model based on these principles has the following structure.

(a) The precipitate volume is taken as twice the amount of copper precipitated to account for the mixture of iron and copper.

(b) Lattice recombination is neglected, but the irradiation-enhanced diffusion coefficient includes a flux-dependent unstable microvoid sink term.

(c) The synergistic interaction between copper and nickel is based on the availability of copper to precipitate under irradiation. It is postulated that some copper is precipitated or removed from the matrix by segregation during stress relief heat treatments or other phases of the TMT (termed here, pre-precipitation); nickel is presumed to decrease the pre-precipitation or segregation or both.[6]

Further, it is assumed that there is a threshold copper content below which there is no copper-precipitate embrittlement contribution. Finally, the effect of phosphorous is also modeled as a precipitation hardening mechanism; however, rather than introducing a separate submodel, an effective phosphorous content is added to the copper concentration used in the precipitation model. These mechanisms are combined in terms of an effective impurity content (I_e) to predict an impurity-induced shift (ΔT_i). A number of refinements or alternate ways to model these effects might be proposed and should be investigated; however, the use of an effective impurity concentration available for precipitation is convenient for application to data correlations.

(d) Based on SANS data in the literature and the results of this study for irradiated iron-copper alloys and copper-bearing steels, the precipitate density is assumed to be a function of I_e and the temperature.

(e) Based primarily on the analysis of the MTR data, a copper-independent radiation damage term was added to the precipitation-induced shift component. The radiation damage component (ΔT_d) is enhanced by nickel following Eq 3. No particular mechanism is specified, but it is postulated that the radiation damage is in the form of stable microvoids (perhaps

---

[6] Note that other nickel effects can be hypothesized [3,24]. For example, nickel might alloy with the copper-rich precipitates, increasing their volume fraction; or it might increase the number density of matrix precipitates. Both of these effects would increase the hardening and shifts due to a given amount of precipitated copper.

growing), although other candidate irradiation-induced microstructures are possible.

Thus, the general form of the shift model is

$$\Delta T = \Delta T_i(\text{Cu,Ni},T_i,\phi,\phi t) + \Delta T_d(\text{Ni},\phi t,T_i) \tag{7}$$

Note that alloy TMT cannot yet be treated explicitly; however, broad classes of thermal history can be accounted for, in part, by applying the correlation models separately to weld and base shifts and the hardness data. Similarly, separate fits to the surveillance data base may account, in part, for the effects of the flux on the radiation damage component of embrittlement not explicitly contained in Eq 7.

This semi-empirical model is clearly oversimplified and has a number of unknown parameters. Hence, it can be considered neither physically rigorous nor unique. However, most of the parameters can be estimated from, or at least severely constrained by, independent sources of information, namely, MTR data and the results of fundamental experiments. Other parameters and optimal parameter values can be obtained from statistical least square fits (LSF) to surveillance embrittlement data. The model and associated calibration are described in more detail in the Appendix.

Emphasis to date has been on quantitatively modeling the surveillance welds and hardness data sets. Table 2 gives the impurity precipitate component of shift (ΔT_i) for welds irradiated at the nominal temperature of 288°C in terms of the effective impurity content (I_e) and an effective fluence (ϕt_e). The effective impurity content is given by

$$I_e = \text{Cu}\{0.6 + 0.4[1 - \exp(-0.55\ \text{Ni})]\} + 3\text{P} - 0.125 \tag{8}$$

and the effective fluence is given by

$$\phi t_e = \phi t/(0.984 + 0.0328\ \phi) \tag{9}$$

The shift contribution due to the radiation damage term is

$$\Delta T_d = (8 + 30\ \text{Ni})\ \sqrt{\phi t} \tag{10}$$

As discussed in the Appendix, slightly different expressions are applicable to the hardness data (possibly due to microstructural and TMT differences between weld, base, and model alloys) and minor variations in only two of the six LSF parameters for weld. (Note, the plate and model alloys used only four LSF parameters).

Figure 17 illustrates the application of the model to predict trends in some of the irradiation hardening data measured in this study as a function of temperature,

TABLE 2—Predicted impurity-induced shifts, ΔT_i (°C).

$\log\phi t_c$	I_c, % by weight										
	0.0	0.025	0.05	0.075	0.10	0.125	0.15	0.20	0.25	0.30	0.40
−1.00	0	0	0	0	6	12	18	27	35	42	56
−0.90	0	0	0	7	15	22	27	37	46	54	68
−0.80	0	0	7	15	22	29	35	46	55	64	68
−0.70	0	0	13	20	29	36	42	54	64	73	89
−0.60	0	0	18	26	35	42	49	61	72	81	97
−0.50	0	2	22	31	40	49	56	68	79	88	104
−0.40	0	7	27	36	46	54	62	74	85	94	110
−0.30	0	10	31	41	51	59	67	79	90	99	114
−0.20	0	14	35	45	55	64	71	83	93	102	116
−0.10	0	17	38	49	59	67	74	86	96	104	118
0.00	0	20	41	52	62	70	77	88	96	105	118
0.10	0	23	44	55	64	72	78	89	98	105	118
0.20	0	25	46	57	66	73	79	89	98	105	118
0.30	0	27	47	58	67	73	79	89	98	105	118
0.40	0	29	48	59	67	73	79	89	98	105	118
0.50	0	31	49	59	67	73	79	89	98	105	118
0.60	0	32	49	59	67	73	79	89	98	105	118
0.70	0	33	49	59	67	73	79	89	98	105	118
0.80	0	33	49	59	67	73	79	89	98	105	118
0.90	0	33	49	59	67	73	79	89	98	105	118
1.00	0	33	49	59	67	73	79	89	98	105	118

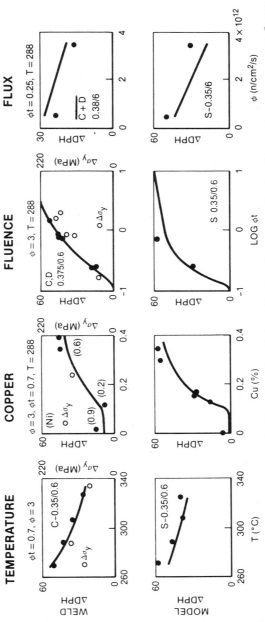

FIG. 17—*Comparison of the revised and calibrated model predictions of hardness increases as a function of temperature, copper content, fluence, and flux for both model and commercial alloys. The yield stress change data were taken from the literature.*

copper content, flux, and fluence for both model alloys and commercial welds. Clearly, the overall agreement is excellent. Indeed, the agreement with the entire hardness data base is also good; the mean residual error is less than 8 DPH, which is close to the estimated uncertainty in the hardness measurements. Figure 18 shows a predicted-versus-measured plot for the same model applied to the surveillance data base for welds. The original data base (65 points) has been supplemented with an additional 32 recent data points. The mean residual error for the original data base is about 15°C and for the expanded base about 18°C. When the fluence data below 0.75 are excluded, the errors are reduced to 12 and 14°C, respectively.

Note that higher scatter can be anticipated at lower fluences due to an inherently larger influence of factors such as microstructure and flux in the kinetically sensitive precipitate nucleation and growth regime compared to the thermodynamically-dictated, fully-precipitated regime found at high fluences. The residual errors are comparable to those found in the previous correlations [3]. However, the revised model has a better physical basis and the ability to predict trends in a much wider range of data. The revised model also provides a good fit to individual heats, particularly for high sensitivity steels. This is illustrated in Fig. 19 for the Maine Yankee (MY) weld, which has the highest shifts in the surveillance data base.

The surveillance model was also compared to a large collection of MTR shift

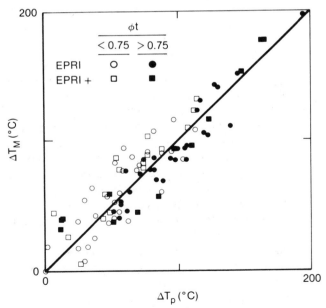

FIG. 18—*Scatter plot of predicted shifts versus measured shifts in the surveillance weld data base.*

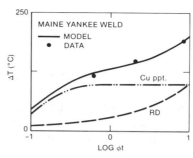

FIG. 19—*Comparison of the model predictions and measured shifts as a function of fluence in a high sensitivity (MY) weld.*

data; the results showed good consistency with the MTR data trends, but with larger mean residual errors (>30°C). This is probably in part due to failure to fully account for differences in variables such as flux and TMT for individual subsets of the MTR data. For example, a fixed "nominal" MTR flux was used in this analysis, and there was no quantitative treatment of flux in the independent nickel shift term. Further, some of the MTR data are for compositions not found in the surveillance data base; and differences in the relationship between yield stress increases and shift, as a function of the unirradiated CVN properties and the magnitude of the yield stress increase, have not been accounted for. When applied to particularly well-characterized MTR irradiations of steels similar to those found in the surveillance data base, the agreement was most often found to be quite good [6].

Summary Discussion and Outstanding Questions

This work has provided a basis to integrate surveillance and MTR CVN shift data with the results of more fundamental experiments to provide a unified model of irradiation embrittlement. For steels with intermediate to high copper and phosphorous contents, precipitation makes the dominant contribution to shifts in the range of low to intermediate fluences; the precipitation term saturates due to impurity depletion. Quantitative models of precipitation, with very few disposable parameters are in good agreement with observed data trends. Two possible effects of nickel on increasing shifts have been identified: (1) a synergistic interaction with copper that is dependent on TMT, which is modeled assuming nickel increases the copper available for precipitation; and (2) an unidentified radiation damage component, which is independent of copper, but which is enhanced by nickel. It is postulated that the radiation damage component is due to the formation of microvoid defects. The radiation damage term roughly follows a square root fluence dependence and becomes increasingly important at high fluences. The overall fluence dependence depends on the balance between the relative contributions of precipitation and radiation damage. At copper contents below about 0.1, the phosphorus (precipitation) and radiation damage contributions are dominant, with the latter resulting in large shifts in high nickel alloys at high fluences.

For the surveillance weld data base, the radiation damage term contributes on average about 25% of the shift. In some cases, this is even higher, for example, the MY weld at high fluence where the contribution is about 50% (see Fig. 19). This is somewhat surprising since an embrittlement contribution of nickel independent of copper has not been clearly identified in most previous studies [3–5]. Further, it is notable that the nickel-enhanced radiation damage term does not appear to change much in going from high flux MTR irradiations to the low flux surveillance data base. Indeed, a stronger rate dependence might be anticipated based on theoretical considerations, although a detailed model has not yet been developed. The synergistic contribution of nickel also depends on the overall composition and fluence; for surveillance welds, going from low to intermediate nickel levels (~0.2 to 0.7) increases the precipitation contribution to the shift by an average of about 15%. Within the range of the surveillance weld data base, the predictions of the revised model represented in Eq 9 are similar to those calculated from the semiempirical correlation function given in Eq 1. The largest differences are for modern clean steels, which are largely outside the compositional range of the existing data base. At very low impurity content (that is, Cu < 0.05) the new model predicts somewhat higher shifts, and at slightly higher impurity contents (that is, 0.05 < Cu < 0.1), the revised predictions are lower up to intermediate fluences.

Finally, we note that the models and analyses described here have not addressed the critical question of embrittlement recovery by post-irradiation annealing (PIA). This is requisite for a comprehensive model. A qualitative evaluation indicates that the relatively rapid recovery observed in most studies to date [6] is not consistent with purely thermal copper precipitate coarsening kinetics; such coarsening would require longer times or higher temperatures or both. This may suggest that under test reactor conditions the radiation damage, in the form of microvoids, is a more important source of embrittlement than suggested by the precipitation-dominated model. Such microvoids would be stabilized by copper [25] as well as by nickel, leading to a second mechanism of copper-enhanced embrittlement. Not only would the strengthening (hence embrittlement) due to such defects recover more quickly during PIA, but the excess vacancies released from microvoids could also accelerate the precipitate coarsening rate. If the precipitates are located on dislocations, perhaps due to PIA-induced climb-precipitate pinning mechanisms, associated pipe diffusion would further enhance coarsening kinetics. Pipe diffusion and coarsening would also be enhanced by excess vacancy absorption at dislocations. Thus, an efficient coupled microvoid-precipitate recovery process might be postulated. Unfortunately, very little information is available on the recovery kinetics for low flux-long time surveillance irradiations; since the balance of embrittling microstructures may vary with flux, there are serious questions regarding the applicability of MTR PIA data for predicting recovery kinetics of embrittled pressure vessels.

The model presented here cannot be considered final, and future research can be expected to result in many modifications and refinements. Nevertheless, the broad outlines of a fairly comprehensive theory of irradiation embrittlement have

been developed in this work. Indeed, this analysis demonstrates that it should be possible to develop a unified physical model of embrittlement that can treat the full array of important irradiation and metallurgical variables. Such models promise significant improvements in the accuracy and reliability of embrittlement forecasting.

Acknowledgments

The authors wish to express their gratitude for the guidance and many useful discussions with T. Griesbach and T. U. Marston. Additional thanks go to J. W. Sheckherd, C. Glinka, P. Lombrozo, R. Maiti, H. R. Chen, and D. Klingensmith for many important contributions to this work. This work was performed under contracts with the Electric Power Research Institute, RP-1021-7, and the National Science Foundation, CPE-8025300-1.

APPENDIX

A quantitative formulation of the models is presented here, along with a brief description of the basis for selection of the model parameters.

Copper Precipitation

Effective Impurity Content (I_e)

The copper available for precipitation ($Cu_a \leq Cu$) was taken to be a function of nickel content as follows

$$Cu_a = Cu(A - (1 - A)) (1 - \exp(-BN_i)) \qquad (11)$$

where A and B vary with thermal history. For the base and model alloys, A was taken as 1 (that is, $Cu_a = Cu$); for the weld with a more complex thermal history, they were treated as adjustable parameters in a least square fit (LSF) regression analysis (discussed later). The potential precipitation hardening contribution from phosphorus was treated by adding a C (constant) $\times P$ term to Cu_a; and the threshold copper (and P) content, below which little precipitation effect is observed, was taken as a constant (D) and subtracted from the total impurity content available for precipitation. Hence, the effective impurity content, I_e, is taken as

$$I_e = Cu_a + C \times P - D \qquad (12)$$

For the range of copper contents of alloys dealt with in this study ($Cu \geq 0.05$), a value of C equal to about 3 is consistent with MTR data. Note that this value might indicate the presence of M_3P precipitates; hence, this value was fixed in the subsequent analysis. The MTR data base further suggests a threshold impurity content parameter of D equal to about 0.1 ± 0.05. However, D also appears to be a function of temperature and may be somewhat sensitive to other material and irradiation variables. Hence, optimal "average" values witin this range were selected based on a LSF analysis of pertinent data sets.

Precipitate Growth Model

Based on data in the literature and the results of the SANS observations just described, the precipitate density was assumed to vary with copper content and irradiation temperature as

$$NP = P(I_{eff})^{0.5} \exp(E_p(1/T_i - 1/561)/k) \tag{13}$$

where P is equal to $10^{23}/m^3$ was taken for commercial materials and P is equal to $3 \times 10^{23}/m^3$ for the model alloys; E_p was estimated from SANS studies and analysis of thermal precipitation hardening data taken from the literature to be roughly 0.5 eV. Estimated values of the precipitate nucleation size was 0.3 nm and fluence ϕt_n of 0.05; the results are insensitive to the choice of these parameters except at very low fluence. Based on a combination of rate theory and the results of SANS experiments, the copper diffusion coefficient under irradiation was taken as

$$D_0 = 3 \times 10^{-8} \phi/(S_d + [1 + 0.1 \phi] \times 10^{14}) \tag{14}$$

where S_d is the measured dislocation density taken as $2 \times 10^{14}/m^2$ for the commercial alloys and $2 \times 10^{13}/m^2$ for the annealed model materials. The last two terms in the denominator of Eq 14 account for additional flux-independent and flux-dependent (microvoid) sink terms, respectively. The diffusion-controlled growth model can be solved in terms of the time (t) needed to precipitate a fraction (f) of the available impurity as

$$t = [0.38/(N_p^{2/3} D_c a)][g(x) - g(x_n)] + t_n \tag{15}$$

where

$$g(x) = [0.167 \ln\{x^2 + ax + a^2)/(x - a)^2\} + 0.577 \tan^{-1}\{(2x + 1)/(a\sqrt{3})\}] \tag{16}$$

and where a is $I_e^{1/3}$, x is $f^{1/3}$, and x_n is the nucleation fraction at the nucleation time $(t_n = \phi t_n/\phi)$. Equation 15 must be inverted to obtain the fractional precipitation as a function of time (or fluence).

Strengthening and Shift Models

The fraction of copper precipitated and precipitate size can be related to the yield strength change through the modified Russell-Brown model [37] as

$$\Delta\sigma = 23448(1 - G^2)^{0.50} \sqrt{f'}/r_p \sin^{-1} G \text{ (MPA)} \tag{17}$$

or

$$\Delta\sigma = 29310(1 - G^2)^{0.75} \sqrt{f'}/r_p \sin^{-1} G \text{ (MPA)} \tag{18}$$

where f' is taken as $2f$ to account for the iron content of the precipitates, and where G is given as

$$G = 0.20 \log(r_p/0.625) + 0.33 \log(650/r_p) \tag{19}$$

Equation 17 was used for $\sin^{-1} G < 50$.

Since there was no information readily available on the unirradiated value of the elastic fracture temperature, the relationship between shift and irradiation-enhanced precipitation

hardening was approximated by the simple proportional relationship

$$\Delta T_i = 0.65\Delta\sigma \tag{20}$$

where the coefficient was taken as the observed empirical value for surveillance welds [3,23,40]. This value is consistent with the results of the more detailed analysis based on unirradiated CVN properties and yield stress increases just discussed. Finally, an empirical relationship between yield stress increases and hardening (ΔVHN) was assumed in the form [41]

$$\Delta\text{VHN} = \Delta\sigma/3.6 \tag{21}$$

Equations 11 to 21 can be used to calculate shifts (or hardness/yield stress changes) as a function of the copper, phosphorus, nickel ϕ, ϕt, and T_i. Note, the only free parameters in the impurity precipitation model are A, B, and D, which relate to the effective copper concentration, I_{eff}. Further, the A, B parameter set only applies to welds, and the D parameter has a restricted range based on MTR data trends. Thus, agreement between the precipitation-induced shift model predictions and observation is *not* simply the consequence of curve fitting using arbitary parameters. However, this does not mean that the model is rigorous or that the fixed parameters are exact.

Independent Nickel Contribution to Hardening and Shift

As discussed previously, there appears to be a radiation damage contribution to the shift that is independent of copper and that is enhanced by nickel in the form

$$\Delta T_d = (E + F\text{Ni})(\phi t - G)^{0.5} \exp(E_d(1/T_i - 1/561)/k) \tag{22}$$

The MTR data can be used to estimate values for these parameters (see Figs. 4 to 7): the inherent embrittlement term (E) is about 10 ± 5 (°C); the nickel enhancement coefficient (F) is about 25 ± 10 (°C/Ni% by weight); and the threshold fluence term (G) is less than about 0.5. The value of E_d was fixed at 1.0 eV. These values are derived from intermediate to high flux MTR data. Hence, the optimal parameters for the low flux surveillance welds and low-intermediate to intermediate flux hardness data may be different and were established in the LSF analysis of the pertinent data subset.

The total shift is simply given as

$$\Delta T = \Delta T_i + \Delta T_d \tag{23}$$

and the total change in ΔVHN hardness is

$$\Delta\text{VHN} = 0.42\Delta T \tag{24}$$

from Eqs 20 and 21.

The correlation model as represented by Eqs 11 to 24 was fit to the various data subsets using a grid search procedure. Starting with best guess values, the parameters A to F were adjusted to minimize residual sum of the squares (RSS) deviations between predicted (p) and observed (o) property changes as

$$\text{RSS} = \sum_i^m [\Delta T_p \text{ (or } \Delta\text{VHN}_p) - \Delta T_o \text{ (or } \Delta\text{VHN}_o)]_i^2 \tag{25}$$

where m is the number of data points. Note that establishing absolute minimum in the

TABLE 3—*LSF parameters.*

	A	B	D	E	F	G
			HARDNESS			
Plate	NA[a]	NA	0.10	8	30	0.25
Model	NA	NA	0.10	8	30	0.25
Weld	0.6	0.55	0.10	8	30	0.25
			SHIFT			
Weld	0.6	0.55	0.125	8	30	0.00

[a] Not available.

RSS is not possible due to covariance between some of the variables and the coarseness of the grid; further, the local search procedure does not guarantee a global minimum. However, in view of the inherent uncertainties in the data and physical and empirical constraints on the model parameters, these approximations to a unique mathematical LSF are not serious. The results are summarized in Table 3 for fits to the surveillance weld shifts and the hardness data. Similar parameters give reasonable fits to the surveillance base metal and MTR base metal and weld data; however, detailed analysis of these data subsets has not been completed.

The least squares fit results are highly consistent. The values of A equal to 0.6 and B equal to 0.55 for the weld data suggests that in going from low nickel of about 0.2 to high values of about 0.8, the copper availability increases from about 80 to about 95%. The threshold impurity content varied from a value of D of about 0.1 for the hardness data to about 0.125 for the surveillance weld shift data. The threshold fluence for the independent nickel-enhanced embrittlement term also decreased from a G of about 0.25 for the hardness data (similar to that observed for the MTR shift data) to about 0 for the surveillance weld shift data. These slight differences may reflect the variations in the ranges of and uncertainties in metallurgical variables, temperatures, fluence, and fluxes applicable to the respective data sets, or deficiencies in the model. More significant, however, is the fact that all the data can be effectively fit by the same model using nearly identical parameters. It is particularly notable that the inherent embrittlement term (E) of 8°C and nickel-enhanced embrittlement term (F) of 30 (°C/Ni) are nearly identical for all data sets and are very close to values estimated from the analysis of the MTR shift data.

References

[1] *Effect of Residual Elements on Predicted Radiation Damage to Reactor Vessel Materials*, Regulatory Guide 1.99, Rev. 1, Nuclear Regulatory Commission, Washington, DC, 1977.
[2] Varsik, J. D., "Evaluation of Irradiation Response of Reactor Pressure Vessel Materials," EPRI NP-2720 1553-1, Electric Power Research Institute, 1982.
[3] Odette, G. R. and Lombrozo, P., "Physically-Based Regression Correlations of Embrittlement Data from Reactor Pressure Vessel Surveillance Programs," EPRI NP-2720 1553-1, Electric Power Research Institute, 1982.
[4] Heller, A. S. and Lowe, A. L., "Correlations for Predicting the Effects of Neutron Radiation on Linde 805 Submerged Arc Welds," BAW-1803, Babcock and Wilcox Co., 1984.
[5] Guthrie, G. L., "Charpy Trend Curves Based on 177 PWR Data Points," *LWR Pressure Vessel Surveillance Dosimetry Improvement Program Quarterly Progress Report*, April-June 1983, W. N. Lippincott and W. N. McElroy, Eds., NUEG/CR-3391-2, HEDL-83-22, Nuclear Regulatory Commission, Washington, DC, 1984.
[6] Odette, G. R., unpublished research.

[7] Stahlkopf, K. A., Odette, G. R., and Marston, T. U., "Radiation Damage Saturation in Pressure Vessel Steels: Data and a Preliminary Model," *Proceedings*, Fourth International Conference on Pressure Vessel Technology, Institute of Mechanics, London, 1980, p. 265.

[8] Hawthorne, J. R., Menke, B. H., and Hiser, A. L., "Light Water Reactor Pressure Vessel Dosimetry Program, Post-Irradiation Notch Ductiliity and Tensile Strength Determinations for the PSF Simulated Pressure Vessel Through-Wall Specimen Capsules," NUREG/CR-3457, Nuclear Regulatory Commission, Washington, DC, 1984.

[9] Hawthorne, J. R., *Nuclear Engineering and Design*, Vol. 17, 1971, p. 116.

[10] Davies, L. M., Ingham, T., and Squires, R. L. in *Effects of Radiation on Materials, ASTM STP 782*, H. Brager and J. Perrin, Eds., American Society for Testing and Materials, Philadelphia, 1982, p. 433.

[11] Hawthorne, J. R., *Radiation Effects Information Generated on the ASTM Reference Correlation Monitor Steels, ASTM DS-54*, American Society for Testing and Materials, Philadelphia, 1971.

[12] Stelzman, W. J. and Berggren, R. G., "Radiation Strengthening and Embrittlement in Heavy-Section Plates and Welds, ORNL-4871, Oak Ridge National Laboratory, 1973.

[13] Steele, L. E., Davies, L. M., Ingham, T., and Brumovsky, M. in *Effects of Radiation on Materials, ASTM STP 870*, F. Garner and J. Perrin, Eds., American Society for Testing and Materials, 1986, pp. 863–894.

[14] Anderson, S. L., DeFlitch, C., Jouris, G. M., Lott, R. G., Mager, T. R., Mancuso, J. F., Meyer, T. A., Rishel, R. D., Schlonski, J. S., Shogan, R. P., Spitznagel, J. A., and Yanichko, S. E., "Feasibility of and Methodology for Thermal Annealing an Embrittled Reactor Vessel," Vol. 2, EPRI NP-2712, Electric Power Research Institute, 1982.

[15] Hawthorne, J. R., Menke, B. H., Loss, F. J., Watson, H. E., Hisler, A. L., and Gray, R. A., "Evaluation and Prediction of Neutron Embrittlement in Reactor Pressure Vessel Materials," EPRI NP-2782, Electric Research Institute, 1982.

[16] Odette, G. R., "Blind Predictions of the PSF Blind Test Results," to be published in HEDL/NUREG Report.

[17] Guionnet, C., Houssin, B., Brasseur, D., Lefort, A., Gros, D., and Perdreau, C. in *Effects of Radiation on Materials, ASTM STP 782*, H. Brager and J. Perrin, Eds., American Society for Testing and Materials, Philadelphia, 1982, p. 412.

[18] Pachur, D. and Sievers, G., *Irradiation Program for Pressure Vessel Steels*, KFA Jülich, April, 1974.

[19] Leitz, C., Gerscha, A., Hofmann, G., and Stobel, H. J. in *Effects of Radiation on Materials, ASTM STP 782*, H. Brager and J. Perrin, Eds., American Society for Testing and Materials, Philadelphia 1982, p. 412.

[20] Hawthorne, J. R. and Watson, H. E. in *Properties of Reactor Structural Alloys After Neutron or Particle Irradiation, ASTM STP 570*, C. J. Baroch and F. R. Shober, Eds., American Society for Testing and Materials, Philadelphia, 1975, p. 54.

[21] Hawthorne, J. R., *Nuclear Technology*, Vol. 59, 1982, p. 440.

[22] Hawthorne, J. R., "Evaluation of Reembrittlement Rate Following Annealing and Research Investigations on RPV Steels," *Proceedings*, NRC Water Reactor Safety Meeting, Nuclear Regulatory Commission, Washington, DC, Oct. 1983.

[23] Odette, G. R., *Scripta Metallurgica*, Vol. 17, 1983, p. 1183.

[24] Lucas, G. E., Odette, G. R., Lombrozo, P. M., and Sheckherd, J. W., *Effects of Radiation on Materials, ASTM STP 870*, F. Garner and J. Perrin, Eds., American Society for Testing and Materials, Philadelphia, 1985, pp. 900–930.

[25] Odette, G. R. and Sheeks, C. K. in *Phase Stability During Irradiation*, J. R. Holland, L. K. Mansur, and D. I. Potter, Eds., Metallurgical Society of the American Institute of Mining, Metallurgical and Petroleum Engineers, 1982, p. 415.

[26] Smidt, F. A. and Sprague, J. A. in *Effects of Radiation on the Substructure and Mechanical Properties of Metals and Alloys, ASTM STP 529*, J. Moteff, Ed., American Society for Testing and Materials, Philadelphia 1973, p. 78.

[27] Brenner, S. S., Wagner, R., and Spitznagel, J. A., *Metallurgical Transactions*, Vol. 9A, 1978, p. 1761.

[28] Little, E. A., in *Effects of Radiation on Materials, ASTM STP 870*, F. Garner and J. Perrin, Eds., American Society for Testing and Materials, Philadelphia, 1980, pp. 1009–1026.

[29] Miller, M. K. and Brenner, S. S., *Res Mechanical*, 1984, p. 161.

[30] Fisher, S. F., Harbottle, J. E., and Aldridge, U. B., "Microstructures Related to Irradiation

Hardening in Pressure Vessel Steels," *Proceedings*, Conference on Dimensional Stability and Mechanical Behavior of Irradiated Metals and Alloys, British Nuclear Energy Society, Brighton, UK, 1983.

[31] Jones, R. B. and Buswell, J. T., "Preliminary Results of an Investigation of the Structure of Pressure Vessel Steels by Small-Angle Neutron Scattering," see Ref 30.

[32] Frisius, F., Kampmann, R., Beaven, P. A., and Wagner, R., "Influence of Copper on the Defect Structure and Radiation Strengthening of Iron," see Ref 30.

[33] English, C. A., "Microanalytical Studies of Pressure Vessel Steels," in this volume.

[34] Wagner, R., Frisius, F., Kampmann, R., and Beaven, P. A., "Defect Microstructure and Irradiation Strengthening in Fe/Cu Alloys and Cu-Bearing Pressure Vessel Steels," *Proceedings*, Fifth ASTM-Euratom Symposium on Reactor Dosimetry, FKSS Geesthacht, West Germany, 24–28 Sept. 1984.

[35] Goodman, S. R., Brenner, S. S., and Low, J. R., *Metallurgical Transactions*, Vol. 4, 1972, p. 2363.

[36] Youle, A. and Ralph, B., *Metal Science Journal*, Vol. 6, 1972, p. 149.

[37] Russell, K. C. and Brown, L. M., *Acta Metallurgica*, Vol. 20, 1972, p. 969.

[38] Hornbogen, E. and Staniek, G., *Journal of Materials Science*, Vol. 9, 1974, p. 879.

[39] Hornbogen, E. and Glenn, R. C. in *Transactions, AIME 218*, American Institute of Mining, Metallurgical and Petroleum Engineers, 1960, p. 1064.

[40] Odette, G. R., Lombrozo, P. M., and Wullaert, R. A. in *Effects of Radiation on Materials, ASTM STP 870*, F. Garner and J. Perrin, Eds., American Society for Testing and Materials, Philadelphia, 1985, pp. 840–860.

[41] Mancuso, J. F., Spitznagel, J. A., Shogan, R. P., and Holland, J. R. in *Effects of Radiation on Materials, ASTM STP 725*, J. Sprague and D. Kramer, Eds., American Society for Testing and Materials, Philadelphia, 1981, p. 38.

[42] Davies, L. M., et al, *Analysis of the Behavior of Advanced Reactor Pressure Vessel Steels Under Neutron Irradiation*, UK Atomic Energy Authority, 1983.

[43] Weertman, J. R. in *Nondestructive Evaluation: Microstructural Characterization and Reliability Strategies*, O. Burke and S. Wolfe, Eds., Metallurgical Society of the American Institue of Mining, Metallurgical and Petroleum Engineers, 1980, p. 147.

[44] Kostorz, G., *Treatise on Materials Science and Technology-15*, Academic Press, 1979, p. 227.

Randy G. Lott,[1] *Thomas R. Mager,*[2] *Regis P. Shogan,*[1] *and Stephen E. Yanichko*[2]

Annealing and Reirradiation Response of Irradiated Pressure Vessel Steels

REFERENCE: Lott, R. G., Mager, T. R., Shogan, R. P., and Yanichko, S. E., "**Annealing and Reirradiation Response of Irradiated Pressure Vessel Steels,**" *Radiation Embrittlement of Nuclear Reactor Pressure Vessel Steels: An International Review (Second Volume), ASTM STP 909,* L. E. Steele, Ed., American Society for Testing and Materials, Philadelphia, 1986, pp. 242–259.

ABSTRACT: This paper summarizes the results of a series of tests on irradiated, annealed, and reirradiated welds performed to provide a data base for annealing a reactor pressure vessel. Specimens from three test welds were irradiated to neutron fluences of 8×10^{18} n/cm^2 and 1.5×10^{19} n/cm^2 ($E > 1$ MeV) with most of the high-fluence specimens receiving an intermediate anneal. Anneals were performed at temperatures ranging from 340 to 454°C with the primary emphasis placed on one-week anneals. Partial recovery of the yield stress, Charpy transition temperature, Charpy upper-shelf energy, and upper-shelf fracture toughness (J_{Ic}) was noted after annealing at all temperatures. The least recovery was observed in the upper-shelf fracture toughness. In sharp contrast, the Charpy upper shelf was fully recovered after the 454°C, one-week anneals.

The increases in the yield stress and the Charpy transition temperature during the second cycle of irradiation were significantly smaller than the increases in the first cycle. The increase in these properties during the second cycle was only marginally larger than the increase in the irradiated but not annealed materials. These results indicate that the beneficial effects of annealing on the Charpy transition temperature are maintained during reirradiation.

A model of irradiation embrittlement and annealing based on copper precipitate coarsening is described. It has been previously demonstrated that a primary cause of embrittlement in these steels is the formation of small copper precipitates. The coarsening of the precipitate structure during annealing would produce a stable structure, which would cause a recovery of mechanical properties and not be subject to large embrittlement rate on reirradiation.

KEY WORDS: radiation effects, pressure vessel steels, annealing, embrittlement, Charpy V, tension tests, yield stress, fracture toughness, J_{Ic}, welds, aging, irradiation

The radiation-induced loss of toughness in pressure vessel steels may be recovered by post-irradiation annealing. The annealing of an irradiated pressure vessel has been suggested by the U.S. Nuclear Regulatory Commission (NRC)

[1] Senior engineer and supervisor of Nuclear Services, respectively, Westinghouse R & D Center, Pittsburgh, PA 15235.
[2] Consultant engineer and senior engineer, respectively, Westinghouse Water Reactors Division, Monroeville, PA 15230.

as a means of recovering upper-shelf fracture toughness if an adequate safety margin cannot be demonstrated. Annealing may also be considered as a means of recovering the ductile-to-brittle transition temperature for pressure vessels that do not satisfy the requirements for pressurized-thermal-shock analysis. Westinghouse has undertaken a project, with Electric Power Research Institute (EPRI) sponsorship, to study the feasibility of annealing an irradiated pressure vessel [1]. To evaluate the practicality of an anneal, both the annealing response and the reirradiation response of the steel must be determined. Therefore, an important aspect of the Westinghouse study has been a large irradiation program to determine the properties of irradiated, annealed, and reirradiated steels. Charpy V-notch, tension and J_{Ic} fracture toughness tests were performed to determine the materials' response. This work provides a basis for determining the annealing requirements and selecting an annealing method.

Due to the difficulty in performing irradiation and annealing experiments, it is unlikely that a data base large enough to cover all of the possible combinations of material chemistry and irradiation conditions will ever be available to the utility considering annealing a pressure vessel. Therefore, extrapolation from the existing data base will be necessary. The ability to extrapolate from a data base is largely dependent on the understanding of the process being considered. If the mechanisms of irradiation embrittlement are understood, it may be possible to develop models of the irradiation and annealing response of the material. This model could then be used to improve the extrapolation technique and increase the confidence in the extrapolation. Such a model could also be used to evaluate apparent trends in the data.

Materials and Procedures

The limiting material in most reactor vessels is the weld metal in the reactor beltline region. Therefore, three test welds prepared by Combustion Engineering for EPRI were selected for use in this study. The chemistry and properties of these welds are summarized in Table 1. These welds were all fabricated using the same A533 Grade B Class 1 plate material and manganese-molybdenum-nickel weld wire. The copper contents of the welds were varied by doping with

TABLE 1—*Summary of chemistry and unirradiated properties of weld materials.*

	EP-19	EP-23	EP-24
Weld flux	Linde 80	Linde 80	Linde 0091
Charpy transition temperature	−16°C	−21°C	−69°C
Charpy upper shelf	83 J	91 J	180 J
Ni, % by weight	0.59	0.59	0.59
Cu, % by weight	0.40	0.23	0.35
Mn, % by weight	1.36	1.40	1.30
S, % by weight	0.013	0.013	0.010
Si, % by weight	0.50	0.50	0.17

a separate copper filler wire. Two of the welds (designated EP-19 and EP-23) were prepared with Linde 80 flux. These Linde 80 welds contained approximately 0.5% by weight silicon and had unirradiated Charpy upper shelves in the range of 80 to 95 J. The third weld was prepared with Linde 0091 flux with a correspondingly low silicon content of 0.17% by weight. The Charpy upper-shelf energy for the third weld was 180 J.

The specimen irradiations were conducted in the University of Virginia Research Reactor. Specimens were irradiated in sets of 27 Charpy V-notch specimens, nine ½T-CT (compact tension) fracture toughness specimens, and three tension specimens. The specimens in a given set were evenly divided between the three materials. Each set was loaded into an irradiation canister with separate dosimetry and thermocouples. The neutron irradiation was divided into two cycles. Each cycle lasting three months and producing a neutron fluence of 8×10^{18} n/cm^2. The irradiation capsules were mounted externally to the core and rotated in mid-cycle to balance the flux distribution in the capsule. Internal heaters were used to maintain an irradiation temperature of 288°C ($\pm$17°C) and to perform intermediate anneals. After the first cycle of irradiation, half of the specimens were removed and returned to the Westinghouse R & D Center for annealing and testing. Most of the remaining sets were annealed using the internal specimen heaters prior to the second cycle of irradiation. The primary emphasis was on anneals one week (168 h) in duration at temperatures ranging from 350 to 450°C. The annealing temperatures were maintained to within $\pm$3°C. Due to the large set-up times and costs associated with annealing a reactor pressure vessel, shorter annealing times did not seem to offer any significant advantage. A limited number of shorter-time anneals were also performed but will not be discussed here [1].

Charpy V-notch, tension, and J_{Ic} fracture toughness tests were used to evaluate the irradiated and annealed materials. All of the tests were conducted according to pertinent ASTM standards. The test procedure used for these tests were identical to the procedures for testing surveillance capsule specimens. The tension specimens were slightly smaller than the typical surveillance specimen, with a 20-mm gage length and a 6.35-mm diameter. Most of the J-integral measurements exceeded the measurement limits outlined in ASTM Test Method for J_{Ic}, a Measure of Fracture Toughness (E 813-81) [2]. However, the toughness levels measured appear to give reasonable indications of the material toughness and to serve the requirements of a research program.

Annealing Results

The evaluation of the annealing results require that the radiation response of the material be determined to provide a base line for comparison. The welds used in this program contained moderate to high levels of copper and nickel. Therefore, significant amounts of embrittlement were expected for all three materials. The measured embrittlement levels were generally consistent with the results from similar materials from reactor vessel surveillance programs. Predic-

tions based on surveillance data correlations match the shift in Charpy transition temperature closely. The second cycle of irradiation produced a slightly higher state of embrittlement than the correlation indicated. The higher rate of damage production in these test reactor irradiations may have contributed to the higher levels of embrittlement. The significance of these observations will be discussed in a following section.

For the purposes of this discussion, annealing recovery is measured as a percentage of the irradiation-induced property change. Using this definition, 100% recovery in any property implies a return to the unirradiated value. This definition allows a quick comparison between materials and properties. Figure 1 summarizes the response of these welds to one-week anneals at 454 and 371°C. This figure compares the recovery of the Charpy upper-shelf energy, Charpy 41-J transition temperature, yield stress, J_{Ic} fracture toughness, and tearing modulus (T) for all three materials. The values of J_{Ic} and T plotted in Fig. 1 are average values based on repeated measurements on the upper shelf. In the vast majority of the cases, the Charpy upper shelf exhibited the largest recovery. In the 454°C anneals, the Charpy upper shelf exceeded the unirradiated value in all three materials. Significantly less recovery was seen in the Charpy transition temperature at 454°C, which exhibited between 78 and 98% recovery. The relationships between annealing temperature recovery for the 41-J transition temperature and the Charpy upper shelf are illustrated in Figs. 2a and b. Similar trends in recovery were seen in all three materials. Weld EP-24, which was fabricated with the

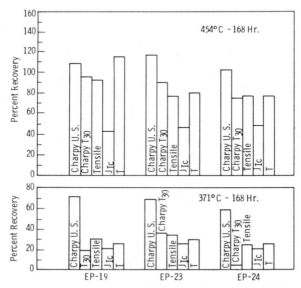

FIG. 1—*Comparison of annealing recovery of Charpy, tensile, and upper-shelf fracture toughness properties for Welds EP-19, EP-23, and EP-24.*

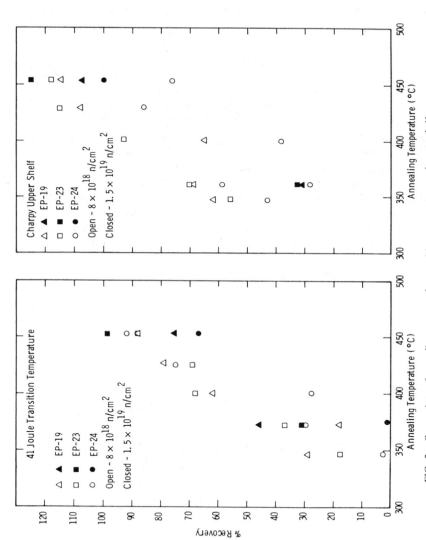

FIG. 2—*Comparison of annealing recovery for transition temperature and upper-shelf energy.*

Linde 0091 weld flux and had the highest initial Charpy shelf and the lowest initial transition temperature, seems to fall on the low sides of the trend bands in both Figs. 2a and b. The amount of recovery observed on annealing after two cycles of irradiation (1.5×10^{19} n/cm^2) appears to be the same as the recovery on annealing after one cycle (8×10^{18} n/cm^2). A comparison of Figs. 2a and b clearly illustrates that recovery in the Charpy upper shelf was larger than the recovery in the 41-J transition for all annealing temperatures. The tensile properties seemed to correlate well with the Charpy transition temperature in the 454°C anneals. This correlation was more obvious in the 454°C anneals than in the 371°C anneals, due the effects of uncertainty on the relatively small amount of recovery seen at the lower temperature.

The loss of upper-shelf fracture toughness is one of the primary reasons for considering a post-irradiation anneal. However, the property that exhibited the least recovery in post-irradiation annealing was the upper-shelf fracture toughness as measured by J_{Ic}. The resistance to tearing as indicated by the tearing modulus, T, recovered in a manner consistent with the behavior of Charpy transition temperature and yield stress. The evaluation of upper-shelf toughness for reactor vessels, as described in NRC document NUREG 0744 [3], is based on the materials' R-curve and is therefore sensitive to both J_{Ic} and T. One interesting aspect of the annealing results was the lack of correspondence between the Charpy upper-shelf energy, which was the property most easily recovered, and J_{Ic}, which was the property least easily recovered. This lack of correspondence makes it extremely difficult to base any evaluation of upper-shelf fracture toughness on a simple correlation with Charpy upper-shelf energy. Figure 3 presents a comparison of the radiation response of both J_{Ic} and Charpy upper-shelf energy. There did appear to be a general correspondence between the radiation response of these properties. However, the variability inherent in the J_{Ic} measurements made the interpretation of these results difficult. In particular, the decreases in J_{Ic} for welds EP-19 and EP-23 were relatively small.

Reirradiation Results

The re-embrittlement rate is an important factor in determining the practicality of annealing a reactor vessel. The beneficial effects of annealing must be maintained long enough to produce a reasonable extension of vessel life. The kinetics of embrittlement also provide an important insight into the physical processes causing embrittlement. The re-embrittlement rates in this study were measured using Charpy V-notch and tension tests. No J_{Ic} tests were performed on the irradiated, annealed, and reirradiated specimens. All of the sample sets for the reirradiation study were annealed between the first and second irradiation cycles for one week (168 h) in the University of Virginia Research Reactor.

The results of the yield stress determinations are presented in Fig. 4. The annealing recovery was approximately 50% at 427°C and 75% at 454°C. During the second cycle of irradiation, the increase in yield stress was similar for both

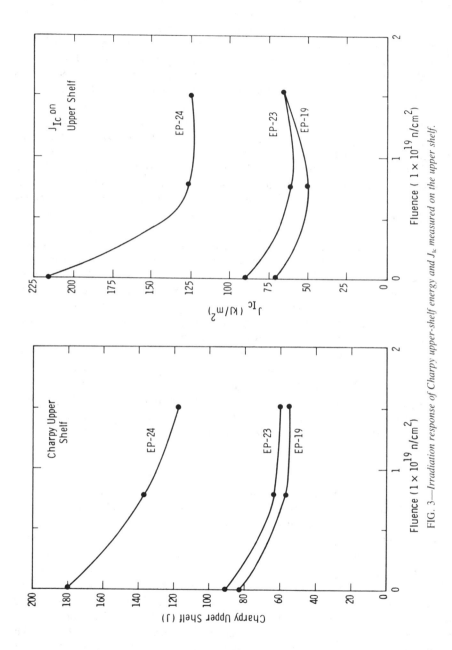

FIG. 3—*Irradiation response of Charpy upper-shelf energy and J_{Ic} measured on the upper shelf.*

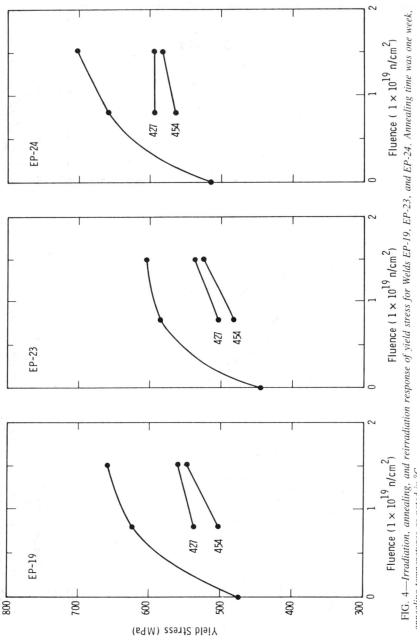

FIG. 4—*Irradiation, annealing, and reirradiation response of yield stress for Welds EP-19, EP-23, and EP-24. Annealing time was one week, annealing temperatures as noted in °C.*

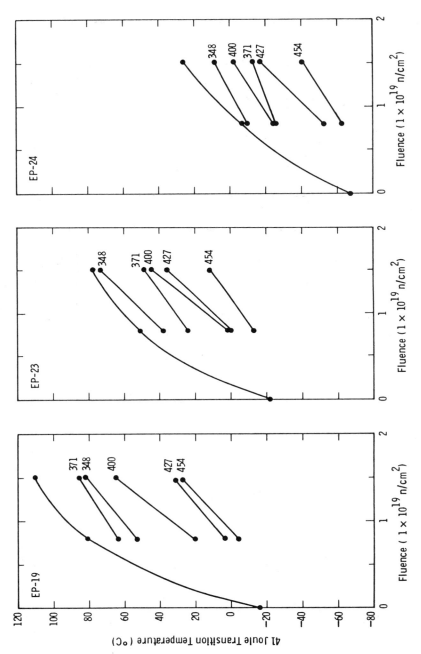

FIG. 5—*Irradiation, annealing, and reirradiation response of Charpy transition temperature for Welds EP-19, EP-23, and EP-24. Annealing time was one week, annealing temperatures as noted in °C.*

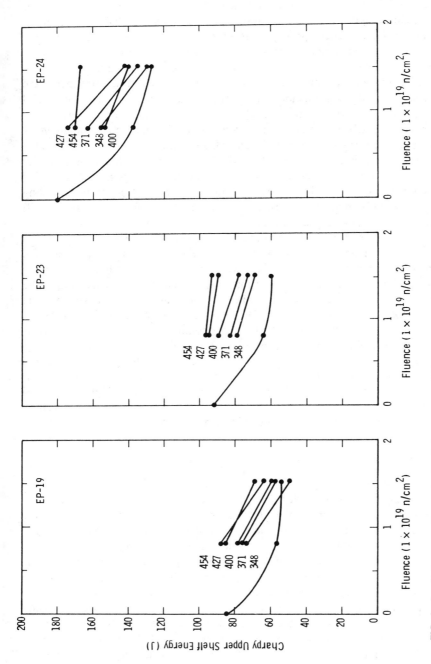

FIG. 6—Irradiation, annealing, and reirradiation response of Charpy upper-shelf energy for Welds EP-19, EP-23, and EP-24. Annealing time was one week, annealing temperatures as noted in °C.

the unirradiated and the annealed specimens. Consequently, the yield stress after the second cycle of irradiation was lower than the pre-anneal value for all of the 427 and 454°C annealed specimens. If the post-anneal rate of increase in yield stress had been comparable to the original rate, the yield stress after both of these annealing treatments would have exceeded the pre-anneal value.

The Charpy V-notch transition temperature behaved in a similar manner to the yield stress during reirradiation. The reirradiation results for the Charpy 41-J transition temperature are summarized in Fig. 5. Intermediate anneals were conducted at temperatures ranging from 348 to 454°C. The rate of embrittlement as measured by Charpy transition in the annealed specimens was comparable to the rate in the unannealed specimens. Only the lowest annealing temperatures, with the least recovery, underwent enough re-embrittlement to surpass the unannealed transition temperature. The decrease in transition temperature from annealing was permanently maintained during reirradiation. This effect appears as a shift vertically downwards in the reirradiation curves shown in Fig. 5.

The Charpy upper-shelf energy did not show the consistently lower embrittlement rates after annealing observed in the yield stress and Charpy transition behavior. As noted previously, the Charpy upper shelf exhibited the largest recovery upon annealing. However, the drop in Charpy upper shelf during the second cycle of irradiation for the annealed materials was also larger than the drop in the unannealed materials. This behavior is illustrated in Fig. 6. Welds EP-19 and EP-24 both re-embrittled at rates comparable to the original embrittlement rate in the unirradiated material. Weld EP-23, which had the lowest copper content, apparently re-embrittled at a lower rate. Although the exact nature of the mechanism controlling the Charpy upper-shelf drop is not well understood, both the annealing results and the reirradiation results demonstrated that there are significant differences between that mechanism and the mechanism controlling the yield stress increase and the transition temperature increase.

Annealing Model

The objective of this research was to develop a model of annealing and re-embrittlement consistent with the experimental data. This model was intended to provide a description of the physical processes rather than a quantitative analysis of the data. Descriptive models can play an important role in substantiating experimental observations and focusing future research.

The primary component of damage in irradiated pressure vessel steels is a fine distribution of copper precipitates. Copper forms a supersaturated solid solution in the unirradiated steels. Precipitation is inhibited by the low mobility of copper at temperatures near the irradiation temperature. Radiation-enhanced diffusion leads to the formation of precipitates in the irradiated steel [4]. Surveillance capsule data from a number of different welds has been used previously to develop a model of irradiation embrittlement [5]. This model describes the irradiation-induced increase in yield stress, $\Delta_i\sigma_y$, using a copper precipitation hardening

model [6]. Small additional terms were required to account for nickel-dependent and chemistry-independent contributions. With these assumptions, the yield stress increase was derived as

$$\Delta_i\sigma_y = (A\,f_{Cu}^{1/2} + B\,f_{Ni} - C)(1 - e^{-a\phi t})$$

where

$$
\begin{aligned}
f_{Cu} &= \text{atomic fraction of copper,}\\
f_{Ni} &= \text{atomic fraction of nickel,}\\
\phi t &= \text{neutron fluence,}\\
A, B, C, a &= \text{fitting constants,}\\
A &= 2625\ \text{MPa,}\\
B &= 94.5\ \text{MPa,}\\
C &= -9\ \text{MPa, and}\\
a &= 3.5 \times 10^{-19}\ (\text{n/cm}^2)^{-1}.
\end{aligned}
$$

Using a critical fracture stress model, it was then shown that the irradiation-induced increase in transition temperature, Δ_iT is

$$\Delta_iT = T_o/\sigma_{yo}\,(\Delta_i\sigma_y + g(f_{Ni},\ \phi t))$$

where $g(f_{Ni},\ \phi t)$ is an additional term required to account for the nickel contribution to the Charpy transition temperature shift. The additional term was determined to be

$$g(f_{Ni},\ \phi t) = 4400\,f_{Ni}(\phi t)^{2/3} - 14$$

by fitting high nickel data. This model gives a good fit to surveillance capsule welds.

Two possible mechanisms for annealing were considered, dissolution of copper precipitates and over-aging by an Ostwald ripening process. Based on extrapolations from high-temperature data, the copper concentrations in these steels appear to be well in excess of the solubility limits in the temperature range 300 to 450°C [7]. Therefore, dissolution appeared to be the least likely mechanism. The modeling efforts concentrated on the Ostwald ripening process [8]. In Ostwald ripening, the larger precipitates grow at the expense of the smaller ones. The average particle size increases in a manner such that

$$r_a^3 - r_i^3 = K\,t_a$$

where r_i is the average particle radius after irradiation and r_a is the average particle size after annealing for time, t_a. The proportionality constant, K, is

$$K = (8\,\gamma\,D\,\omega\,C_o)/(9\,kT)$$

where

γ = interface energy of precipitate,
D = diffusion coefficient for copper in steel,
ω = atomic volume of precipitate,
C_o = concentration of copper *in solution*,
T = annealing temperature, and
k = Boltzman's constant.

From the dispersion hardening model, it can be shown that for a given volume fraction of precipitates and for reasonably large precipitate sizes, the increment in yield stress is inversely proportional to the precipitate radius, that is

$$\Delta\sigma_y = G/r$$

where, based on observations in irradiated steels

$$G = 10^{-4} f_{\text{Cu}}^{1/2} \text{ MPa cm}$$

The residual yield strength increment after annealing can then be derived from the foregoing relationships

$$\Delta_a\sigma_y = \Delta_i\sigma_y/(K\ t_a\ \Delta_i\sigma_y^3/G^3 + 1)^{1/3}$$
$$= \sigma_{y_a} - \sigma_{y_o}$$

The critical fracture stress model can then be used to predict the residual increase in transition temperature

$$\Delta T_a = T_o/\sigma_{y_o} (\Delta_a\sigma_y + g(f_{\text{Ni}},\ \phi t))$$

To calculate the reirradiation response of the welds, the following assumptions were made:

1. Copper that has already precipitated cannot cause further embrittlement.
2. Additional hardening during reirradiation is caused by the precipitation of previously unprecipitated copper and the continuation of the nickel mechanism.

The first assumption was based on the observation that the Ostwald ripening process is nonreversible. The net effect of these assumptions was to force the re-embrittlement rate to be equal to the original embrittlement rate at the point of the anneal regardless of the amount of annealing recovery. The total increment in yield stress was then determined from the following logical construction

$$\Delta_r\sigma_y = \Delta_{ri}\sigma_y - (\Delta_i\sigma_y - \Delta_a\sigma_y)$$

where

$\Delta_n\sigma_y$ = yield stress increment predicted with no intermediate anneal,
$\Delta_i\sigma_y$ = yield stress increment prior to anneal, and
$\Delta_a\sigma_y$ = residual yield stress increment after anneal.

The transition temperature was then predicted in a manner similar to the irradiated and annealed model

$$\Delta_r T = T_o/\sigma_{y_o} (\Delta_r\sigma_y + g(f_{Ni}, \phi t))$$

The original embrittlement model predicted the increase in transition temperature from the material chemistry, the original transition temperature, and seven fitting constants. Although the annealing response of the steel is defined in terms of the physical properties of the steel, several of these properties are extremely difficult to measure and therefore the values are ill defined. Therefore, there was some arbitrariness in the value chosen for the rate constant, K. This arbitrariness in the reirradiation model was most evident in the value chosen for the diffusion coefficient. Measurements of copper diffusion in pure iron indicate that the activation energy for diffusion is approximately 3 eV/atom [7]. Copper diffusion in iron requires a vacancy mechanism. The vacancy formation energy in iron is 1.5 eV/atom, and the migration energy is 1 eV/atom [9]. The activation energy used in the annealing model for copper diffusion in the irradiated steel was 1.8 eV/atom. This value is significantly lower than the activation for copper diffusion in iron. The diffusion of copper in iron may be enhanced by the presence of impurities, and it is to be expected that the activation energy for diffusion in a steel will be lower than the activation energy for diffusion in a high-purity single crystal. Also, the irradiated steel may contain vacancies from irradiation trapped as small vacancy loops or at other lattice defects. Cold working of alpha iron to increase the dislocation density and introduce vacancies has been shown to decrease the activation energy to 1.4 eV/atom [10]. Although the values used for the physical constants in the annealing model were not based on any direct measurements, they remain within a reasonable range.

Discussion

The irradiation and annealing model was used to predict the embrittlement for the materials and irradiation conditions described in the section on materials and procedures. The predictions for the yield stress behavior and the transition temperature behavior are summarized in Figs. 7 and 8. These results closely match the data from the annealing study. The temperature where annealing recovery becomes significant was primarily determined by the temperature dependence of the diffusion coefficient. No annealing would be predicted for these materials in this temperature range without enhancement of the diffusion coefficient.

The original radiation embrittlement model underpredicted the extent of em-

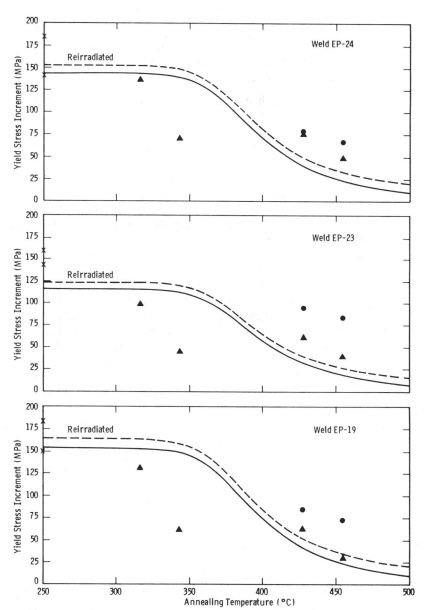

FIG. 7—*Model predictions for yield stress behavior. The annealed data is shown as triangles and the reirradiated data is shown as circles. The predictions of the irradiation and annealing model are shown as solid lines. The reirradiation prediction is shown as a dashed line. The pre-anneal values are noted with "x's" on the left axis of the plots.*

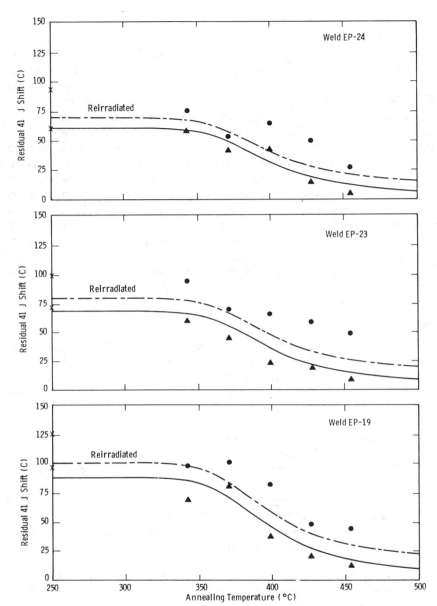

FIG. 8—*Model predictions for Charpy transition temperature behavior. The annealed data is shown as triangles and the reirradiated data is shown as circles. The predictions of the irradiation and annealing model are shown as solid lines. The reirradiation prediction is shown as a dashed line. The pre-anneal values are noted with "x's" on the left axis of the plots.*

brittlement in the second cycle of irradiation for all three welds. This model was developed for surveillance capsule test data where the neutron flux was significantly lower than the test reactor neutron flux used in the annealing study irradiations. Although the test reactor-irradiated specimens generally behave in a manner similar to the surveillance capsule materials, it is possible that the difference in damage rate may have given the higher embrittlement rate [11]. The underestimation of the damage rate in the second cycle of irradiation was also evident in the materials that were annealed and reirradiated. Although the incremental embrittlement in the second cycle was similar in both the unannealed and the annealed specimens, the model underpredicted the extent of re-embrittlement in the annealed specimens due to the higher than expected embrittlement rate for the second cycle. No changes were made in the embrittlement model because it was believed to properly reflect surveillance capsule data. The basic assumption of the model was that the copper precipitates that coarsened on annealing would cause no further embrittlement during the second cycle of irradiation. This assumption is justified by the observation that the incremental embrittlement in the second cycle of irradiation was independent of the annealing condition.

Summary

An irradiation embrittlement and annealing study, which included Charpy V-notch, tension and J-integral fracture toughness tests has been described. A unified model of irradiation embrittlement and annealing based on previous experience with surveillance capsule data and the results of this annealing study was presented. The important implications of this work include:

1. Annealing in the temperature range 350 to 450°C produced recovery of irradiation embrittlement.
2. The post-annealing embrittlement rate was equivalent to the second cycle embrittlement rate in the unannealed material.
3. Charpy upper-shelf energy and Charpy transition temperature show different responses to both annealing and reirradiation.
4. The Charpy upper-shelf energy exhibited more recovery during post irradiation annealing than the upper-shelf fracture toughness as measured by J_{Ic}.
5. A copper precipitate coarsening model that predicts annealing of the yield stress and of the Charpy transition temperature in the temperature range 350 to 450°C has been presented.
6. This annealing model explains the low re-embrittlement rates in the annealed materials.
7. If the physical basis for this model can be confirmed, it should be possible to relax the surveillance requirements for an annealed pressure vessel.

Acknowledgments

This work was sponsored by the Electric Power Research Institute under Contract RP 1021-1, T. U. Marston, project manager.

References

[1] Mager, T. R., et al, "Feasibility of and Methodology for Annealing an Embrittled Reactor Vessel," Technical Report NP-2712, Electric Power Research Institute, 1982.

[2] ASTM Test for J_{Ic}, a Measure of Fracture Toughness, (E-813-81) *Annual Book of ASTM Standards*, 1984.

[3] Johnson, R. E., et al, "Resolution of the Reactor Vessel Materials Toughness Saftey Issue; Task Action Plan A-11," NUREG-0744, U.S. Nuclear Regulatory Commission, Washington DC, Sept. 1981.

[4] Odette, G. R., *Scripta Metallurgica*, Vol. 17, 1983, pp. 1183–1184.

[5] Lott, R. G., in *Proceedings*, Topical Conference on Ferritic Alloys for use in Nuclear Energy Technologies, J. W. Davis and D. J. Michel, Eds., TMS-AIME, American Institute of Mining, Metallurgical, and Petroleum Engineers, 1983, pp. 37–44.

[6] Russell, K. C. and Brown, L. M., *Acta Metallurgica*, Vol. 20, 1972, pp. 969–974.

[7] Salje, G. and Feller-Kniepmeier, M., *Journal of Applied Physics*, Vol. 48, 1977, pp. 1833–1839.

[8] Markworth, A. J., *Metallography*, Vol. 3, 1970, pp. 197–208.

[9] Doyama, M. and Koehler, J. S., *Acta Metallurgica*, Vol. 24, 1976, pp. 871–879.

[10] Soeno, K., in *Transactions*, Japan Institute of Metals, Vol. 11, 1970, pp. 185–189.

[11] Lucas, G. E., Odette, G. R., Lombrozo, P. M., and Sheckherd, J. W., in *Effects of Radiation on Materials. Twelfth International Symposium, ASTM 870*, F. A. Garner and J. S. Perrin, Eds., American Society for Testing and Materials, Philadelphia, 1985, pp. 900–930.

Miroslav Vacek[1]

Effect of Various Metallurgical Microstructures on the Response of the Nickel-Molybdenum-Chromium BH 70 Steel to Neutron Irradiation at 285°C

REFERENCE: Vacek, M., "**Effect of Various Metallurgical Microstructures on the Response of the Nickel-Molybdenum-Chromium BH 70 Steel to Neutron Irradiation at 285°C,**" *Radiation Embrittlement of Nuclear Reactor Pressure Vessel Steels: An International Review (Second Volume), ASTM STP 909,* L. E. Steele, Ed., American Society for Testing and Materials, Philadelphia, 1986, pp. 260–278.

ABSTRACT: Radiation hardening and embrittlement of the BH 70 steel heat treated to different microstructures (tempered martensite, tempered bainite, and tempered mixed ferrite-perlite, bainite, and martensite after neutron irradiation about 7×10^{23} n/m² > 1 MeV at 285°C) were compared with commercial heat treatment conditions. Only moderate radiation hardening, with small differences for individual conditions, was measured in all four heat treatment conditions (by 29 to 48%). Roughly the same radiation embrittlement $\Delta TT_{41J} = 137$ to 148°C was found in all heat treatment conditions used. The initial (unirradiated) and resultant (irradiated) Charpy-V 41-J transition temperature of the BH 70 steel, however, can be altered appreciably through heat treatment practices, resulting in different microstructure. Initial transition temperatures (TT_{41J}) of individual heat treatments were found in the range from -73 to -143°C.

KEY WORDS: irradiation, radiation effects, pressure vessel steels, steels, embrittlement, nuclear reactors, pressure vessels, temperature of irradiation, ductility, notch sensitivity, neutrons, alloying elements, melting, heat treating, microstructure

Several investigators have found that metallurgical microstructure can significantly affect the response of reactor pressure vessel (RPV) steels to neutron irradiation [1–5]. Such effects were observed, especially with temperature of irradiation lower than 150°C. A ferrite-perlite structure appears to produce radiation embrittlement sensitivity, while tempered bainite and particularly tempered martensite tend to coincide with relative radiation embrittlement insensitivity. Of most significance, however, are irradiation studies conducted at elevated temperature (operational temperature of the power reactor pressure vessel wall), where thermally activated processes can act.

[1] Research worker, Nuclear Research Institute, Rez, Czechoslovakia; on leave at Risø National Laboratory, Denmark.

TABLE 1—*Chemical composition of the BH 70 steel in percent by weight.*

C	Si	Mn	Cr	Mo	Ni	P	S	Ti	V	Cu	Al
0.18	0.25	0.39	0.35	0.39	3.28	0.013	0.014	0.01	0.04	0.15	0.015

This paper deals with the effect of the metallurgical microstructure on radiation hardening and embrittlement of the nickel-molybdenum-chromium BH 70 steel at 285°C. The microstructure was changed by heat treatment, otherwise, the steel was the same.

Experimental Details

Material and Heat Treatment

Potential RPV low-alloy BH 70 steel from Rheinstahl Hüttenwerke A/G Hattingen, West Germany (FRG) was selected for this program. The chemical composition of the BH 70 steel is given in Table 1. The steel was vacuum-degassed to a hydrogen content below 2 ppm [6].

The BH 70 steel plate of dimensions 1000 by 3000 by 100 mm was cut into bars 18 by 18 by 80 mm. The longitudinal axis of the bars was parallel to the rolling direction of the plate. The bars have been then given one of the heat treatments listed in Table 2 to get untempered martensite (M), tempered martensite (TM), untempered bainite (B), tempered bainite (TB), and tempered mixed microstructures of ferrite-perlite, bainite, and martensite (TP) consistently with the Cooling Transformation Diagram of the BH 70 steel. For the study, only three heat treatments according to Conditions B, D, and E (Table 2) on small bars just mentioned and commercial heat treatment (CHT) were employed. This means that all specimens were tested in tempering conditions according to Table 2.

TABLE 2—*Heat treatment of the BH 70 steel and corresponding Vickers hardness number of bars.*

Condition	Heat Treatment	Vickers[a] Hardness, VHN 30
A	920°C, 1 h, water	446
B	920°C, 1 h, water + 650°C, 10 h, water	276
C	920°C, 1 h, salt bath 450°C, 0.5 h, water	294
D	920°C, 1 h, salt bath 450°C, 0.5 h, water + 650°C, 10 h, water	254
E	920°C, 1 h, control cooling in the closed furnace to 630°C[b] + 650°C, 10 h, water	253
F	commercial heat treatment: (870 to 930) °C, water + (600 to 700) °C, 7 h, air	246

[a] Mean value minimally of 15 tests.
[b] From 920°C to 740°C in 1.5 h (120°C/h), to 710°C in 3 h (10°C/h), to 630°C in 1.5 h (53°C/h).

Corresponding microstructures for all heat-treated conditions including commercial heat treatment are presented in Figs. 1 to 6. Figures with designation (a) are from optical microscope and (b) and (c) from electron microscope (carbon extract replica).

Figures 1a, b, and c illustrate typical martensite needles. At higher magnification (Fig. 1c) a very fine dispersed acicular phase (probably Fe_2C), formed by self-tempering of martensite during quenching, was found. In Fig. 2, a largely tempered martensite structure is shown that consisted mainly of precipitated cementite and finer carbides. The former martensite needles can often be distinguished (Fig. 2b). Photomicrographs of isothermal transformation of bainite are presented in Fig. 3. In ferrite regions, finer globular particles are seen. Largely tempered bainite microstructure in Fig. 4 is evidenced by considerably spheroidized cementite particles. Finer globular particles are still seen in ferrite. Figure 5 shows the largely tempered mixed microstructure of ferrite-perlite, bainite, and martensite. Figure 6 illustrates tempered mixed microstructures of martensite, bainite, and perlite. Cementite is not fully spheroidized everywhere. Cooling rate was probably much less than in Fig. 2 because there is a big difference between the dimensions of bars and the plate of the same steel.

Considering that mechanical properties of the BH 70 100-mm-thick steel plate, do not vary much from surface to surface [6], bars from randomly different plate depths were chosen for the examination.

Specimens

Smooth and notched tension specimens according to the Figs. 7 and 8, respectively, and standard impact specimens according to the ASTM Notched Bar Impact Testing of Metallic Materials (E 23–82), Type A (V-notch) were machined from bars heat treated in accordance with Table 2 Conditions B, D, E, and F. Charpy V-notch specimens had L-T orientation according to the ASTM Test Method for Plane-Strain Fracture Toughness of Metallic Materials (E 399–83). Subsequent to fabrication and designation, all specimens were given a stress relieving anneal of 30 min at 600°C in the vacuum 1.3×10^{-4} Pa (1×10^{-6} mm Hg).

Irradiation Details

The irradiation was carried out in the middle core of the Danish Reactor DR 3, Position B 3, at Risø National Laboratory, in an electric furnace temperature controlled Standardrigs No. II and III. Standardrigs No. II and No. III contain 28 (14) tension specimens and 6 (12) Charpy-V specimens [7], respectively. Four Standardrig No. II and two No. III were used for the program. The average irradiation temperature of tension and impact specimens of each rig was 285 ± 10°C. Temperature was measured continuously by chromel-alumel thermocouples. During irradiation, the specimens were surrounded by an inert gas atmosphere.

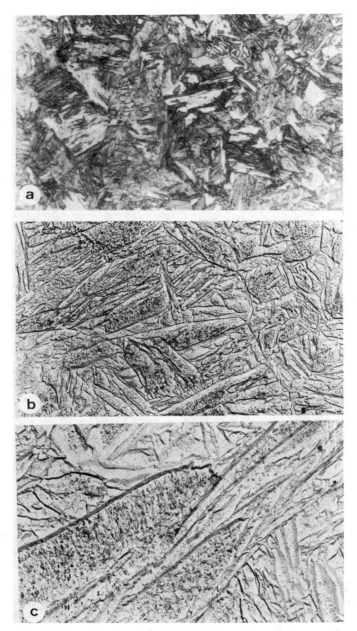

FIG. 1—*Microstructure of the Condition A heat-treated BH 70 steel (untempered martensite); original magnifications:* (a) ×1000, (b) ×3000, *and* (c) ×7500.

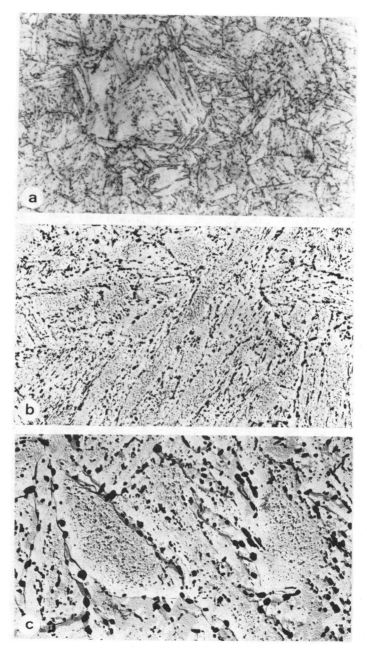

FIG. 2—*Microstructure of the Condition B heat-treated BH 70 steel (tempered martensite); original magnifications:* (a) ×1000, (b) ×3000, and (c) ×7500.

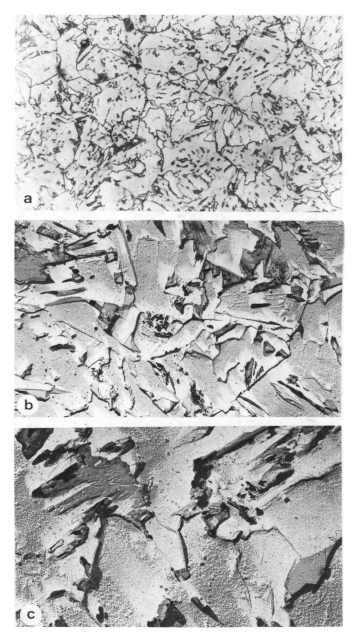

FIG. 3—*Microstructure of the Condition C heat-treated BH 70 steel (untempered bainite); original magnifications:* (a) ×1000, (b) ×3000, *and* (c) ×7500.

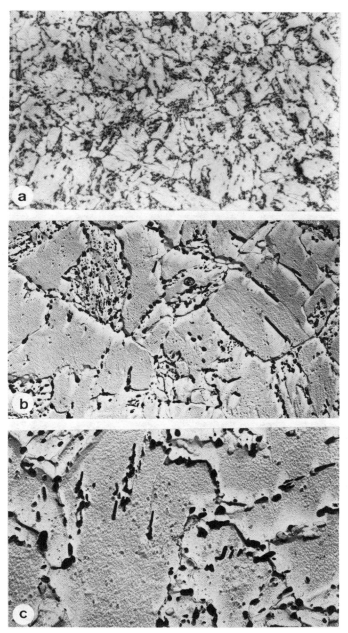

FIG. 4—*Microstructure of the Condition D heat-treated BH 70 steel (tempered bainite); original magnifications:* (a) ×1000, (b) ×3000, *and* (c) ×7500.

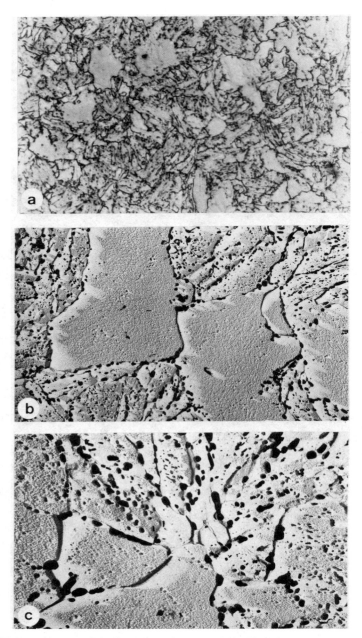

FIG. 5—*Microstructure of the Condition E heat-treated BH 70 steel (tempered mixed ferrite-perlite, bainite, and martensite); original magnifications:* (a) ×*1000,* (b) ×*3000, and* (c) ×*7500.*

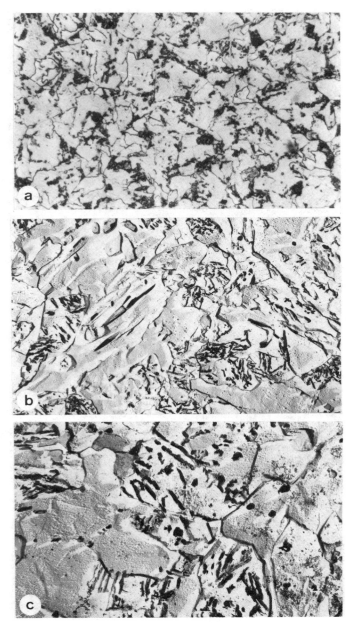

FIG. 6—*Microstructure of the Condition F commercial heat-treated BH 70 steel (tempered mixed martensite, bainite, and perlite); original magnifications:* (a) ×1000, (b) ×3000, and (c) ×7500.

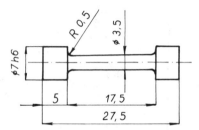

FIG. 7—*Smooth tension test specimen.*

Fast and thermal neutron fluence were measured using nickel, BH 70 steel, and cobalt monitors. The cross sections and half-lives used in calculating the results were as follows:

Monitor	Reaction	Cross Section	Half-live
Nickel	Ni^{58} (n,p) Co^{58}	107×10^{-27} cm^2	71.3 days
BH 70 steel	Fe^{54} (n,p) Mn^{54}	78×10^{-27} cm^2	312.6 days
Cobalt	Co^{59} (n,δ) Co^{60}	37.4×10^{-24} cm^2	5.27 years

Fast fluence values measured by means of nickel and BH 70 steel monitors were in reasonably good agreement. Henceforth all neutron fluences reported will be from the Fe^{54} (n,p) Mn^{54} reaction in the units above 1 MeV.

Testing Procedures

Tension tests were conducted using an Instron-type in-cell tension testing machine (100 kN) at strain rates of 2×10^{-4} s^{-1} and 2×10^{-2} s^{-1} (smooth specimens in accordance with Fig. 7) and 2.5×10^{-2} s^{-1} and 2.5 s^{-1} (notched specimens in accordance with Fig. 8).

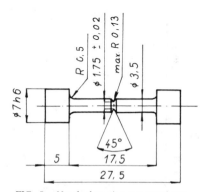

FIG. 8—*Notched tension test specimen.*

TABLE 3—Tensile properties of unirradiated and irradiated smooth and notched tension specimens of four heat treatments[a] of BH 70 steel.

Type of Specimen	Strain Rate, s^{-1}	Neutron Fluence n·m^{-2}, (E > 1 MeV) × 10^{23}	Yield Stress, MPa	Δ Yield Stress MPa	Δ Yield Stress %	Fracture Stress, MPa	Ultimate Tensile Stress, MPa	Reduction of Area or Notch Reduction of Area, %	Total Elongation, %	Uniform Elongation, %	Number of Tested Specimens	Notch Strength Ratio
CONDITION B (TM)												
S^b	2 × 10^{-4}	...	761	...	...	1738	822	73.1	18.4	7.3	3	...
S	2 × 10^{-4}	7.3	982	221	29	1732	1002	63.6	17.2	6.8	4	...
S	2 × 10^{-2}	...	775	...	...	1744	842	73.1	19.7	9.3	2	...
S	2 × 10^{-2}	7.3	1033	258	33	1775	1039	62.4	16.5	6.6	2	1.78
N^c	2.5 × 10^{-2}	...	1491	...	...	2050	1501	36.2	...	...	3	1.81
N	2.5 × 10^{-2}	7.3	1878	387	26	2261	1885	25.1	...	...	3	1.76
N	2.5	...	1497	...	...	2259	1520	35.1	...	...	2	1.74
N	2.5	7.3	1859	362	24	2305	1875	19.4	...	...	2	
CONDITION D (TB)												
S	2 × 10^{-4}	...	653	...	...	1538	743	71.3	21.0	8.2	3	...
S	2 × 10^{-4}	7.0	899	246	38	1618	938	61.3	15.8	6.2	3	...
S	2 × 10^{-2}	...	676	...	...	1526	761	70.0	21.0	10.4	2	...
S	2 × 10^{-2}	7.3	936	260	38	1594	958	60.7	15.6	5.9	2	1.81
N	2.5 × 10^{-2}	...	1365	...	...	1880	1377	37.7	...	...	4	1.92
N	2.5 × 10^{-2}	7.3	1833	468	34	2206	1841	25.5	...	...	3	

N	2.5	...	1370	...	...	2101	1394	37.9	...	...	2	1.78
N	2.5	7.0	1836	466	34	2275	1859	18.4	...	...	2	1.90
CONDITION E (TP)												
S	2×10^{-4}	...	668	...	...	1688	760	74.0	21.1	9.0	3	...
S	2×10^{-4}	7.0	944	276	41	1716	982	63.6	17.3	7.2	3	...
S	2×10^{-2}	...	681	...	...	1753	769	73.9	21.4	10.3	2	...
S	2×10^{-2}	7.0	977	296	44	1746	997	63.2	17.5	7.4	2	...
N	2.5×10^{-2}	...	1309	...	...	1851	1328	39.3	...	...	3	1.73
N	2.5×10^{-2}	7.0	1794	485	37	2211	1804	24.0	...	...	3	1.81
N	2.5	...	1316	...	...	2198	1369	40.2	...	...	2	1.76
N	2.5	7.0	1821	505	38	2540	1837	27.8	...	...	2	1.81
CONDITION F (CHT)												
S	2×10^{-4}	...	643	...	...	1504	773	65.0	17.8	8.0	3	...
S	2×10^{-4}	7.3	952	309	48	1697	1023	58.4	15.1	5.9	3	...
S	2×10^{-2}	...	655	...	...	1522	784	65.7	19.2	9.7	2	...
S	2×10^{-2}	7.3	979	324	49	1660	1037	58.7	16.1	6.5	2	...
N	2.5×10^{-2}	...	1408	...	...	1875	1426	33.8	...	...	3	1.82
N	2.5×10^{-2}	7.3	1791	417	30	2069	1836	18.1	...	...	3	1.77
N	2.5	...	1382	...	...	2087	1408	35.4	...	...	2	1.77
N	2.5	7.3	1857	475	34	2285	1869	18.0	...	...	2	1.78

[a] See Table 2.
[b] S = smooth tensile specimen.
[c] N = notched tensile specimen.

Charpy-V impact tests were performed with a Wolpert (FRG) 300-J in-cell impact tester with ISO Striker. The striking velocity at impact was 5.5 m/s.

Vickers hardness was measured only before irradiation on using a 300 N Vickers Armstrongs hardness tester.

Results and Discussion

Tension Tests

Tensile properties of the unirradiated and irradiated specimens are given in Table 3. Because of the limited number of specimens, only two to four specimens were used in obtaining the average values of the properties reported in Table 3. Tensile properties of all heat-treatment conditions are very similar. Only tempered martensite (Condition B) showed a little higher yield and ultimate strength for unirradiated and irradiated specimens than the three other heat treatments. Small differences in radiation hardening were observed for individual heat treatments. The smallest radiation hardening was found in tempered martensite (Condition B; ΔR_p 0.2 = 221 MPa; that is, increase by 29%) followed by tempered bainite (Condition D; 246 MPa; 38%), tempered ferrite-perlite (Condition E; 276 MPa; 41%), and commercial heat treatment (Condition F; 309 MPa; 48%).

The fracture stress is defined as ratio of the load of the tension specimen at fracture (an engineering load-elongation curve) and the cross-sectioned area of the specimen at fracture. The effect of neutron irradiation on the fracture stress in Table 3 is not unambiguous. It is a little different for smooth and notched tension specimens. The increase and, in fewer cases, the decrease of the fracture stress owing to neutron irradiation were observed at smooth specimens. At notched specimens, only the increase was observed. The increase was, on average, more significant at notched than at smooth specimens.

Total elongation of irradiated smooth specimens was always above 15%, uniform elongation was above 5%, and reduction of area was above 55%.

Notch sensitivity was not essentially affected by neutron irradiation. The notch strength ratio (NSR) was a little increased after irradiation, except for commercial heat treatments where a slight reduction was measured. According to McClintock [8], if the notch strength ratio is less than about 0.70, there is a strong probability that an unstable fracture would develop in service. However, our NSR values are far above the limit value.

The increased strain rate resulted in the moderate increase of yield and ultimate strength of unirradiated and irradiated specimens (Table 3).

Impact Tests

Charpy V-notch impact energy transition curves for all unirradiated and irradiated heat-treatment conditions are shown in Figs. 9 to 12. The Charpy-V 41-

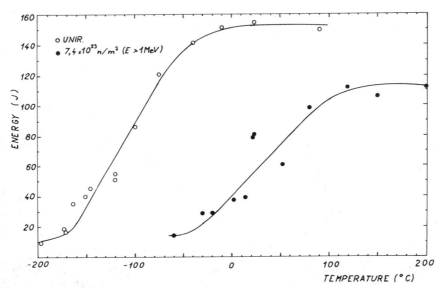

FIG. 9—*Charpy V-notch impact energy transition curves for unirradiated and irradiated BH 70 steel, heat treated according to Condition B (tempered martensite).*

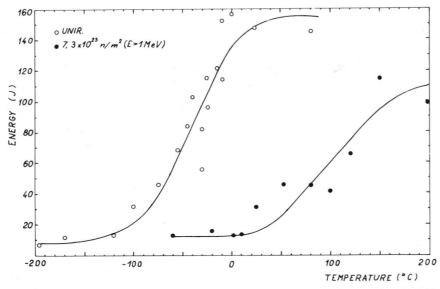

FIG. 10—*Charpy V-notch impact energy transition curves for unirradiated and irradiated BH 70 steel, heat treated according to Condition D (tempered bainite).*

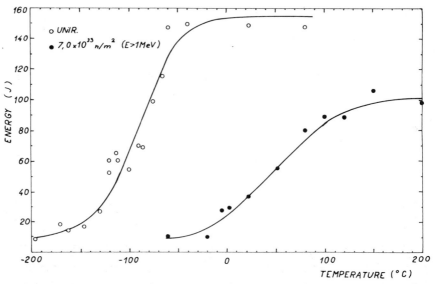

FIG. 11—*Charpy V-notch impact energy transition curves for unirradiated and irradiated BH 70 steel, heat treated according to Condition E (tempered mixed ferrite-perlite, bainite, and martensite).*

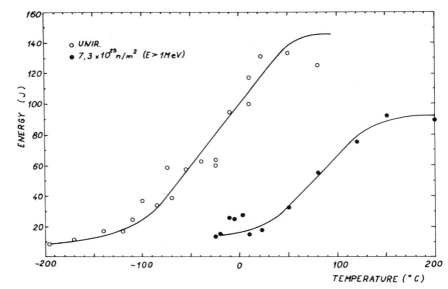

FIG. 12—*Charpy V-notch impact energy transition curves for unirradiated and irradiated commercial heat-treated BH 70 steel (tempered mixed martensite, bainite, and perlite).*

J transition temperature for unirradiated and irradiated impact specimens are summarized in the Table 4.

Evaluation of transition temperature curves was performed using fitting procedure according to Oldfield [9] to the equation

$$KV(T) = A + B \tanh \frac{T - T_o}{C} \tag{1}$$

Radiation embrittlement is roughly the same for all heat treatment conditions used ($\Delta TT_{41} = 137$ to $146°C$). However, higher differences are in the 41-J transition temperature before and after irradiation. For unirradiated specimens, the lowest initial transition temperature ($-143°C$) was found in tempered martensite (Condition B in Table 2) and in tempered mixed ferrite-perlite, bainite, and martensite ($-118°C$; Condition E); the highest one in commercial heat treatment ($-74°C$; Condition F) and tempered bainite ($-73°C$; Condition D). A similar sequence was found after irradiation (Table 4).

The 41-J transition temperature after irradiation of the tempered martensite is still lower, at least by $50°C$, than for Conditions D and F; and the same transition temperature of Condition E is still lower, roughly by $35°C$, than Conditions D and F. Heat-treatment conditions are therefore very important for initial as well as resultant transition temperature of the RPV steels. For a comparison, Fujimura and Oku [10] found in the A 533-B steel after irradiation $8.1 \times 10^{23} n/m^2 > 1$ MeV at $277°C$ the increase of 41-J transition temperature by $146°C$. This means an increase from initial 41-J transition temperature, $-6°C$, up to $+140°C$ after irradiation. The A 533-B and A 508 steels with a maximum content of 0.10% copper, (representing improved production of West Germany, Japan, France, and the United States) [11] show, however, lower increase in the 41-J transition temperature after similar neutron irradiation.

Only a moderate decrease of upper-shelf impact energy was found after irradiation of all heat treatments used (Table 4). The percentage decrease in upper-shelf energy due to irradiation was from 25 to 34%.

Conclusions

Radiation hardening and embrittlement of the BH 70 steel heat-treated to different microstructures of tempered martensite, tempered bainite, and tempered mixed ferrite-perlite, bainite, and martensite after neutron irradiation about 7×10^{23} $n/m^2 > 1$ MeV at $285°C$ were compared with a commercial heat-treated condition. This study has made it possible to draw the following conclusions:

1. Only moderate radiation hardening was measured in all four heat-treatment conditions (by 29 to 48%). The smallest hardening was found in tempered martensite (Condition B) and the highest one in commercial heat treatment (Condition F).

TABLE 4—*The Charpy-V 41-J (30 ft·lb) transition temperatures and upper-shelf energy of four heat treatments of BH 70 steel.*

Heat Treatment Condition (Table 2)	Neutron Fluence, $E > 1$ MeV (n·m^{-2})	Charpy V-Notch 41-J (30 ft·lb) Transition Temperature			Upper-Shelf Energy		ΔUpper-Shelf Energy	
		Unirradiated, °C	Irradiated, °C	ΔTT_{41}, °C	Unirradiated, J	Irradiated, J	J	%
B Tempered martensite	7.4×10^{23}	−143	+1	144	153	114	−39	−25
D Tempered bainite	7.3×10^{23}	−73	+73	146	155	110	−45	−29
E Tempered mixed pearlite, ferrite, bainite, martensite	7.0×10^{23}	−118	+28	146	155	103	−52	−33
F Commercial heat treatment	7.3×10^{23}	−74	+63	137	145	93	−52	−34

2. Notch strength ratio was a little increased after irradiation except commercial heat treatment, where slight reduction in NSR was found.
3. Total elongation of all heat-treatment conditions of irradiated smooth tension specimens was above 15%, uniform elongation was above 5%, and reduction of area was above 55%.
4. Roughly the same radiation embrittlement (ΔTT_{41} = 137 to 146°C) was found in all four heat-treatment conditions. The measured difference, 9°C, is in the testing method range accuracy. The radiation embrittlement sensitivity of the BH 70 steel is not then influenced by different microstructures or different heat treatment at the irradiation conditions used.
5. The initial unirradiated and resultant irradiated Charpy-V 41-J transition temperature of the BH 70 steel, however, can be altered appreciably through heat-treatment practices, resulting in different microstructures. The lowest initial transition temperature (TT_{41} = -143°C) was found in tempered martensite (Condition B) and in tempered mixed ferrite-perlite, bainite, and martensite (-118°C; Condition E). The highest initial transition temperature was found in tempered bainite (-73°C; Condition D) and in commercial heat treatment (-74°C; Condition F). The similar transition temperature sequence was found after irradiation, also.
6. The moderate decrease of the upper-shelf energy (by 25 to 34%) was found after irradiation in all heat-treatment conditions for Charpy-V specimens.
7. To arrive at a more complete understanding of the possible alteration of radiation sensitivity of RPV steels through modification of microstructure, a continuing experimental and research effort is needed.

Acknowledgment

The author wishes to thank the Danish Atomic Energy Commission for the opportunity to carry out this work and to the technical staff of the Risø National Laboratory for irradiation and testing services. He particularly thanks N. Hansen, Head of the Metallurgy Department, for the helpful discussions, consultations, and support through the course of this work; and H. J. Gabel for assistance in the hot-cell operations.

References

[1] Trudeau, L. P., *Radiation Effects on Reactor Structural Materials*, AEC Monograph Series, American Society for Metals, Rowman and Littlefield, New York, 1964.
[2] Wechsler, M. S., *The Interaction of Radiation with Solids*, North Holland Publishing Co., Amsterdam, 1964.
[3] Hawthorne, J. R. and Steele, L. E., in *The Effects of Radiation on Structural Metals*, ASTM STP 426, American Society for Testing and Materials, Philadelphia, 1967, pp. 554–572.
[4] Steele, L. E., *Atomic Energy Review*, Vol. III, No. 2, International Atomic Energy Agency, Vienna, 1969, p. 108.
[5] Vacek, M. and Vrtěl, J., *Radiation Damage in Reactor Materials*, Vol. I, International Atomic Energy Agency, Vienna, 1969, pp. 333–349.

[6] Winther, A. C., "Mechanical Properties and Microstructure of a Pressure Vessel Steel Plate of BH 70 as a Function of Temperature and Position in the Plate," Risø Report-M-775, July 1968.

[7] Qvist, J., "Rigs for Irradiation of Structural Materials," Risø Report-M-852, 1969.

[8] McClintock, F. A., *Welding Journal,* Research Supplement 26, 1961, p. 202s.

[9] Oldfield, W., *ASTM Standardization News,* Nov. 1975, pp. 24–29.

[10] Fujimura, T. and Oku, T., "Irradiation Embrittlement of A 533-B Pressure Vessel Steel (HSTT Plate 03)," Co-ordinated Research Programme on Irradiation Embrittlement of Pressure Vessel Steels, IAEA-176, International Atomic Energy Agency, 1975, pp. 27–83.

[11] Hawthorne, J. R., in *Radiation Embrittlement and Surveillance of Nuclear Reactor Pressure Vessels: An International Study, ASTM STP 819,* L. E. Steele, Ed., American Society for Testing and Materials, Philadelphia, 1983, pp. 100–115.

Summary

This meeting of specialists continues a pattern of approximately triennial meetings on the subject of radiation embrittlement of reactor pressure vessel steels. As with the most recent prior meeting, the theme continues to be the understanding of radiation embrittlement of steels so as to better assure the structural integrity of the primary containment vessels of power reactors. The sponsoring organization within the International Atomic Energy Agency (IAEA), the International Working Group on Reliability of Reactor Pressure Components, has assured the continuity through periodic sponsorship of an appropriate meeting of specialists. The last most recent meeting was held in October 1981 in Vienna. The proceedings of that meeting were published by the American Society for Testing and Materials (ASTM) as Special Technical Publication (STP) 819. The contents of the present meeting reflect changes in the nuclear power business occurring since 1981; that is, it reflects two divergent trends, strong pressure from antinuclear groups coupled with escalating capital requirements opposed by a growing worldwide dependence on nuclear power for electricity production. The former fosters close regulatory control and a growing urgency to understand and overcome the potential negatives of radiation embrittlement. These two influences were evident in the contents of the meeting's formal papers and related discussion.

Forty-five specialists from 18 countries presented 21[1] formal and two informal papers in the two and one-half day meeting wherein detailed discussion was encouraged and became a critical part of the meeting's results. Besides a special final session for discussion to summarize and make recommendations, there were four technical sessions: I. Overview of National Programs, II. Surveillance and other Radiation Embrittlement Studies, III. Pressure Vessel Integrity and Regulatory Considerations, and IV. Mechanisms of Irradiation Embrittlement. The four formal sessions are reviewed briefly as a prelude to a more detailed statement of status and a summary of recommendations.

Session I was highlighted by national overviews from Czechoslovakia, the Federal Republic of Germany (West Germany), the United Kingdom, and the United States in which presentations collectively included: changes to regulatory

---

[1]For reasons of clearance limitations or others, several papers that were presented were not included in the proceedings. Nevertheless, this summary reflects all papers presented and related discussions as well.

guides or rules, delineation of research directions and needs, reactor design alternatives, and the means for dealing with transients. The revision to a crucial U. S. regulatory guide was based upon a new and growing base of data from the surveillance programs in U. S. reactors, but resulted in slightly more conservative data trends that seemed appropriate based upon data generated by the IAEA Coordinated Research Program and that of the German National Program. Nevertheless, the severe nature of possible transients, especially the so-called over-cooling accident that might lead to pressurized thermal shock in some U. S. reactors, was deemed crucial to decisions on both the regulatory guides and the direction of research studies that strongly emphasize data aimed toward answers in the latter area. Data presented by each author validated the value of controlling steel composition to reduce embrittlement and also to design new plants to reduce life-time exposure and, hence, embrittlement. The positive outcome of such presentations are to encourage the use of improved steels as well as design modifications to reduce the chance of placing welds in high fluence regions of the vessel and to generally reduce vessel exposure to neutron radiation both for current and future systems. Research directions emphasized by each national overview presented included, specifically or implicitly, need for added fundamental studies to better understand the nature of the embrittlement process, need for improved quantitative fracture approaches using small specimens, the need for criteria to produce a better quality of steels in terms of high initial toughness and low sensitivity to neutron radiation, and the need to be able to better model both physical processes involved and the consequences in terms of damage or embrittlement trends as a function of the neutron environment and the vessel steel involved. The latter are most important as they often form the basis for regulatory rules. Recommendations growing out of the whole conference impinge significantly upon the suggested directions of national programs.

Session II contained recent results of surveillance programs and research studies as well as descriptions of specific surveillance programs including a newly modified program of the Babcock and Wilcox Company in the United States and that used in India's Tarapur Reactor (with initial results) and Yugoslavia's Krsko Reactor. Specialists' described ways of obtaining the best possible fracture toughness data from small specimens by (1) extracting small notched tension specimens from remnants of tested Charpy specimens, (2) the use of side-grooved precracked Charpy-sized specimens for J_{Ic} determination, and (3) the modification to impact test machines to allow measurement of dynamic fracture toughness. A massive systematic Italian program for predicting the reference transition temperature increase trends from irradiated specimens was described. Its basis is the chemical composition and related irradiation-induced changes for the steels studied. The results are expected to yield a better equation for establishing trends for embrittlement for regulatory and operational control purposes. The adequacy of various data bases and approaches to their use was discussed in detail considering the relative value of test reactor and surveillance data. The latter seem to have higher merit for trend limit establishment but a strong recommendation was made

for developing a "standardized" data base. This was judged by the specialists to be a proper, even necessary function of the IAEA as a unique international body having the resources, the charter, and the continuity necessary to data base maintenance.

The papers and discussion of Session III on Pressure Vessel Integrity and Regulatory Considerations rested heavily upon the U. S. Nuclear Regulatory Commission (USNRC) Regulatory Guide 1.99, its latest revision and the related German Rule, Safety Standard KTA 3203, which establishes a severe limit on projected fluence at end of life (nominal reactor life). Because of the relative stages of development of nuclear power in these two countries, the very different approaches were deemed to be feasible in each but not necessarily transferrable between the two. The modeling of an "overcooling accident" or pressurized thermal shock condition leads to the conclusion that radiation embrittlement as well as the existing or potential flaws and local stress conditions are of crucial interest on a plant-by-plant basis for those vessels of "old" or sensitive steel compositions. Underlying the papers presented and the discussion following were several strong recommendations for controlling embrittlement, limiting severe conditions of service, as well as criteria for assessing critically the potential for degradation to the point of possible failure.

Session IV concentrated on two main issues, the effect of annealing of irradiation damage and modeling this effect as well as the mechanisms underlying damage. One study of annealing showed nearly complete recovery at 454°C and, with reirradiation, found reduced sensitivity toward reembrittlement. The latter observation was contrary to some earlier results. Discussion of annealing, especially the modeling of effects on copper-defect centers led to the conclusion that much is to be learned about the phenomena affecting steel embrittlement. A brief report of the practical benefits of annealing the vessel of an operating reactor, the BR-3 at Mol, Belgium, was reported to have been fully successful based on annealing at 343°C (650°F) after the reactor's operation at 260°C (500°F). This operation was described as "wet annealing," that is, it was based on the use of the nuclear system to raise the coolant temperature to 343°C and to hold it there for one week. (This paper was offered only for discussion, not for publication.) Discussion of annealing, especially the USNRC attitude of its nonuse in the pressurized thermal shock analysis led to questions of this attitude and a conclusion that annealing deserves further study and technological evaluation as a "last resort" means for reducing radiation embrittlement in operating reactors having vessels that are sensitive to radiation.

In spite of the early focus on annealing in Session IV, the main result of this session was to highlight the merits of advanced modeling and microanalytical techniques such as positron annihilation, analytical electron microscopy, and small-angle neutron scattering as tools of high potential for developing a better understanding of the physical bases for irradiation hardening and embrittlement. The coupling of statistical modeling procedures with data from microscopic techniques and parallel analysis of mechanical or physical properties shows spe-

cial promise for describing and even predicting steel response to irradiation. Correlations, incorporating physical hardening parameters and irradiation temperature produced coherent results from the most extensive data base available to date. Copper hardening centers were identified as the primary cause of radiation embrittlement but with nickel contributing in a way not yet well understood.

Besides the four focused technical sessions, a final half-day session was held to assess the current state of knowledge and to recommend directions for future efforts. The latter included specific recommendations for the IAEA Working Group as well as general and specific recommendations concerning the future research and surveillance programs attributable to individual organizations within member countries or for collective action. These are outlined beginning with the recommendations for collective action and following with topical reviews and recommendations for any and all interested parties.

Activities to be Supported by the IAEA

The principal function of the IAEA is and has been properly to support collection, interchange, and dissemination of information that will aid the peaceful use of nuclear energy in a safe and efficient manner. The specialists continued to view these functions as primary to the IAEA's role in this subject but with the addition of some more direct support of research as well as of data analysis and storage.

The history of IAEA involvement in steel embrittlement by neutron irradiation is long and illustrious going back to sponsorship of the first major international conference on the subject in 1967. For this reason and because of the strong long-term continuity following the auspicious initiative in 1967, the specialists believe strongly in the merits of continuing the adopted role of the IAEA working group. Recommendations of the specialists relate to information dissemination as well as the encouragement and support of knowledge growth in critical areas. Principal recommendations to meet these goals were delineated:

Recommendations

1. Continue the series of specialists' meetings on a triennial (or more frequent) basis to review progress and research needs in the subject.

2. Assure publication of the results of specialists' meetings with appropriate analysis of results to maintain an international collective and authoritative statement of results and needs. Emphasis should continue to focus on safety-related developments and consequently to serve as a guide to those initially embarking on nuclear power development.

3. Commission special publications, as appropriate, to meet needs of the community for disseminating new research or surveillance data including an update of the volume published by the IAEA in 1975 entitled *Neutron Irradiation of Reactor Pressure Vessel Steels* (TRS 163).

4. Commission consultants' meetings, specialists' meetings, and conferences *as needed* to carry out the mandate of optimizing data dissemination.

5. Promote collaboration with other international bodies to assure optimum data release and minimal duplication of effort. In the development of data bases especially, coordinate with such organizations as the Organizations for Economic Cooperation and Development/Nuclear Energy Association (OECD/NEA), the independent International Association for Structural Mechanics in Reactor Technology (IASMiRT), the International Welding Congress (IWC), and the International Committee on Cyclic Crack Growth (ICCGR). (The latter is cooperating with the IAEA for joint sponsorship of a specialists' meeting in 1985.) These efforts are essential to assure meeting general goals just cited and for retaining the good national institutional cooperation that now exists.

6. In the realm of research encouragement and data acquisition, a program was undertaken by the IAEA in the early 1970s and is encouraged vigorously because of its' continuing high payoff. This effort was called the coordinated research program on Irradiation Embrittlement of Reactor Vessel Steels. It is now in Phase 3. The scope has grown from an effort to establish reproducible results on irradiation of one steel among several investigating institutes to a rather massive new program called Phase 3—"Optimizing Reactor Pressure Vessel Surveillance Programmes and Their Analyses", which is just now getting underway with about 25 different steels and 14 participating countries. Investigators in these countries use different approaches but will contribute to improved fracture criteria, neutron dosimetry and spectrum analysis, better knowledge of composition effects, better fundamental understanding of the physical bases for steel embrittlement and, in general, a better system of understanding of what comprises a good surveillance effort. International comparisons and collaborations will be a common feature of this study with interim reports issued at meetings of principal investigators.

The following is intended to approach the results and recommendations from a topical viewpoint and reflects largely the chairman's (editor's) views of the results and related recommendations. The *key subjects* are clearly radiation embrittlement, surveillance, assessing the fracture potential of vessel steels, and mechanisms of radiation damage. Related topics that are subordinate to these include neutron environmental analysis, thermal annealing to correct damage, the science of radiation damage, and the implications of service "transients" to vessel integrity. However, at the risk of being repetitive and raising the level of emphasis beyond that deserved, these subjects are treated as if they were integral parts of the total presentation and the related discussion. Primary emphasis, however, must reside on the four key elements discussed in the following sections.

Radiation Embrittlement

New information dealt principally with the steel composition effects, comparison of research reactor and surveillance data, the means for measuring such

effects (neutron dosimetry, temperature, and fracture criterion used), the implications to reactor vessel integrity during service transients, and the mechanisms of the radiation damage process. While none of these topics is new, new results and indicators were cited.

Recommendations

1. Looking back, the 1979 meeting dwelt heavily on data suggesting a "rate" or "saturation" effect that later was resolved without evidence of significant effect. The 1981 meeting dealt largely with the theme of independent or synergistic effects of residual or alloying elements, especially copper and nickel. The 1984 meeting introduced more sophistication to the latter without its resolution but with a strong emphasis on statistical and mechanistic studies to address "what levels of what elements" caused significant negative effects. The general consensus appeared to suggest serious damage if the copper level was over about 0.20% with nickel over 0.50%. Significant disagreement surfaced regarding the role of nickel at different levels. The strongest recommendation then came in the form of endorsing the Coordinated Research Programmes (CRP) directions to study a series of laboratory steel compositions having contents using both varying nickel and copper and using both conventional mechanical properties along with fundamental detectors for assessing the nature of the atomic level interactions. This recommendation is now built into the CRP Phase 3 both as to approach and to substantive content.

2. Phase 3 of the CRP program that was being finalized formally concurrently with the Specialists' meeting is not defined in detail but it should suffice to verify that carefully formulated laboratory and commercial-scale heats of varying steel compositions will permit elaboration on synergism or lack thereof between effects of copper, nickel and phosphorous.

3. An almost universal call of the specialists was for more directed scientific programs to assess the mechanisms of neutron interaction with the elements in typical reactor pressure vessel steels. This does not mean that no such results were available but the scope of selected variability within a given type of steel was inadequate to make most effective use of the tools such as field ion microscopy, analytical electron microscopy in general as well as special techniques such as small angle neutron and X-ray scattering and others now available for "seeing" the defects in irradiated steels.

4. New data showed some effects of temperature. Temperatures slightly lower than those typical of current light-water-reactor operation showed significant effects in terms of higher embrittlement. Full understanding of the role of temperature and time as well as strain aging effects, offsetting or abetting neutron exposure, is poorly understood. And, while not crucial for "standard" operating temperatures, it is part of the unknowns in the complex interactions of flux, temperature, time, strain, and steel types that will ultimately provide the "whole" story of neutron irradiation embrittlement. These should, therefore, be studied

from this view as well as the empirical one in which a specific reactor vessel operates at an "abnormal" temperature, whether lower or higher, than the general population.

5. One statistical study of data bank results in the United States suggests that, for reasons not clear, that data from surveillance of power reactor vessel embrittlement provides a more consistent base for analysis and projection of anticipated changes. This is encouraging in the sense that it suggests capsule integrity, good technique in dosimetry and related environmental analyses, but discouraging in that the most flexible tool for full study—research reactor experiments on an accelerated basis—may not be as useful as had been thought. However, the recommendation is that this analytical comparison be done with a weighting process that gives less credit to older research data where dosimetry might have been less well developed. Clearly, much more needs to be done in this realm. From this grew the recommendation that the IAEA assume and retain the role of data base proprietor not just for the CRP but for all available irradiation embrittlement data.

Surveillance

The program content included surveillance from three perspectives, (a) content of national program, (b) redirection with new knowledge, and (c) data for comparison with the "world" data bank. Results came primarily from (a) and (c); the former involved descriptions from India and Yugoslavia both of which sought to enhance their programs by using small fracture specimens and the latter in connection with papers comparing special research data with that from power reactors. The volume of the latter and the redirection of programs (b) seem poised for very rapid growth.

Recommendations

1. While surveillance programs may be locked into old technologies for a while, there is a clear and highly desirable trend toward modifying programs as was described by the Babcock and Wilcox representative to (a) add new fracture mechanics specimens and (b) to assure that the true "weak link" material is prominently included in key surveillance capsules.

2. All representatives endorsed the notion that surveillance is essential and should be updated as is possible. This means both improved specimens and dosimetry as possible. The goal of Phase 3 of the IAEA CRP will build nicely on this effort as the principal goal in this study is to optimize surveillance. Further, where the power level or core configuration has changed significantly for core management reasons or as a result of an overcooling accident and the related condition called pressurized thermal shock, new capsules may need to be added to assure that one can integrate effects over years that may involve significant core changes.

3. New or revised programs should capitalize on research developments just cited as part of ongoing studies. Of special interest is the best knowledge of chemical composition in order to have the best chance to choose the "weak link" material, to locate the capsule at the peak fluence location, to use the best possible miniature specimen for optimum fracture data, and ultimately to contribute to a better data base in the future.

4. Several papers described procedures for using small or modified specimens (before or after irradiation) for obtaining quantitative fracture mechanics numbers. Each surveillance program monitor should maintain his knowledge of such developments to optimize results from available specimens. For example, modifications of Charpy V-notch specimens to obtain J_{Ic} data have been described. (This type of correlation will be a major part of Phase 3 of the CRP.)

Fracture Approaches to Vessel Steels

As just cited (Surveillance) several authors have developed criteria for using small specimens to define fracture potential in the vessel steels. This requires thorough evaluation; this means that the specimen must not be materials or geometry or size dependent. The critical nature of this factor is validated by the fact that this is a crucial part of the plan for Phase 3 of the CRP. The complexity of this task is best described by the fact that one must interpret the structural integrity of a vessel from laboratory tests of a few small specimens, while a direct one-for-one test approach is not possible short of the test of a full-sized irradiated vessel and correlated with fracture mechanics specimens taken from a failed vessel. Barring this possibility, it is crucial to be assured that the fracture analysis is based upon an approach that is clearly conservative (more severe) than can be expected in a real vessel.

Recommendations

1. The overriding significance of this factor required a dedicated effort from all to arrive at a criterion within surveillance or research studies that meets the limits of conservatism implicit to safety.

2. Consideration of the American Society of Mechanical Engineers, Section III, Appendix G basis, the K_{IR} curve, continues to raise two key questions. First is there a K_{Ia} (crack arrest) number that can be defined in a standard manner for use in forming the "ductile" portion of the curve after irradiation? Second, what is the shape of the K_{IR} curve after irradiation for a sensitive steel? While extensive work was carried out on K_{Ia}, the need still exists for a standard approach. On the second point, large section tests of irradiated specimens and of scale vessels suggests the K_{IR} curve to be conservative relative to projected vessel behavior. Recommendations are still to use this approach but to be as careful as possible in use of small specimens to pinpoint RT_{NDT} on the K_{IR} curve while noting results for assessing the shape of the K_{IR} curve beyond the RT_{NDT} point.

3. In the use of quantitative fracture criteria, T or tearing modulus or a tearing instability factor was not used but rather a J-R curve and J_{Ic} from small specimens seemed to be more universally used than ever before. It was recommended that refinements to define the better criteria should be watched carefully and applied as possible but with an effort always to seek a tie to the universally accepted Charpy V-notch specimen.

4. The several papers describing small specimens for K_{Ic} or J_{Ic} determination from criteria formerly applied to the Charpy cross-sectional limits suggested advances in the procedures based on side-grooving, especially ones that create the degree of constraint normally found only in much larger specimens. However, it is recommended that these new techniques be studied in Phase 3 of the CRP effort and that more than one organization cross check the approach on a given steel both before and after irradiation.

5. Because of comprehensive overview papers that all addressed the vessel's structural integrity from the view of fracture mechanics, especially as these may be affected by an overcooling accident (producing pressurized thermal shock) in some systems, great importance was and must continue to be placed on fracture analysis in future studies. This implies, as well, close collaboration with specialists in nondestructive testing and stress analysis in order that the three main factors be simultaneously considered. These are: (1) the vessel's irradiated toughness condition, (2) operating or transient stress, and (3) any existing flaw in a critical location of the vessel. These considerations were made more sensitive by the revelation that flaws of significant size relative to vessel wall thickness have been found in the *outside* wall of a U.S. vessel. This condition is made more serious because of the fact that K_{Ia} or crack arrest considerations were optimistically based on the presence of a flaw on the inside vessel wall. Recommendations were strongly pressed for obtaining the fullest knowledge possible of fracture toughness of a vessel at any point through its thickness and that more conservative considerations of projected flaw sizes and location (as well as the local stresses) be taken. Further, the significance of "low shelf toughness" *must* be quantitatively assessed by an internationally accepted "standard" criterion. Many early reactors are subject to severe analysis on this point. Such analyses can only become more critical with longer operating periods.

6. Analyses for the overcooling accidents that were presented lead once again to the need to minimize radiation and its embrittling effects by all means at the disposal of specialists and for radiation damage specialists to study ever more carefully the opportunities for changing the vessels' condition in service by all available means. (See Summary in *ASTM STP 819* for a review of this topic based on results available at the sister meeting in 1981.)

7. All of the preceding recommendations have crucial implications to criteria development by regulators for assuring structural integrity. There can be no letup in the study by specialists and these studies must integrate the technologies applying to vessel integrity assurance. For example, the question of pressurized

thermal shock (PTS) resulting from an overcooling accident must be related to fracture potential analyses for each reactor vessel, especially those wherein significant radiation embrittlement is possible because of "sensitive" steels or high projected neutron fluence levels during the anticipated life of the vessel. Plant specific analyses are essential to assess all factors that impinge on PTS and related potential for vessel fracture. Other accident or transient conditions that may heighten fracture potential must be assessed in conjunction with embrittlement probabilities.

Mechanisms of Radiation Damage

The early studies and observations of radiation damage of steels were largely empirical in nature and, because of the potentially serious nature of embrittlement observed, studies concentrated on engineering implications in order to minimize the negative consequences of such effects in nuclear plants. Later, programs were undertaken to understand the phenomena involved. These highlighted the role of the residual elements, copper and phosphorus, then later other elements such as nickel, vanadium, and so forth. Empirical results pinpointed copper and nickel as serious actors in this drama and several studies sought clarification of their negative roles. Several papers at the meeting directed further attention to the complexity of this subject while validating the need for better knowledge in this area.

Recommendations

1. Refined tools for microanalytical evaluation of irradiated steels offer opportunities that should be accepted and fully utilized. Techniques such as field ion microscopy, analytical transmission, and scanning electron microscopy, as well as small-angle neutron and X-ray scattering for assessing physical and chemical features of steels after irradiation, plus techniques that simulate neutron bombardment offer hope for further clarification of the embrittlement phenomena and were encouraged by meeting participants.

2. The ongoing CRP sponsored by the IAEA Working Group on Reliability of Reactor Pressure Components should focus attention on fundamental studies. Fullest use of the laboratory steels offered by Japan should permit better knowledge of the role of the cited elements (copper, phosphorus, and nickel) on the process of embrittlement. (It should be noted that nine of fourteen national participants in the Phase 3 CRP will be studying groups of specially formulated laboratory heats of steels containing differing levels of the elements considered most deleterious to properties of irradiated steels.)

3. Besides the composition oriented studies, others must emphasize the nature of the neutron-atom collision processes in order to complement our knowledge of the role of individual elements in the irradiated steels. This relates to the need for the best possible understanding of neutron interactions with the complex steel

matrix as a function of energy spectrum. The outcome should be two-fold: (*a*) a better understanding of neutron-produced defects, their stability, and mobility; and (*b*) better bases for describing the damaging potential of neutrons by energy level (or damage based dosimetry).

4. As knowledge is gained about both the microchemical and microphysical phenomena involved in the embrittlement process, it is desirable, even necessary, that such knowledge be applied to support criteria for specifying improved radiation resistant steels; for clarifying potential failure patterns, such as the through-wall crack arrest potential; and for minimizing radiation embrittlement effects through design modifications (core or vessel) or through thermal annealing.

5. Strong agreement was voiced by most meeting participants for a high priority effort in fundamental studies of steel embrittlement based on the feeling that only full knowledge would permit users to take actions necessary to minimize the negatives of this insidious process and to integrate steps for precluding serious consequences from occurring. Thus, good knowledge becomes the tool for avoiding the problem in new reactors and for ameliorating such effects in existing plants.

General Conclusion

The optimism inherent to all phases of the meeting, especially the discussion and recommendations session, bodes well for the future of our hope for understanding radiation embrittlement of steels. Further, it reflects a global view of active positivism for nuclear power that this volume reflects both implicitly and explicitly. The recommendations cited are believed to be a distillation of substantive opinions on the topic. Strong support for research and development in the subject undergirds confidence in nuclear power. Further, an overwhelming impression was gained that the IAEA provides the best international outlet for information on the specific topic of irradiation embrittlement of reactor pressure vessel steels and, accordingly, that the sponsoring International Working Group must continue to serve this function and to support the knowledge base through the newly undertaken Phase 3 Coordinated Research Program on "Optimizing Reactor Pressure Vessel Surveillance Programmes and Their Analyses."

Lendell E. Steele

Head, Thermostructural Materials Branch, Material Science and Technology Division, Naval Research Laboratory, Washington, DC; specialist meeting chairman and editor.

Author Index

Subject Index

D1614422